Watch out f

The Secret Guide to Pra   ocience

Jaroslav Flegr

First Publication: December 2016

Publisher: Faculty of Science, Charles University

Cover design & composition: Petr Tureček

Typeset: Tomáš Lavička

Editor: Julie Novakova

ISBN: 978-80-7444-046-5

Contents

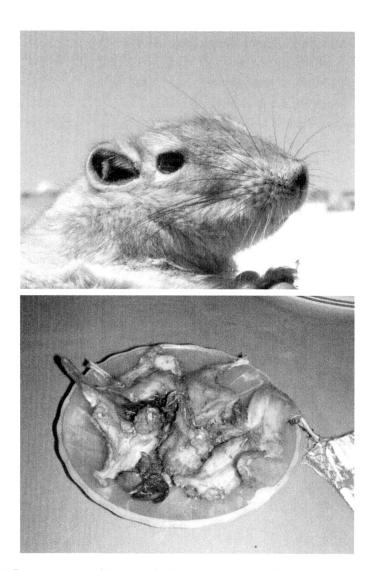

Fig. 1 Common gundi (*Ctenodactylus gundi*), the first host in which *Toxoplasma* was discovered. Before and after culinary preparation. Photo taken by Jan Votýpka, Tunisia.

Preface

Just to be clear – this is not an autobiography. This book builds upon the story of how we came to recognize the effect of latent toxoplasmosis on the human psyche and behavior (as well as on reproduction, immunity, physical appearance, and fitness), and because I or one of my colleagues had been present at most of the described discoveries, the text may in some places, as in the first chapter, dangerously resemble autobiography. But appearances indeed may be deceiving. The story of recognizing toxoplasmosis' effect on man provides a sort of framework, which is arrayed with various curiosities of modern biology, along with general and even specific observations and suggestions as to how one should – and, above all, should not – do science. Considering that not every reader is interested in an explanation of principle of isoelectric focusing, or in the propriety of applying a Bonferroni correction to multiple tests, I have separated this array into individual boxes, which one can easily skip between. But personally, I think these boxes are precisely the most important aspect of this book, and readers, particularly those pursuing professional science, should not skip over them. The effect of toxoplasmosis on man is certainly a fascinating phenomenon (otherwise I would not have dedicated 20 years of my life to its study), but the very process of acquiring scientific knowledge is much more compelling. So, please, don't skip over the boxes.

What is *Toxoplasma* and toxoplasmosis? *Toxoplasma* is a parasitic protozoan, Latin name *Toxoplasma gondii,* discovered in 1908, incidentally within a fairly exotic rodent, the Saharan gundi (*Ctenodactylus gundi,* Fig. 1). In fact, this parasite targets almost any warm-blooded animal, including man. It is very widespread: an estimated third of the world's population carries a latent form of this successful parasite. Even I carry *Toxoplasma* in my body and, with about a 30% probability, so do you. Once infected, you will never get rid of your quiet companion.

Toxoplasmosis is the disease caused by *Toxoplasma* and has three forms in man: acute, congenital, and latent. An attack of acute toxoplasmosis occurs immediately after infection and is usually accompanied by symptoms we associate with common bacterial and viral diseases – furthermore, patients usually experience swelling of the neck lymph nodes. In the vast majority of people, toxoplasmosis subsides of its own accord – that is to say that it passes into its latent phase, during which only quiescent state *Toxoplasma* parasites are present in the body. Yet the most notorious and dangerous form of toxoplasmosis is congenital toxoplasmosis, which can afflict newborns whose mothers were infected while pregnant. Transfer of the parasite from mother to developing fetus can result in miscarriage or serious developmental disease in the child. Doctors' main interest lies in understanding congenital toxoplasmosis, which, while a relatively rare disease, effects serious health consequences. By contrast, my particular professional interest, and simultaneously the central theme of this book, is latent (hidden) toxoplasmosis. This form of the disease consistently afflicts about a third of the world's population. Physicians generally rule that latent toxoplasmosis is asymptomatic and does not present a serious health issue, but they are almost certainly wrong. Our results indicate that, in connection with latent toxoplasmosis, thousands of people die every year just as a result of the heightened risk of car accidents. The work of American and Turkish authors further confirms that latent toxoplasmosis markedly raises the risk of suicide. In addition, many epidemiological studies show that in sensitive people latent toxoplasmosis can trigger schizophrenia, a very serious mental disease afflicting about 1% of people at some point during their lives. Apart from the health risks attending latent toxoplasmosis, this parasitic disease is also curious in that it characteristically alters the behavior and temperament of infected persons. Large comparative studies even show that some differences in national temperament can be explained by the amount of people infected in individual countries[1]. Latent toxoplasmosis raises the level of the sex hormone testosterone in infected men and changes their physical appearance. Women infected by *Toxoplasma* parasites are showier, more sociable and frivolous, give birth to more boys than girls, and have a somewhat longer pregnancy. In addition, studies on the effect of toxoplasmosis on the human organism have led to a number of discoveries, which, though not directly related to the disease, may for this reason have an even broader impact on our understanding of the workings of the human body and psyche. Several of our studies have clearly shown that the organism of people with blood group Rh plus reacts differently to latent toxoplasmosis (and perhaps also to a range of other influences, including fatigue and aging) than does the organism of people with blood group Rh minus.

Who is this book written for? (Now I can reveal that this chapter is just a prologue in disguise…) Well, firstly, for myself – for when I reach old age, and have trouble recalling how I spent my youth and what I actually discovered, I'll undoubtedly be grateful for this book (hopefully, I'll still be able to understand it… just to be safe, I'll try to explain it all in the simplest terms, and avoid words that are hard to remember or pronounce with dentures). Beyond that, this book is directed towards anyone interested in biology, particularly in the field known in Prague as "white biology". (Before we all started wearing jeans to work, the white biologists, pouring homogenized mice from one test tube into another, wore white lab coats. Green biologists, on the other hand, wore khaki-colored field clothes as they chased after butterflies or counted up the number of sedge seedlings in the meadow.) Furthermore, this book will likely be opened by someone who has personal experience with toxoplasmosis. And finally, *Watch out for Toxo!* is directed towards the reader interested in the workings of modern science. Maybe I am overly optimistic, but the boxes devoted to methodology could be very helpful to even my current colleagues (but they, unfortunately, have neither the time to read books nor to work with the above-mentioned homogenized mice and sedge seedlings, because they are ceaselessly writing papers, grants, and grant reports), and to future colleagues – that is, students who are interested in similar topics, primarily biology and medicine (I've heard that such students do occasionally read books – probably when their internet connection happens to be broken). Though this book covers mostly methodology for researching behavior, a large part of this applies to science in general.

Usually, the last paragraph of preface is the place for acknowledgments, but for most readers, that's the signal to skip to the first chapter. So instead, I'll extend an apology: An uninitiated reader of this book might get the impression that the author is an unbearable braggart, who struts around, acting like Mr. Know-it-all; like he's been everywhere and seen everything; and more importantly, as though he has single-handedly (at worst, with some help from his team) made every discovery regarding latent toxoplasmosis. Therefore, I sincerely apologize to the unenlightened reader for any ineptitude in my writing style, which might lead to this false impression. The truth is that the author isn't boasting (because, among other wonderful qualities, he is both modest and meek) – he and his team are really that good.

I. How I didn't become an immunologist
nor a molecular taxonomist

How did it all begin? Quite differently than I tell the reporters, who come sniffing through the laboratories each year when silly season rolls around. They're hunting for stories on how scientists battle with nature, day and night, to wrest away her closely guarded secrets. Dear readers, know this: It's not true that "it all started when I joined the department of parasitology in the 90s, and cast around for a research topic that might encompass both parasitology and evolutionary biology". Period. Don't listen to journalists – they'll believe and publish anything.

I'd say that the reality was much more interesting. After about four years working in the Department of Immunology of the Institute of Molecular Genetics of Czechoslovak Academy of Sciences, I returned to the Department of Parasitology at Charles University. My primary goal was to form a laboratory of molecular biology, and to dedicate myself to molecular phylogenetics – in other words, to continue with the topics I had researched before leaving the university. Most of all, I was determined to avoid immunology, though Jaroslav Kulda, the department head at the time, had originally invited me to his workplace to study this topic. Since I arrived in the department with my own salary fund, I didn't feel tied to my bosses' expectations (however, I always tend to play by my own rules, so the salary fund probably had little to do with it) (Box 1 *How to arrive in the department with your own funds*).

Maybe it wasn't very nice or responsible of me, but I think that I finally gave the head of the department a sufficiently convincing explanation for why I wanted to form a molecular biology instead of immunology lab (neither of these existed in the department at that time). I told him: "Immunology is an interesting scientific discipline, but under the conditions of the department, which has no history of immunological research, it could not be conducted at a decent level." Not only did we lack the basic equipment, but we also were missing contacts with top international workplaces, as well as sources for literature, chemicals – everything you can think of.

Box 1 How to arrive in the department with your own funds for salaries

This story reminds me of that common scenario in fairytales: kind-hearted Jack, on his way to save an enchanted princess, meets a hungry, weary traveler on the road. Out of the goodness of his heart, Jack shares his last piece of food with the traveler. The weary traveler then turns out to be a powerful sorcerer, who had taken this disguise to test Jack, and now rewards him for his altruistic behavior. About a month or two after the Velvet Revolution, with the country in disarray, several of us former members of the Faculty of Science arranged a meeting. We thought of returning to Charles University and establishing there a new workplace, which would study and teach theoretical and evolutionary biology. One of those present was Zdeněk Neubauer, who had been pressured to leave the university in the 80s; with his unorthodox opinions (and this is a very moderate term), he infuriated his more conformist colleagues like a red Soviet flag does an exceptionally irritable Western-oriented bull. At the end of the meeting, Zdeněk asked each and every one of us, whether we really wanted him on the team. I told him that while I usually disagree with his opinions, I'd be happy for him to be part of our project. At the time, I had no inkling that Zdeněk Neubauer was a good friend of both future president of Czechia Václav Havel, and of Radim Palouš, the first president of Charles University after the revolution. In the stormy post-revolutionary period, Neubauer had a say in what happened with the salary funds of the former Marxism-Leninism department. Unlike Neubauer, I had no way of knowing that he would be the one to select employees for his Department of Philosophy and Natural History. After ensuring salary funds for most of his conspirators (evidently, not everyone passed the weary traveler test), he told us that we could stay at his new department, or were free to transfer to a department of our choice, along with salary funds. I was among the people who chose the second option (though only transiently, as it turned out).

Furthermore, we lacked experience: in the Institute of Molecular Genetics, I primarily cloned interleukin genes, an activity closer to molecular engineering than to real immunology. Not even my about fourteen months in the Department of Immunology at the University of Tokyo made up for my lack of experience in the field. Rather, they showed me that immunological research is difficult to carry out under the conditions of our university's Department of Parasitology. I continued: "The most I could do here was assistant work, like preparing antibodies for the experiments of other colleagues, developing a diagnostic system to detect parasites, or look for a way how to monitor the immune response of an infected host." (Saying this, I got the feeling that something flickered in the eyes of the department head. It might have been that proverbial spark of hope, or just a trick of the light.) "But spending my time running a service laboratory was the last thing I wanted to do in a new, or really any, workplace." (The light in the eyes of the department head dimmed.) If I remember correctly, Jaroslav Kulda never reproached me for moving to molecular biology, and evolutionary parasitology, and made peace with the situation.

In contrast, we at the university had all the necessary equipment for studying molecular biology of parasites and I had much more practical experience in this field. In my undergraduate work, I had looked for DNA in the organelles of the parasitic protozoan trichomonad (Fig. 2). The search was unsuccessful, which might have had something to do with the fact that the particular organelles in this protozoan (hydrogenosomes) have no orgenellar DNA, as was discovered many years later (notice how carefully the scientist formulates his conclusions). In the ancestors of trichomonads, all the hydrogenosome genes moved into the cell nucleus (see Box 2 *Why some cellular organelles have their own DNA, while others, like hydrogenosomes, don't*).

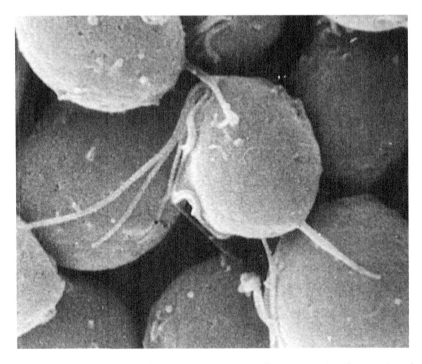

Fig. 2 The protozoan Trichomonas. *A sexually transmitted parasite that was the subject of my undergraduate and later graduate study. Scanning electron microscope picture by Pavol Demeš.*

Box 2 Why some cellular organelles have their own DNA, while others, like hydrogenosomes, don't

Some of the important modern cellular organelles, such as mitochondria and chloroplasts, developed from symbiotic – and in my opinion, probably originally parasitic – bacteria. Chloroplasts and mitochondria kept remnants of their bacterial DNA (most of it gradually moved into the nucleus of their host cell). Hydrogenosomes, on the other hand, a type of peculiar mitochondria found in some protozoans, handed over all their DNA to the cell nucleus. The reason organelles move their DNA into the nucleus is pretty clear. Chloroplasts and mitochondria act as cellular power plants. In the process of converting energy, these organelles produce highly reactive chemical substances that are damaging to DNA and cause mutations. In the cell nucleus, the genes are much better protected. Furthermore, a single cell often has several hundred or even thousands of these organelles, so if each of them had their own DNA, subject to possible mutations, these organelles would begin competing among themselves to reproduce. The victors of the competition will be the organelles with mutations allowing them to reproduce the fastest, even if it detracts from their primary function – producing energy for the cell. So eventually, the predominant organelles will be those that reproduce faster than their competitors, but don't provide the cell with energy. The fewer genes present in these organelles, the lower the risk that they will mutate and start reproducing faster, while abandoning their power plant function. So transferring organelle genes to the nucleus is a preventative measure against the formation and take-over of "selfish" organelles. But this prevention is not a hundred percent effective. Although the total number of genes in today's mitochondria and chloroplasts (a couple dozen in mitochondria, a couple hundred in chloroplasts) is negligible when compared to the number of genes in the nucleus, many genetic diseases are caused by mutations in mitochondrion and chloroplast genes. Many of these genetic diseases are probably the result of the cell being overwhelmed by mutated, "selfish" organelles.

It's a bit harder to explain why mitochondria and chloroplasts, unlike hydrogenosomes, kept some of their genes. Because of their handful of leftover genes, these two types of organelles have to maintain a complicated apparatus to copy the genes, transcribe them into RNA, and translate them into proteins. At the moment, I'm inclined towards the hypothesis that an individual mitochondrion or chloroplast needs these genes in order to directly regulate the activity of its respiratory chain. This respiratory chain produces energy in a mitochondrion or chloroplast. The individual molecules that make up a respiratory chain are anchored in the organelle's membrane, and during energy production, the molecules pass electrons along the chain while pumping hydrogen ions (protons) from one side of the membrane to the other. The resulting proton gradient is used by the cell to synthesize ATP, a molecule that serves as the cell's primary source of immediate energy. The activity of the respiratory chain in each organelle must be tuned precisely. The wrong level of molecules in the organelle could quickly lead to the formation of the above-mentioned dangerous chemicals (radicals), which would first damage the proteins and DNA in the organelle, and then spread to the rest of the cell. So each component of the chain must be synthesized in the organelle, because otherwise its rate of synthesis cannot be adjusted to meet the conditions of the specific organelle.

If the genes for respiratory chain were found in the nucleus, then it would be impossible to transport a protein from the nucleus to only the mitochondria that needed it, without the protein also ending up in hundreds of other mitochondria. This hypothesis additionally explains the lack of DNA in hydrogenosomes, which are organelles present in certain protozoan species that live in low-oxygen environments, and therefore cannot use normal mitochondria to produce energy. These strange mitochondria don't use a respiratory chain, but synthesize ATP using a different, less dangerous method.

Partly thanks to this, my undergraduate work acquainted me with a variety of interesting techniques from molecular biology, which I used in an effort to find DNA in this trichomonad organelle. I should mention that I selected the topic of my undergraduate work myself, despite emphatic warnings from my mentor Jiří Čerkasov, as well as his remarkable wife and co-worker, Apolena Čerkasová. Instead of organelle DNA, I finally discovered the first dsRNA virus in a protozoan cell, as well as the presence of repetitive DNA in the *Trichomonas* nucleus. My graduate work included further study of this virus in different strains of trichomonads.

Unfortunately, we published the discovery of dsRNA in *Trichomonas*, along with the subsequent proof of virion particles, later than our American competitors[2], but at least it was in a significantly worse journal. However, in those days, that was our workplace tradition. (I say "we" when discussing the *Trichonomas* experiments – not as a majestic plural – but rather to express the fact that experiments performed by undergraduate and graduate students are usually financed, planned, or co-planned by the student advisor; and usually several lab members are involved in the study, including other students and lab technicians.)

Nevertheless, this time our American competitors didn't have to try as hard. Unlike me, they didn't have to drop their research for a year to become a tank platoon commander. Instead of running nucleic acids across an electrophoretic gel in the lab, I found myself running four tanks and fifteen mischievous scamps across the snow-covered plains on a military base in the Doupov Mountains. I apologize to Captain Šic, the proud head of my battalion – who was famous for saying that hell would freeze over before any of us bean-sprouts (meaning us university types) would get an officer's star, and yet probably spared me from future military call-backs (I suspect that he scribbled in his report: "Arm Flegr only if all has been lost!") – again, I hope Captain Šic will forgive me when I say that my American competitors didn't miss much in military service. The landscape of the Doupov Mountains might look nice from the vantage point of a horse-back rider, but certainly not to the shivering soldier sitting on the steel seat of a T-55 tank. After returning from the mandatory military service, we struggled to catch up to the Americans. Sometimes, in our lab experiments, we even closed the gap, but when it got to the final sprint – getting our work published – we usually came in second place. Even to this day, there are several interesting discoveries about *Trichomonas* dsRNA viruses that we haven't yet published (Box 3 *Trichonomas double-stranded RNA*).

Box 3 *Trichonomas* double-stranded RNA

I'll never forget the day when, after three years of scrutinizing electrophoretic agar gels in the dim red light of the darkroom, I finally shouted "Eureka!" I had discovered something that looked like organelle DNA. I saw a strong, narrow band at the place that normally marks DNA which is three micrometers long (Fig. 3).

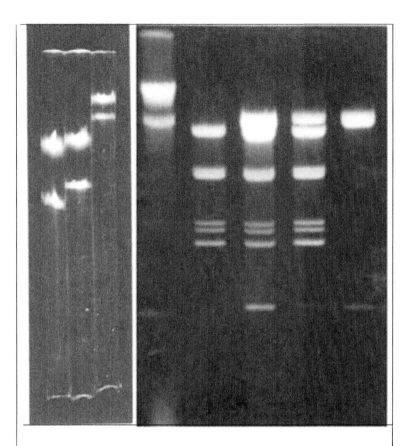

Fig. 3 Electrophoretic analysis of Trichomonas *nucleic acids. Aside from the nuclear DNA band (on top), other bands are visible. I originally thought that these nucleic acid bands came from hydrogenesomes, the protozoan's modified mitochondria. It was later determined they actually come from the double-stranded RNA (dsRNA) of a virus that had infected* Trichomonas. *This was the first dsRNA virus described for a protozoan. On the left are the results of dsRNA capillary electrophoresis; having no machine ourselves, we resourcefully used a potty chair as the electrophoretic tank, and a car battery as the electric power source. The capillary tubes (from left to right) were filled with increasing concentrations of agarose gel. The picture on the right shows the results of a more modern agarose slab-gel electrophoresis (this time created from a plastic sewing box). The leftmost lane is a sample of total*

Trichomonas *nucleic acids, whereas the last lane represents the same sample treated with DNA digesting enzyme, so it contains only RNA. The second lane is of reoviral dsRNA, and is used as a marker to determine the size of unknown dsRNA segments. Lanes 3 and 4 show reoviral dsRNA loaded together with various amounts of* Trichomonas *dsRNA.*

It took me about two months to figure out that it wasn't actually organelle DNA. The electrophoretic gel had at least six bands, in positions that corresponded to DNA molecules of various lengths. But most of these bands still showed up in the sample after I added a DNA-digesting enzyme, and disappeared when I added an RNA-digesting enzyme, under conditions in which not only single-stranded but also double-stranded RNA (dsRNA) is destroyed (Fig. 4).

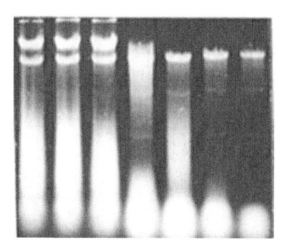

Fig. 4 Results showing that satellite bands on Trichomonas *nucleic acid electrophoretic gel are composed of RNA, not DNA. Samples in each lane (from left to right) were treated with increasing amounts of DNase (an enzyme which digests DNA). In another experiment, the samples were treated with an enzyme which digests double-stranded RNA. This caused all the lower bands to disappear, leaving only the top DNA band intact.*

I confirmed the dsRNA nature of the molecules using a combination of fluorescent dyes that glow different colors under UV-light, depending on which nucleic acid they have bonded to. Eventually, I even developed a quick method for isolating dsRNA from a mixture of nucleic acids[3]. The *Trichomonas* virus forms spherical (icosahedral) shells (capsids) about 35 nanometers in diameter. But some of the dsRNA – the short ones – seems to be found in the *Trichomonas* cell outside these capsids[4-6]. The amount of virus dsRNA in an infected *Trichomonas* cell is immense – comparable to the amount of DNA in the protozoan's nucleus. Yet the presence of the dsRNA doesn't harm the cell; at least under laboratory conditions, it doesn't slow cellular growth. About 30% of the strains in our lab had the virus, but the amount and lengths of dsRNA in the *Trichomonas* cells differed from strain to strain[5]. Interestingly, it's almost certain that at least two types of trichomonad dsRNA molecules are covalently bonded to a protein (and the same is probably true for the killer-factor dsRNA found in yeast), which, as far as I know, nobody has published yet. The killer-factor is a mycovirus that is suspiciously similar to the *Trichomonas* virus, in both the size of its genome and the shape of its capsids. We weren't able to determine whether the *Trichomonas* virus, like the killer-factor, also produces a toxin that kills uninfected cells or, possibly, competing yeasts.

But the study of RNA viruses in protozoans wasn't supposed to be the main research topic in my new laboratory. Already during my post-graduate study, I was well aware that our workplace had two major advantages over labs in other countries. In our department, we had a respectable collection of parasitic protozoans preserved in liquid nitrogen. Outside the liquid nitrogen, we had an equally respectable collection of parasitologists, who, in the quiet sanctuary of the Prague Faculty of Science (which, as my colleague Stanislav Komárek likes to say, is the last traditional German university in the world), waited out the tumultuous evolution of international biology in the second half of the 20th century. By the start of the 80s, in most Western universities, the departments of parasitology were either dissolved or gradually colonized by molecular biologists and biochemists, who knew little about the parasites they used in their studies. In our university, up to the late 90s, most of the scientists in the department of parasitology, and even most of its graduates, were able to find parasites in nature, determine their species, isolate, and, when technically possible, use them to establish a lab culture. And these abilities can be extremely useful. For example, they served me well in the field of molecular phylogenetics, which I began studying sometime in the mid-80s. In the 90s, scientists had not yet determined the zoological or botanical classification of many unusual groups of protozoa. So it seemed that we had a great chance to use our natural advantages, with the aid of modern molecular biology techniques, to fill in the empty spaces of the taxonomic system. This proved to true, as over the years my molecular phylogenetics research team (Box 4 *Research teams*) gradually discovered the phylogenetic positions of several interesting groups of parasitic protozoans[7,8]. Other groups of parasites were classified more quickly by our competitors, be it by a couple of months or a couple of years[9], but that's life.

So how was it that I left my lab of molecular phylogenetics to study *Toxoplasma*'s effect on host behavior – in other words, to study the manipulation hypothesis? Simply put, it was happenstance. When I arrived in the college, I knew very little about the manipulation hypothesis, and I certainly didn't expect to study it. In truth, I wasn't all that interested in it. The manipulation hypothesis states that some parasites alter the behavior of hosts in an effort to spread from an infected host into a new, uninfected one.

Box 4 Research teams

In the Faculty of Science, I always studied whatever seemed most interesting to me at the time. Sometimes, this wasn't well-received by my surroundings. In the department of parasitology, some of my colleagues were taken aback or even scandalized by the fact that I also taught my students topics that were, let's say, only loosely related to parasitology. For example, when studying the effect of parasites on human behavior, I also, incidentally (but rather intentionally), collected data related to general evolutionary psychology. If the secondary topic seemed interesting enough, I didn't hesitate to pursue it. For this reason, I was happy to offer my laboratory as an asylum to students who were unlikely to find support elsewhere, because they had chosen an unusual though interesting topic. So, I might happen to be studying the effect of latent toxoplasmosis on human behavior, the phylogenetics of anaerobic protozoans, the role of scent in choosing a mate, the evolutionary significance of sadomasochistic preferences, and the peptide "dictionary" of parasites and free-living organisms – all at the same time.

For example, a parasite, in order to complete its life-cycle, might need its current host to get eaten by a certain predator (so that the parasite can spread to the predator). The parasite often is able to alter the behavior of its current host, so it is more likely to get caught and eaten. For example, the infected host may be less careful, more noticeable, spend more time in open space, or react more slowly when in danger (Fig. 5). When I arrived in the department, most of what I knew about the manipulation hypothesis came from my favorite books, *The Selfish Gene* and *The Extended Phenotype* by Richard Dawkins (see Box 5 *The Selfish Gene*).

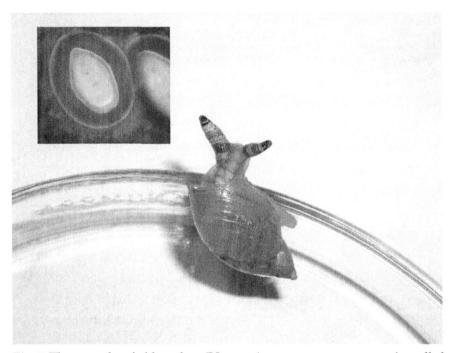

Fig. 5 The green-banded broodsac (Urogonimus macrostomus, *orig. called* Leucochloridium macrostomum *or* Leucochloridium paradoxum), *residing in an amber snail* (Succinea putris). *You can see the large, colorful and swollen broodsacs this parasitic flatworm has created on the snail. During the day, the broodsacs move to the snails' tentacles and cause them to pulse. Insect-eating birds (the definitive hosts of the green-banded broodsac) confuse the tentacles with caterpillars and eat them. Inside the broodsacs (sporocysts) are hundreds of microscopic larvae (see the picture on the top left), which infect the finicky bird. The parasite doesn't harm the bird much; otherwise the bird would be more careful in hunting for caterpillars.*

Among other things, Dawkins discusses the case of the Lancet liver fluke *Dicrocoelium dendriticum*. During its life-cycle, this fluke needs to get from its intermediate host, an ant, into one of its definitive hosts, such as a sheep. Now, sheep don't usually eat ants, but the fluke has a very elegant fix for this minor detail.

Box 5 The Selfish Gene

The book *The Selfish Gene* was published in 1977 by the British author Richard Dawkins. I believe the first copy to come to Prague was brought by Vladimír Jan Amos Novák, author of a world-renowned book about insect hormones, as well as several fairly nonsensical evolutionary theories; the founder and long-time head of the Laboratory of Evolutionary Biology, a practically independent research institute of the Czechoslovak Academy of Sciences; a member of the Central Committee of the Communist party of Czechoslovakia but simultaneously a decent sort. Among other things, Novák is famous for his personal letter to Lysenko, in which he tried to convince the latter to stop incarcerating his scientific opponents. Novák himself got locked up by the Russians for half a year, when, toting a backpack, he tried to illegally cross the border into the Soviet Union; he wanted to see for his own eyes what baffling things were happening during the Lysenkoism in his beloved communist country. (The Lysenkoism was a politically organized witch-hunt of good geneticists and biologists in the name of the obscure, ideologically-backed theories of Trofim Denisovich Lysenko. By the end of the fifties, this persecution spread to the Soviet satellites, including Czechoslovakia, where it fortunately never was as drastic as in the USSR.) Novák apparently got the book from Richard Dawkins in person, and after his return from England, thoughtlessly lent it to my mentor Jiří Čerkasov, who soon lost it to me. I think I was the first Czech to read this book. And if Novák beat me on the trip from London to Prague, it's quite possible that I win the category of being the Czech to have read it the most times. In a very accessible style, Dawkins shows why Darwin's theory of the evolution of adaptations by natural selections fails to explain how evolution works in sexually reproducing organisms. Dawkins proposes the theory of the selfish gene (which is basically an ingenious reformulation of Hamilton's theory of inclusive fitness). This theory states that in evolution, individuals of a species don't compete for the best biological fitness (see Box 58 *How evolution forms useful traits*); rather, gene variants (alleles) compete amongst each other to get the greatest number of copies into the next generation of organisms. Definitely read this book[10] – it's probably the best thing that Richard Dawkins has ever written (and believe me, his writing is not bad at all!). And then, I encourage you to follow up with my book *Frozen Evolution*[11], in which I, in turn, took on Dawkins' theory.

It reprograms the behavior of its host, so that come morning, the ant rushes out of its nest, goes a meter from the ant-pile, and climbs up a blade of grass. At the top, it chomps into the grass and holds on. There it waits until noon, when it climbs down and finds shade to avoid drying out. In the evening, when the air is cooler, the ant returns to its vigil, waiting until a passing sheep chomps up this blade of grass. I read this beautifully-rendered story so many times as a student that I'll never forget the elaborate antics of this clever fluke.

But when I returned to the university in 1991, I had no inkling that I might study something like this. As I mentioned, my primary goal was to form a molecular phylogenetics lab. Above all I tried to get back into normal academic life in the university, but for some reason I could not attain it. I'm not sure, to what extent it was tied to my wandering between the university and the Institute of Academy of Sciences, or to the first symptoms of a mid-life crisis, or to the unexpected arrival of freedom for former Czechoslovakia and the feeling that whatever the future had in store for me, it could not be a wonderful as the fall of communism. Probably a little bit of each.

In 1987, after finishing my graduate study, I had to leave the university, which couldn't find a place for me. Other graduates, who, unlike me, were members of the Communist party, were easily accommodated. But I wouldn't say that reason I "left" was primarily political. Rather, the people in power tried to get rid of independent thinkers, who might someday pose a threat, or at least stand in contrast with the authority's mediocrity. I have no illusions that this happens only in countries with Real Socialism. Nevertheless, there and then, leaders had an automatic system for chasing out such people – independent thinkers usually weren't members of the Communist party, so it was easy to get rid of them under this pretext. In my case, it was probably also a matter of common human envy. At the time, I was invited to an excellent laboratory in a California university, where my more publication-successful competitors were studying the *Trichomonas'* virus. And I, still young and naïve, mentioned in front my department head, who "coincidently" was also the leader of the local Communist party cell, what kind of pay I'd be getting at this American laboratory. As a result, I had to find a position outside the university. With a measure of good luck, I finally got a job in the Institute of Molecular Genetics at the Czechoslovak Academy of Sciences, in the laboratory of Vladimír Holáň. But my departure from Charles University lost me the opportunity to go the USA and continue researching *Trichomonas* viruses. In retrospect, I think it might have been for the better, because otherwise I wouldn't have begun studying the manipulation hypothesis, nor made the acquaintance of *Toxoplasma* (however, I say this primarily for the benefit of that department head; if she happens to read this, I hope she stews in her envy).

At my new workplace, I was officially working in biotechnology, developing the already-developed monoclonal antibodies for pregnancy tests (in other words, this is what I got paid for). Unofficially, I did genetic engineering; I subcloned sneakily-obtained interleukin genes into expression vectors (the job I was given by my boss); semi-illegally, I worked on proteomics, studying the peptide dictionary of parasites; and finally, I worked in immunology, researching DNA synthesis in white blood cells in the presence of nucleotide synthesis inhibitors (a situation under which no DNA synthesis should occur) (see Box 6 *DNA synthesis in white blood cells in the presence of a nucleotide synthesis inhibitor*).

Box 6 DNA synthesis in white blood cells in the presence of a nucleotide synthesis inhibitor

A lipopolysaccharide, extracted from the cell walls of bacteria, is thought to stimulate the division of B cells (white blood cells (WBCs), or leukocytes, that create antibodies). Scientists have determined this by adding a radioactively-marked DNA building block – thymidine (one of four types of nucleotides) into the culture medium given to the leukocytes. If the B cells are dividing, they should incorporate the thymidine, along with the radioactive marker, into the DNA of the new cells. We conducted this experiment using the mouse WBCs. Vladimír Holáň noticed that when we added the nucleotide synthesis inhibitor aminopterin (more specifically, purine nucleotide synthesis inhibitor) into the medium, then intensity of radioactive thymidine incorporation significantly increased. Actually, one would expect the opposite: in the presence of aminopterin, cells shouldn't be able to synthesize purine nucleotides, and therefore should not be able to synthesize the new DNA they need for cellular division. We never figured out why our B cells had no regard for theories and cheerfully incorporated radioactive thymidine into their DNA, even in the presence of the inhibitor. However, it is possible – and, I think, quite probable – that thymidine incorporation into WBC DNA, which is generally considered to be a measure of how quickly these cells are dividing, is actually tied to a completely different process, which, unlike DNA synthesis, doesn't require a supply of new nucleotides and therefore is not inhibited by the presence of aminopterin. My guess is that in certain areas, WBCs continuously degrade and re-synthesize their own DNA, which might be related to the antibody affinity maturation (see Box 22 *Antibodies and myths about them*). If I hadn't left the Institute of Academy of Sciences for the university, I probably would have continued solving the mystery of what lipopolysaccharide-stimulated B cells are actually doing, when immunologists think they are synthesizing new DNA. If one of the readers wants to take a crack at this problem, then I must warn him – only some lipopolysaccharides have this effect on lymphocytes (of causing thymidine incorporation even in the presence of a nucleotide synthesis inhibitor).

I wasn't too happy in the academic institute, probably because I had been spoiled by the atmosphere in the university. To say it more positively, in my time at the Faculty of Science, I was most grateful for the fact that people on different research teams helped each other, borrowed each other materials and equipment, gave advice and most of all, had a true interest in their work – an interest which often even bordered on enthusiasm. They did science for the sake of science, not for money or their career. In the Institute, I got to study something I was interested in (by that I mean the semi-illegal part of my work), and I had incomparably better equipment than at the university, but I felt out of place. There was great rivalry among the research teams, and when I needed to borrow a certain chemical from a friend, I had to creep into his lab after working hours, so that his boss wouldn't see. And so it's not surprising, that immediately after the fall of communism, I happily returned to my former position at the university. But to my dismay, soon after I got the unshakable feeling that I no longer belonged there. You can never step into the same river twice. Fortunately, it all straightened out after a couple years, but the first few years back in the college were strange and certainly not pleasant.

Maybe for this reason, for the first time in my life, I began paying attention to my own psyche.

I began considering past events in which my reactions had surprised me, but which I'd had neither the time nor the inclination to dwell on. As long as I can remember, maybe since I was six years old, my opinions and way of thinking haven't really changed. In any case, the mistakes I make are the same. But suddenly it seemed that in certain situations, I behaved differently than I would've expected. I've always considered myself to be someone who doesn't give up easily, and who carries out important things to the end. Usually, I am very reluctant to submit to authority, and even less to "authority"; and if I must do so, then it is only for strategic or tactical reasons, decided after serious consideration and borderline self-denial. Life taught me not to insist upon my opinions at any cost. Nevertheless, I am sometimes unsuccessful, which has gotten me into several tight spots. But to tell the truth, I didn't mind the occasional "tight spot". I was quite happy to tussle, from time to time, with an unwelcoming environment. Of course, if only due to my physical disposition, I rarely fought physically; but that's probably because in today's cushy times, conflicts between adults are rarely addressed with a stick or a fist. Furthermore, several times in my childhood (and also a few times later on), I was able to avert a physical conflict at the last minute with an unexpected psychological maneuver: You'd be surprised at how quickly an enthusiastic aggressor on the ridge of the Krkonos mountains will be thrown off balance when you politely inquire after the soonest bus to Neratovice. In any case, I must agree with a friend who would always say: "Whenever you see a hornet's nest, then you pick up a stick and start poking at it, to see what the stupid insects will do. And then you have to find a way to get out of the mess."

And certain recent behavior patterns did not fit my personality. A simple example: buying salami sold by weight. In my childhood, butcher and delicatessen shops – and actually, pretty much any shop – that sold goods by weight cheated their customers. Today, of course, they still do, but impersonally and on a professional basis – the cashier scans your vacuum-sealed bag of ham with added water, wishes you a good meal and hopes you'll come again (or you can go to another store, if you think their water is better).

During my childhood, salespeople apparently considered it a matter of personal pride to cheat their customer of a couple ounces on each portion they sold. So when a person bought ten ounces of ham, he could count on either receiving less of the meat, or at least getting the wrong amount of change – or possibly, both. Of course, this also happened to me. And instead of protesting and causing a nice ruckus (and losing the possibility of returning to the store), I kept quiet. And what's more, keeping quiet for some reason seemed more beneficial. As if staying mum and accepting the scam would somehow gain me a future advantage over the salesman. "I sure fooled him, letting him cheat me for the salami."

All in all, completely irrational behavior, which in retrospect, try as I might, I cannot see as beneficial. And after leaving the store, I could not understand the motive behind my actions, nor the feelings that accompanied them. Could the salesperson have hypnotized me?

Now for a different example. The house I live in had bad electrical wiring, so from time to time I blew a fuse. One day I was particularly successful, and blew not only the secondary circuit breaker, but also the main circuit breaker, and finally the power inlet box on the outside of my house. I knew that there are high currents running through this area, and that it's safer not to approach it, but rather to call the professionals. I also happened to know that replacing this fuse positioned in front of the electricity meter is the business of Electrical Company (or whatever its name is) and that it's free of charge. And I told myself – few people know that it's free of charge, so when the repairmen arrive, they'll probably ask to be paid. No doubt they'll say that I caused the damage, therefore I should pay for their trip and the broken fuse.

And I was right. The contractors arrived, changed the fuse, and told me to pay them ten bucks. At the time, five bucks was something like fifty bucks today. I knew that they had no right to the money; and what's more, I had anticipated their maneuver. But precisely because I knew it was a scam, and they thought that I didn't know, then, with a feeling of superiority, I gave them those ten dollars. All the while, I told myself: there, that will show them. Of course, I didn't show them anything – there was nothing to show. The contractors cheerfully stuck the ten dollars into their pocket and drove off.

I stood there in disbelief, waiting for the punch line. How is it possible that whenever I let somebody cheat me, I have a strong feeling that I'm actually winning? At that moment, I understood that the feeling of superiority is only illusion, and incompatible with reality. The person who cheats me leaves with a feeling of smug satisfaction (he'd probably be even more pleased to know that I let him cheat me) and I am left only with the strange feeling, that I cannot grasp how I let it happen, and why on earth I thought it was a good idea.

Like I said, after my return to the Faculty of Science, I started to see this pattern of strange behavior as an interesting psychological problem. I asked around whether others had experienced something similar, and discussed the problem with my friends. I inquired whether anyone ever got the feeling that in a particular situation they behave according to a foreign will and foreign interests, even though it seems like they are acting voluntarily. We probably discussed hypnosis and suggestion, since I thought they might be related. We tossed around the idea that certain people could be able to impose their will upon other people, so that victim behaves (with a feeling of superiority) in a way that benefits the suggester. I don't recall what we concluded, but it was clear that none of my acquaintances had experienced this situation.

About a month after one such debate, played out in a cozy, poorly lit corner of a pub close to the college building, Jaroslav Kulda stopped in my lab, in dire need of volunteers to test a new *Toxoplasma* antigen. For a long time, the department of parasitology had been conducting a study of toxoplasmosis. When I arrived in the Faculty of Science, this study was nearing its end, but a small part of original activities still existed, namely the testing of *Toxoplasma* antigens.

The method for producing this antigen for toxoplasmosis diagnosis was probably developed by the former researchers in the department of parasitology. By the time I arrived, the antigens had long been commercially produced by the Institute of Sera and Vaccines; but whenever they came out with a new batch of antigens, it brought them to our department for testing. In addition, several clinics sent us pregnant women suspected of having toxoplasmosis, and we were to screen them using a method known as the skin test.

In this test, a *Toxoplasma* antigen (a mixture of macromolecules obtained by solubilization of *Toxoplasma* cells) is injected into the skin. Within two days, people infected with the parasite – who are Toxo positive – get a red spot surrounding the injection site. Based on the size of the spot (scientifically-speaking, based on the intensity of the delayed hypersensitivity reaction), we could determine how long ago a person had been infected, as well as the risk of health complications for a pregnant woman (see Box 57 *How dangerous is Toxoplasma in pregnant women?*).

Testing antigens and screening pregnant women went well together; we had a regular supply of fresh antigen to test, and simultaneously a regular stream of patients who we could screen using the antigen. But before screening the women, we had to quickly determine how the antigen worked, and in what concentration we'd use it. And that was when Jaroslav Kulda ran from lab to lab, looking for volunteers for antigen testing.

Today, of course, it would probably be impossible for a parasitologist who was not a physician to inject people with an antigen, but back then, they weren't so strict about it. The times were a bit wilder, and such things weren't as tied down by various regulations. For example, in one of the labs for the parasitology class, students injected each other with antigens to test for toxoplasmosis.

In 1993, we even had an undergrad student in her second or third year of study conducting the skin test. I get goose bumps when I imagine the mess we'd be in if someone had complained about it, or even reported us to the authorities. For this reason, we quickly abandoned this method of testing, and switched over to the classic serological method. Serological tests, which determine the level of antibodies in a blood sample, are neither as sensitive nor as specific as a skin test, which means that one risks a false positive or false negative result (see Box 7 *The specificity and sensitivity of diagnostic tests*). On the other hand, the researcher doesn't risk getting in trouble. One of our doctor friends, who came to the college once or twice a year, would draw (and still does) the blood for testing. The student volunteers would enter the "office" in four-minute – in later years, even three-minute – intervals, sign the informed consent form, get about 4 mL of blood drawn by the doctor, and pick up a psychological questionnaire to fill in. And we were lucky to have the doctor we did, because just his name guaranteed that the students would come in droves to have their blood drawn. Whenever I lured the students to this testing, I always emphasized that the doctor's name was Zdeněk Hodný – something like "Joe Gentle" – and therefore that the blood draw wouldn't hurt a bit. The students probably didn't believe me, so they came to see for themselves.

Box 7 The specificity and sensitivity of a diagnostic test

The quality of a diagnostic test is primarily based on its specificity and sensitivity. A test with low **sensitivity** is one unable to detect low concentrations of a particular substance; therefore, it sometimes gives us a false negative result. So a person with low levels of *Toxoplasma* antibodies may be diagnosed as Toxo negative by an immunological test, even though he has actually been infected. On the other hand, a test with low **specificity** is one unable to distinguish *Toxoplasma* antibodies from antibodies against a different parasite. Such a test might diagnose someone who never had the parasite as Toxo positive – in other words, a false positive reading. Unfortunately, the specificity and sensitivity of a test often work like two communicating vessels. A test with high specificity has low sensitivity, and vice versa. Therefore, physicians select a test based on whether a false negative result or false positive result would do less harm to the patient. (In which case, they would select a high sensitivity low specificity, or high specificity low sensitivity test, respectively.) But in basic research, low specificity or sensitivity usually doesn't pose such a serious problem, and the test is chosen according to different criteria. If a cheaper and faster, but less specific or sensitive method allows us to test ten times as many individuals than a more expensive and time-consuming, albeit more specific or sensitive method, then it's usually better to go with the former, "inferior" method. The possible greater error will be made up for by the opportunity to test substantially more people.

To get back to the start of our research: when Jaroslav Kulda came looking for volunteers, I naturally stepped forth. In the first place, I was interested in the testing process; and furthermore, in whether or not I was infected. To my surprise – and by that, I don't mean pleasant – I found, two or three days after the testing, that I am Toxo positive. A red spot had formed around the injection site on my arm, and based on its size, I'd been infected relatively recently. At the time, I suspected this had happened in Japan, where I'd sampled raw or undercooked meat, and where the *Toxoplasma* prevalence is about the same as in the Czech Republic – that is, around 30%. But my infection probably happened before my Japan trip, maybe when I was handling hay from a rabbit run (see *Toxoplasma* risk factors, discussed in chapter XXI).

At the time of my testing, I knew little about *Toxoplasma* and toxoplasmosis (the disease caused by this parasite). Although I worked in the department of parasitology, and even in the room where *Toxoplasma* research was conducted; and my undergraduate work was carried out on protozoans in a lab shared by the department of parasitology and the department of animal physiology, my research focused on a different protozoan, the sexually-transmitted parasite *Trichomonas*. In any case, by education I was more of a physiologist or cellular physiologist; at heart an evolutionary biologist; and in terms of professional experience, primarily a molecular and cellular biologist. And as I mentioned, I'd spent four years working in immunological labs. The most I knew about *Toxoplasma* was that it's some protozoan; but I sometimes mixed it up with *Toxocara,* which is a parasitic helminth (or, as an old-timer would say, a parasitic worm). When I discovered that I was *Toxoplasma*-infected, I quickly got to know my enemy. The first thing that caught my attention was the interesting life cycle of this parasite (Fig. 6). *Toxoplasma* is a coccidium, and thus related to the protozoan which causes malaria. Both *Toxoplasma* and malaria belong to the group known as the Apicomplexa. *Toxoplasma* reproduces sexually in the intestinal epithelium of felids. Cats, therefore, are *Toxoplasma*'s definitive hosts (see Box 8 *Intermediate and definitive hosts*).

Box 8 Intermediate and definitive hosts

In their life-cycle, many parasites go through several host species, each of which plays a specific role. The most important role is that of the **trophic host**, whom the parasite pumps for maximum nourishment – resources used to form the biomass of its offspring. Then the vector, or **transport host**, ensures a transfer into a new host, and, if possible, an uninfected population. Finally, the **definitive host** is the organism in which the parasite reproduces sexually – in the other, intermediate host(s), it reproduced only asexually. Whereas in the trophic host, the parasite's primary concern was the number of offspring, in the definitive host it's also concerned about variety. Therefore, the definitive host serves as the place for the parasites' "rendez-vous." The parasite usually doesn't harm the definitive host, because it needs this host to survive as long as possible and accumulate as many distinct strains of the parasite as possible. Quite often, the definitive host also serves as a vector, and the intermediate host also serves as a trophic host, although it's not a rule – there are plenty of exceptions. Beyond that, parasitologists define a **paratenic host**, as a host in which the parasite cannot reproduce, but can sometimes accumulate. Through such a host, a parasite can get into an intermediate or definitive host – usually when the **paratenic host** is eaten, intentionally or unintentionally, by the new host. Sometimes the existence of a **paratenic host** increases a parasite's chances of getting into another host; but other times, it's to the parasite's disadvantage. The parasite might get into the **paratenic host** by accident, and only get to the definitive host if it's lucky.

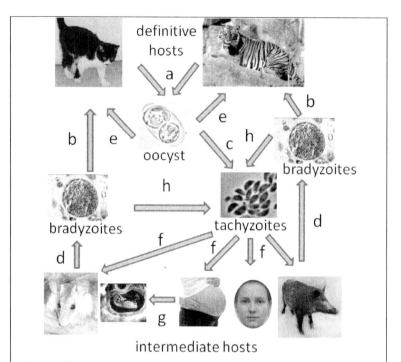

definitive hosts

a

oocyst

b
e

b
e

h
c

bradyzoites

h

bradyzoites

tachyzoites

f

f f f

d

d

g

intermediate hosts

Fig. 6 The life cycle of Toxoplasma gondii. *The definitive felid host releases oocysts in the feces (a). Oocysts reside in the soil and enter intermediate (c) and definitive hosts (e). In their bodies the oocysts quickly become rapidly dividing tachyzoites (d). Tachyzoites spread the infection through the body (f), often using the host's free-moving cells, such as white blood cells, as vectors. In host tissues, particularly in muscular, nervous, and connective tissue, tachyzoites change into slowly dividing bradyzoites (d), which remain in the host in the form of tissue cysts. If the infected individual is eaten (b), the tissue cysts release bradyzoites, which change into tachyzoites in the new host (h). If the consumer is felid, then the parasite differentiates in its intestinal cells. The tachyzoites first become merozoites and finally gametocytes, which fuse in pairs and form resistant oocysts. In a pregnant woman (or gravid female of any host species), tachyzoites can infect the developing fetus (g). Humans can be infected with oocysts from unwashed vegetables; or with bradyzoites from sources like raw or improperly cooked meat. Other sources of infection include contaminated water, and blood transfusion or organ transplantation from infected donors.*

Toxoplasma's intermediate host, on the other hand, can be any warm-blooded animal – so under normal circumstances, a mammal or bird. It's rumored that under "abnormal" circumstances, a fish can also become a *Toxoplasma* host, if kept at warm enough temperatures. It probably wouldn't work with a carp – I doubt it would appreciate water at 30 or more degrees Celsius (86 °F) – but with a tropical fish, it might be feasible. *Toxoplasma*'s life-cycle begins when an infected cat, the definitive host, excretes cysts in its scat. A cat is usually infected as a kitten, and releases cysts for only two or three weeks, although in large amounts. Then it stops, and thereafter is not contagious. Through the feces, the cysts make their way into the soil. From there they can infect any organism, be it mouse or man, that digs in the dirt or eats something with dirt on it. (For example, a child playing in the sandbox, or an adult munching on a carelessly-washed carrot.)

When a mouse becomes infected, it usually suffers only a mild illness (although this depends on how "bad," or virulent, the strain of *Toxoplasma* is, and how many parasites got into the mouse); something similar happens with a human. Certain mammals get sicker than others. Upon reaching the intestines of an intermediate host (mouse or man), the protozoan exits the cysts and form tachyzoites, a motile form of *Toxoplasma*. Tachyzoites attack various cells in the body, and inside, they quickly reproduce. A healthy immune system deals with these tachyzoites pretty quickly. It develops a strong immune response, and the tachyzoites have to "retreat into illegality." The quickly-reproducing tachyzoites become slowly-reproducing bradyzoites, which remain in the body as tissue cysts until the host's death. If the infected intermediate host is eaten by a felid, the protozoan begins sexually reproducing in the cells on the internal surface of the intestines, and releasing hardy cysts into the feces. And so it comes full circle. If the intermediate host (mouse or man) is eaten by an organism other than a felid, it behaves just as it would in any intermediate host, reproducing only asexually and eventually forming tissue cysts. Immediately after infection, a person undergoes a phase known as acute toxoplasmosis, during which the tachyzoites are rapidly reproducing. In someone with a healthy immune system, this resembles a mild virosis, and is often accompanied by swelling of the lymph nodes. The following phase, in which the parasites withdraw in tissue cysts, is known as latent toxoplasmosis. From a clinical standpoint, it is asymptomatic. Only in a small fraction of cases does a person ever realize that he was infected, and that he will carry *Toxoplasma* tissue cysts in his body for the rest of his life (Fig. 7).

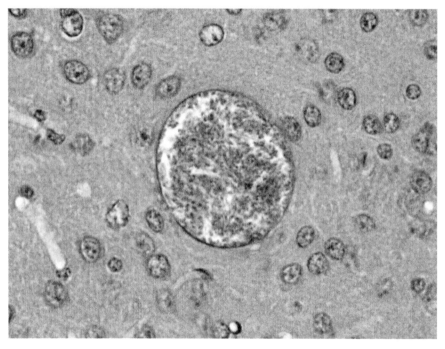

Fig. 7 A Toxoplasma *cyst in a murine brain. The small particles inside the cyst are individual bradyzoites, "silently" awaiting the moment when the host is eaten by a predator (hopefully by a felid, the definitive host of* Toxoplasma*). The bradyzoites will be released by the action of digestive enzymes and penetrate the host from the intestinal lumen through the endothelium. Photo by Mirka Pečálková-Berenreiterová.*

When reading up on *Toxoplasma*, one thing in particular caught my notice. This parasite can serve as a model organism for studying the manipulation hypothesis, because it seems that *Toxoplasma* alters the behavior of its intermediate host in order to up its chances of getting into a definitive host. In the 80s, an English team led by notable parasitologist William M. Hutchison (who discovered the life-cycle of *Toxoplasma*) tested this hypothesis.

They published a number of studies showing that, in certain situations, *Toxoplasma*-infected mice behave differently than healthy mice. And in a natural setting, some of the behavioral differences of uninfected mice could have made them more likely to get eaten by the definitive host, a cat.

It wasn't long before this new knowledge about *Toxoplasma*'s "lifestyle" clicked with what I had observed regarding my own behavior. In my muscle and nervous tissues lies a protozoan whose interests are undoubtedly different from my own.

Whereas evolution programmed me to survive and reproduce, it programmed *Toxoplasma* to try to manipulate me into getting eaten by a felid. Well, at least in the case of mice it can do so by altering their behavior (see Box 9 *Manipulative parasites: body snatchers*).

So why couldn't it also manipulate a human? Hidden in its tissue cysts, Toxoplasma has no way of knowing that it's in a human instead of a mouse brain; and even less so, of knowing that, for several millennia now, the chances of humans becoming cat chow are very slim. (I wanted to write that the chances are non-existent; but not long after I started my studies, one of our students was killed by a tiger in the Prague Zoo. I don't know whether the student was Toxo positive, but seeing as he climbed into the enclosure, I wouldn't be surprised.)

Box 9 Manipulative parasites: body snatchers

A manipulating parasite, figuratively speaking, battles over the body with its host. The host was evolutionarily programmed to behave in a manner that would get as many copies of its own genes into the next generation; whereas the parasite was programmed to make the host behave in a way that would pass on the parasite's genes. At first glance, it might seem that the host will win the tug-of-war; after all, he's fighting on his own turf. But in reality, the parasite is usually the victor. The main reason is because, evolutionarily, the parasite is much more experienced than his host in battling over body and behavior. The parasite battles with a host in every generation; and only the parasites who win will pass their genes to the next generation. In contrast, only a part of the host population battles the parasite in a particular generation. Moreover, it's still possible for hosts who would lose the battle to pass on their genes – for example, by reproducing before getting infected or manipulated. Because of these two reasons, the parasite is exposed to more systematic selection than the host; so he usually wins the evolutionary battle. Probably the most sophisticated "body snatcher" is a type of barnacle, which belongs among marine crustaceans. These parasites don't waste time re-programming the behavior of their host, but instead take over the whole body. The miniature larva of the barnacle genus *Sacculina* penetrates the body of a crab and then grows into network of threads, which most closely resembles the mycelium of wood-decaying fungi (and I'll have you know that barnacles are actually the distant cousins of crawfish and crabs!). They hormonally castrate their host and divest him of the ability to shed his cuticle, so that

> he won't waste energy on such trivialities like his own growth and reproduction. After some time, the reproductive organ of the barnacle bursts out of the crab's abdomen, and from then on the crab produces the larvae of his parasite. The great marine robbery is complete. The crab lives as he would normally, but instead of producing his own offspring, he makes that of the parasite. So the next time you're in Hawaii, you can easily find one of these crabs. In some areas, the majority of the population has been infected, and already from a distance you can distinguish them by the fact that their shells are overgrown with barnacles and algae – the crabs, you see, aren't allowed to molt.

Toxoplasma continues doing what it learned from its evolution, from those tens of millions of years that it's lived on this planet, attacking warm-blooded animals. It lies in its cysts, awaiting its opportunity, and manipulating its intermediate host so that he'll quickly wind up in a felid's stomach.

Suddenly I had an explanation for my strange behavior, for those situations in which I sought to be the victim of an attack and voluntarily cooperated with the person doing me harm. Even this irrational behavior is, from an evolutionary standpoint, an advantageous adaptation – of course, it's not good for me, the unwilling host of *Toxoplasma*, but it's very useful for the parasite trying to get into a felid's body. All the pieces fit. And I realized that, if my hypothesis were correct, then its implications applied not only to myself, but to an enormous amount of people. A third of the world's population was Toxo positive in the early 90s. In the Czech Republic, it was also a third; in France, 60 to 70%; in Germany and Hungary, 50 to 60%; and in USA, about 20%. Although in China, or at least in those areas covered by the studies, the prevalence of toxoplasmosis is significantly lower – usually between 5 and 10% –

in South America more than 60% of the population is infected, and in parts of Africa, over 90%. Just the number of potentially afflicted people is very disturbing; without taking into consideration the possible health and economic impacts. At this point, my primary concern wasn't just my own behavior, but rather the possible effects of *Toxoplasma* on a third of the world's population. And I immediately began planning how to attack my hypothesis.

II. How I accidentally discovered that *Toxoplasma* changes human personality

I got very lucky in selecting my research method. And in truth, I basically selected the first method at hand. At the time, we had practically no equipment for studying animal behavior. But we did have a constant inflow of human test subjects – female patients got the toxoplasmosis test administered one day, and returned two days later for us to check the test results. And I told myself that I could simply hand them a questionnaire, in which I would ask about those strange behavioral patterns I had observed in myself. Then I'd compare the answers of the women who turned out to be Toxo positive (infected), with those of the Toxo negative (uninfected) women, and see if there was a significant difference.

I prepared a set of maybe ten questions that I thought I would have answered differently before and after my infection. Besides questions about an unwillingness to defend oneself against a swindler, I included questions about behavior I thought could prove advantageous to a parasite. For example, I asked how quickly and in what way the answer reacted to immediate danger; whether they startle easily and jump away quickly, or rather remain calm, reacting slowly or not at all. I had noticed that now I was rarely startled. If I heard a rustling above my head, instead of jumping to the side, I was more likely to look up for the source of the sound. This sort of behavior could be advantageous for a parasite trying to make its way into a felid's stomach. Felids usually ambush their prey, taking advantage of the moment of surprise. If, in this moment, the prey acts effectively and quickly enough, then the felid will miss its meal. But if the prey hesitates for any sort of deliberation, instead of reacting reflexively, then it will find itself in the felid's jaws.

By the way, there are some situations of immediate danger in which an unnaturally cold-blooded reaction can actually be an advantage. For example, I was surprised by my own emotionless and entirely rational reaction to a machine-gun attack by Kurdish units on a small town near Diyarbakir in eastern Turkey. With a group of four students, we were staying the night in a truck bed among bags of cement (that evening, our Kurdish hosts had emphasized that this night we really *could not* sleep on the flat roof of the house, as we were accustomed to in Turkey), and for about 20 minutes, machine gun bullets blazed a few meters above our heads. I checked that everyone was huddled between the spaces between the bags, safe from ricocheting bullets, and then fell to contemplating what the angry Turkish soldiers would do after the attack. Fortunately, they were content with simply blowing out the window panes of all the Kurdish shops in the town and left our cement truck in peace.

Another question asked the person how startled, frightened, repulsed, or uncomfortable he is when he sees a spider or a snake. At the time, I created the questions according to intuition – I'm not exactly sure why I included this one. It might have been related to situation I heard about from one of my colleagues from the university, Jan Buchar, when I was recruiting him as a guinea pig for this testing, and told him about my hypothesis. He told me that, in the wild, he himself had seen a frog hop straight into the jaws of a grass snake. And all the while, the frog was wailing in fear; nevertheless, it hopped all the way to the snake, who summarily snapped it up. So the ability of a snake to hypnotize its prey could be more than a myth. Perhaps the snake is aided in his hunt by the parasite waiting in the brain of its prey – the parasite that needs to get into the snake.

A further question asked the subject whether he would fight to the end if physically attacked. Twice when I found myself in such a situation (thankfully, I haven't been physically attacked more times), I prematurely gave up the fight. And this was despite the fact that I had done karate a number of years after college, and so it wasn't a technical problem for me to incapacitate my attacker. But for reasons unknown, it was a problem psychologically.

Some of my questions sounded pretty strange, and if they'd been posed individually, then no doubt the questionee would wonder what on earth I was actually trying to figure out. For this reason, I judged it better to disguise my ten questions among a larger number of inquiries, preferably taken from a standard psychological questionnaire. Entirely by chance, I selected Cattell's 16-factor personality questionnaire, because the mother of one of our students was working with it at the time. I copied the questionnaire onto the computer, mixed my ten questions into its 187, and then handed it out to patients at the screening. But soon it because apparent that this method wasn't very effective.

Although we got three to five patients every week, only some of them were willing to dedicate an hour to answering nearly 200 questions. Many of the patients were either in a rush, or had no sympathy for my science, so the data accumulated slowly. I decided to focus my efforts on my colleagues. During each week of testing, I dashed from lab to lab, asking all the scientists and students I find whether they could volunteer. I explained to them the concept behind the testing, which stirred their interest, and about 80 to 90% took part in the testing. I also recruited friends and acquaintances, and the friends and acquaintances of my friends and acquaintances. So every Tuesday I made my rounds, convincing employees and students to get themselves tested for toxoplasmosis, and then complete that obnoxious, 200-question questionnaire. Over the course of six months, I gathered data from about 200 people. In the end, I didn't include the data from those couple of dozen patients that I tested at the very beginning, and in my statistical evaluation of the testing used only the data from the university students and employees in order to keep the study population as homogeneous as possible (see Box 10 *Statistical evaluation of data*).

Of course, I was most interested in the answers to my ten questions; but I incorporated those from Cattell's questionnaire into the analysis as well. This questionnaire primarily explores 16 psychological factors, such as Sociability, Warmth, Emotional stability, Dominance, and Intelligence.

Box 10 Statistical evaluation of data

Statistics is a set of methods which allows us to detect relationships in imperfect data that have been "sullied" by the effects of chance. In the real world, random factors affect almost all the data a scientist works with. **Exploratory statistical methods**, such as factor, cluster, and discrimination analysis, allow us to reveal relations partially hidden by the effects of various (in the present context) random factors – i.e. factors other than the one(s) we are currently studying. **Confirmatory statistical methods** allow us to estimate the probability that the **null hypothesis** is true – in other words, the probability that the observed phenomenon, such as an average greater body mass measured for 30 Toxo positive people than for 30 Toxo negatives, is only due to chance. If we create two entirely random groups – for example, by tossing a coin for each person – and then measure the mass body of the individuals, then the average body mass of the two groups will undoubtedly be different. If the two groups are very large, and their members are truly selected by chance, then the difference between the group averages should be small. But if either of the groups is small, or was affected by an outside factor (for example, if we weighed the people in one group first, and in the meantime, the other group of people lost weight – for example, some of them simply went to the bathroom), then the difference in average body mass can be quite large. Based on whether or not the observed difference is large for the given group sizes and the given variability in the measured variable– that is, whether or not an outside factor influenced played a role – we select the appropriate statistical method. In this case, it would be a t-test (Student's t-test). The result of statistical data analysis is the **P value**, which reflects the probability that the observed phenomenon – in the example above, this is the difference in the average body mass of the two groups – is just due to chance. If this P value is lower than 0.05, or 5%, then the difference is statistically **significant**. This means that the probability of the null hypothesis is so low that we have the right to lean towards the opposite conclusion: that the observed difference is caused not just by chance, but also by an outside factor. (In the framework of classical statistics, the P value is not the probability that the null hypothesis is true. Rather, it is the probability of obtaining the results you did (or more extreme) even if the null hypothesis applies – in other words, getting "false positive data." But don't worry about this – even among researchers who regularly use statistics in their work, only a few understand this difference[12].)

I expected that none of these factors would be related to toxoplasmosis, though some of the 200 questions in Cattell's questionnaire could be. They might ask something similar to what my question did; or they might ask about something that hadn't occurred to me, but could be related to *Toxoplasma* infection. But the situation was a bit risky, because two hundred questions meant two hundred statistical tests, and when analyzing so many tests, one must use a correction for multiple testing (see Box 11 *Bonferroni correction for multiple testing*). Without this correction, we risk false positive results; but with it, we risk false negative ones.

Box 11 Bonferroni correction for multiple testing

When we pose 200 different questions to students divided randomly into two groups, then the average answer of the two groups will have a statistically significant difference for every twentieth question. This is because of the way statistical tests work. A statistical test primarily gives us the P value, which reflects the probability that an observed phenomenon, such as the difference in the average answer of infected versus uninfected people to a certain question is only due to chance (see also Box 10 *Statistical evaluation of data*). But if we are asking whether the two groups differ in their average answer to not one specific question, but to at least one of any 200 questions, then the probability that the difference is only due to chance is much greater than what we are given by the statistical test. Whenever I'm explaining this concept to students, I use this analogy: When I toss a piece of chalk into a trash can across the room, the chances that I'll make it in are about 1%. Whereas if I throw 200 pieces of chalk, then the chances that at least of these will make it in are 200 times greater – meaning that I most probably get two piece of chalk in. So if we're conducting several unrelated statistical tests, we must use the **Bonferroni correction**, which involves multiplied the obtained P value by the number of tests. A more precise (and not as strict) corrective method for multivariable tests substitutes the P value into the following formula: $P' = 1 - (1 - P)^n$. But after applying the Bonferroni correction, many originally statistically significant results are no longer statistically significant; many of them rightfully, but other unrightfully so. This means that we risk overlooking an interesting result. But of course, the whole matter is a bit more complicated (see also Box 85 *When and when not to use a Bonferroni correction*). Today, the statistician usually tries to replace a set of several individual tests with a single test that tries out all the hypotheses simultaneously. So if we're comparing the average temperature in five localities, we don't have to use ten separate tests to compare the temperature of all ten pairs of localities, and then fix the resulting P values using the Bonferroni correction (by multiplying them by ten). Instead we use the ANOVA (analysis of variance), and only if the ANOVA gives us a statistically significant result will we check each pair of localities for a difference. This is a better approach, because it involves a much lower risk of false negative results. Therefore, today multiple tests followed by a Bonferroni correction should only be conducted if we don't have the appropriate test for several independent variables (e.g. multiple regression or ANOVA) available – for example, if we have data whose analysis requires a nonparametric test (see Box 25 *Parametric and nonparametric tests*).

To my pleasant surprise, the questionnaire study was successful, although a bit differently than I expected. For some of my ten questions, there was a difference in the answers of infected and uninfected people, but these differences weren't very big, and weren't statistically significant after a Bonferroni correction. But much more interesting were the results regarding Cattell's psychological questionnaire, which I had only included to keep the test subjects from suspecting the study's true purpose. When looking at the individual questions, none of the differences were statistically significant – and definitely not after the Bonferroni correction – so there was nothing interesting in that aspect. But out of those 16 psychological factors determined by Cattell's questionnaire, several were different in infected versus uninfected men, and one of these was statistically significant even after the Bonferroni correction. In women, differences in the same factors tended to be flipped (for Toxo positives versus Toxo negatives), and weren't statistically significant. However, differences in two other factors were almost statistically significant. In reality, the differences may have missed statistical significance because there were a lot fewer women than men in our test group. Back then, substantially more men attended the department of natural sciences than women; over time, the ratio reversed, and today we have almost three times as many female than male students.

Toxo positive and negative men differed most in the psychological factor L (Protension), or Suspiciousness (Toxo positive men were more suspicious); and then in factor G (Superego strength), which tells us how willing people are to follow social norms. Toxo positive men had significantly lower Superego strength than did Toxo negative (uninfected) men. So one can say that my Toxo positive colleagues and students were more suspicious and less willing to respect social norms (Fig. 8).

A weaker, and not statistically significant effect of toxoplasmosis manifested in a lowered factor A (Affectothymia) (sociability, warmth, and openness), as well as in factor Q_3 - Self sentiment integration (they have less self-control). In contrast, infected women had a slightly greater willingness to respect social norms (factor G), higher affectothymia (factor A), and slightly greater intelligence (factor B).

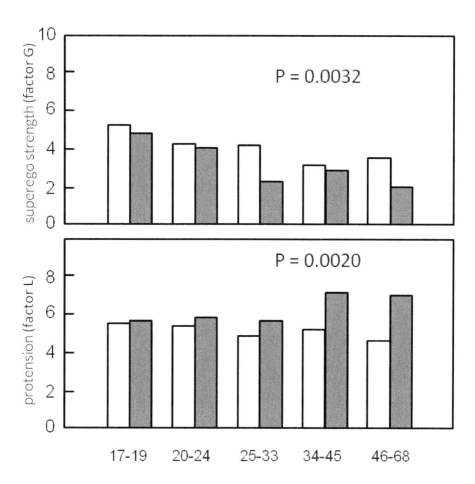

Fig. 8 A bar graph demonstrating the differences between the Toxo positive versus negative male students and teachers of our college, regarding Cattell's factor G (Rule consciousness), which measures Superego strength, e.g. the tendency to follow social norms, and factor L (Suspiciousness, or Protension). Since older people are more likely to be Toxo positive, the difference between Toxo negatives (white columns) and positives (gray columns) could be result of their age. Therefore, we had to statistically filter out the effect of age by including age in the analysis as a covariant (as an "unimportant" variable that influences the studied variable but is outside our interest), or by analyzing individual age groups separately (see x-axis). The graph shows that the effect of toxoplasmosis is statistically significant in all analyzed age groups.

I happily presented my results at a conference of Czech and Slovak protozoologists, and, as could be expected, it brought some much-needed excitement. By that I mean that most of those present welcomed the diversion in an otherwise fairly boring program; I sincerely doubt that they believed our results. I myself wasn't really sure what I thought about the data. If there had been unambiguous differences between the infected and uninfected subjects in their average answers to my ten questions, I would have said: yes, I clearly confirmed my hypothesis; *Toxoplasma* probably manipulates the behavior of its host.

But I had no clue how Suspiciousness or Superego strength could be related to toxoplasmosis. I think that my presentation, called "Show me your parasites and I'll tell you who you are," concluded that the observed differences between infected and uninfected men might be a side-effect of *Toxoplasma*'s manipulatory activity. The parasite tries to do the same thing in man that works in mice, and it manifests in this bizarre manner. But I myself wasn't too sure about this conclusion. I knew only too well that when one obtains and unexpected positive result in one study, then, regardless of statistical significance, he must be very careful in his conclusions – and certainly verify the result with new, unrelated data (see Box 12 *Why to be wary of unexpected results*).

Box 12 Why to be wary of unexpected results

Unexpected results are treacherous, especially when one can't come up with a convincing explanation after obtaining them. If, before starting the study, we decide to look whether infected versus uninfected people differ in any of the 16 psychological factors, then we can use the Bonferroni correction to determine the probability that the observed difference in that factor is due to chance as opposed to toxoplasmosis (see Box 10 *Bonferroni correction for multiple testing* and Box 85 *When and when not to use a Bonferroni correction*). But if we first collect the data and discover a relationship during the following analysis – for example that all the people whose last name starts with a vowel differ in a certain factor from those whose last name starts with a consonant – then we certainly need to confirm the result on a different subject group before publishing it, regardless of how statistically significant the correlation is. There are infinite nonsense hypotheses that we could test in our data; thus it's not surprising that one of these would be supported by the statistical test. As I already mentioned in relation to the Bonferroni correction, the obtained P value, which indirectly reflects probability that a certain phenomenon is only the result of chance is only correct when you are checking a single test. If we're examining data after the experiment, we are unwittingly or even wittingly testing an enormous number (of mostly nonsensical) hypotheses. If something in the data catches our interest, to the extent that we decide to formally test the existence of the observed phenomenon (for example, the relationship between the last letter of one's first name, last name, name of residence and the psyche, body height, blood group, or the sum of the digits in one's birth-date, etc., and the test gives us a highly statistically significant result, it doesn't really mean anything (Fig. 9). No Bonferroni correction can help us – there are many nonsensical hypotheses we could think of, and we have no way of knowing how many we tested in our minds when looking at the data. Yes, you should carefully examine the data, because it might contain unexpected results which could be much more interesting than the original reason for the study. (In my opinion, the ability to notice such details it what marks a good researcher.) But unexpected results should be approached very carefully, and always tested in an independent study.

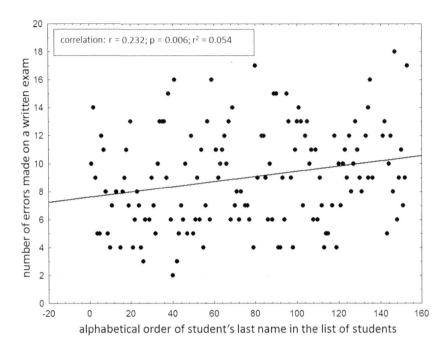

correlation: r = 0.232; p = 0.006; r² = 0.054

number of errors made on a written exam

alphabetical order of student's last name in the list of students

Fig. 9 An example of an unexpected, and therefore probably nonsense correlation revealed subsequently in the data. The X-Y scatter plot shows the number of errors made on a written exam on evolutionary biology according to the alphabetical order of student's last name. The relationship between this order and test result might not be as nonsensical as it seems at first glance. Many elementary and middle school teachers call out students according their alphabetical order in the gradebook, so students at the beginning of the alphabet are often questioned more frequently. Annie Adams is therefore (maybe) better trained to prepare for an examination than Zachary Zuko. Unfortunately, I was not able to reproduce this result in the following years, so it might really be due to chance.

So why did our results seem suspicious to me, and why, when starting the study, did I not expect that any of the 16 Cattell's factors could be influenced by toxoplasmosis? The thing is, most of Cattell's psychological factors are primarily influenced by a someone's personal value system, rather than his natural, spontaneous tendencies. This, at least in my opinion, is what distinguishes Cattell's questionnaire from others like Cloninger's 7-factor Temperament and Character Inventory (TCI) questionnaire, which we began using in later years. Cloninger's factors, such as novelty seeking, reward dependence, and harm avoidance, can be (and apparently are) related to the concentration of a certain neurotransmitter (see Box 13 *Neurotransmitters* and Box 56 *What does Cloninger's TCI measure?*). So by changing the concentration of the neurotransmitter, the parasite can easily affect these factors.

In contrast, Cattell's factors, such as Sociability, Superego strength, and Suspiciousness, are related to the set-up of one's inner values. For example, if someone thinks that it's good not to obey social norms, then he likely won't obey them, and the Cattell's questionnaire will show his low Superego strength. If someone has had his trust broken several times in his life, then he's probably suspicious; but if it hasn't happened to him yet (in which case he must have shipwrecked in time on a deserted island), then he's more trusting and Cattell's questionnaire will show his low Protension. Since one's system of values is established early on in life, and isn't easy to change, it seemed to me quite unlikely that Cattell's personality factors could be significantly affected by toxoplasmosis.

Box 13 Neurotransmitters

The cells of the nervous system communicate with each other and other cells through electrical and chemical signals. The chemical substances that transfer information between nervous cells are called neurotransmitters. There exist a number of neurotransmitters, which differ not only in molecular structure, but also in the location of their synthesis, their effect, and their biological function. Some neurotransmitters act only in area in which they are secreting, binding to the membrane receptors of the surrounding cells. The leftover neurotransmitters are usually reabsorbed into the original cell, to be reused, or are digested by specialized enzymes. But many neurotransmitters act at a greater distance. In this case, they remain in the nervous tissue for a longer period of time at a fairly high concentration. As a result of the higher concentration of neurotransmitters, the number of corresponding receptors on surrounding cells gradually changes (usually by decreasing). The levels of individual neurotransmitters, as well as the number and type of the corresponding receptors, affect how an individual reacts to a certain type of stimulus, or how enthusiastically he seeks it out (see also Box 56 *What does Cloninger's TCI measure?*).

Temporary differences in neurotransmitter and receptor concentration are reflected in mood swings; long-term differences can explain the vast variety of human temperaments. Aside from the stimuli he encounters in his lifetime (i.e. experiences), a person's temperament also depends on genetic predispositions. For example, it's known that individuals have different variants of receptors for the neurotransmitter dopamine. People with a certain variant exhibit a much greater probability of becoming drug addicts and risk-takers. From the perspective of a population and the entire species, it's clearly advantageous for individuals to have different temperaments, and therefore give precedence to different activities, because it facilitates division of both labor and resources. Studies conducted on birds also reveal genetically determined differences in temperament.

After nature exposed my error, and showed that a number of Cattell's factors – including some that I definitely wouldn't have expected – were affected by Toxo infection, I began casting around for a possible mechanism. Finally, I reached the conclusion that there is an explanation, but it requires a fundamentally reevaluation of the generally accepted relationship between one's systems of values and one's behavior. Psychologists usually believe that the reason people act in agreement with their system of values is because they modify their behavior to fit their values. Based on our results from *Toxoplasma* studies, today I picture the relationship as being the other way around. Each individual systematically – even if subconsciously – observes himself, noting how he reacts in various situations. And so that his behavior doesn't conflict with his values system, he gradually adjusts not his behavior (for this would achieve only short-term harmony), but rather his system of values. So today I picture the relationship between Cattell's personality factors and toxoplasmosis as follows: a person has some system of values, a large part of which was constructed during his childhood; then he becomes infected with *Toxoplasma*, and in certain situations, behaves differently than he would've before. After some time, he notices this, just as I did myself, and formulates a rational explanation. Then he reorganizes his system of values to align with his new behavior, which in reality is caused by the parasite.

I am but a self-made amateur in psychology (though my wife would say that this is more of a flattering euphemism). I don't know whether my reverse theory of personality up is correct; nor do I know whether it's new, or whether there are psychologists who look at the relationship between behavior and the values system in this opposite manner. When I asked my colleagues, or the psychologists I worked with, they weren't too sure about it. Perhaps one of my readers will tell me which author I should cite in the future in relation to the above model of building one's value system (see Box 14 *Citations in scientific literature*).

Box 14 Citations in scientific literature

In scientific literature (but not, for example, textbooks), any nontrivial statement must be supported with the appropriate citation – that is, a reference to original author and the source in which he or she published the discovery or hypothesis. There are two reasons for this practice. First off, it enables the reader to look up the source and see the statement in the context of the data and methods. The second reason is social – citations are part of scientific etiquette, and really etiquette in general, because they acknowledge that the cited author was the first to make that discovery. This is why you must cite the first author of a hypothesis, even if you yourself formulated the hypothesis independently. And strictly speaking, it's sometimes quite difficult to know whether you created a hypothesis independently, or whether it somehow (perhaps indirectly) reached you from its original source. Back in the 80s, while reading an immunology textbook (*Fundamental immunology*), I was just overjoyed when I uncovered the role of MHC proteins in antigen presentation. I thought of a model that elegantly explained almost all the peculiarities then known about MHC proteins, including the reason they play such an important role in most immunological processes. Several years later, I realized that, maybe a year before making my "discovery," I had read about the hypothesis in a 1986 article published by Jacques Ninio in the journal *Immunology Today*[13]; only I hadn't quite understood or appreciated it. Meanwhile, the article apparently fell into obscurity; over those several years, it was cited only once (and that was by the author himself). And actually, a year before Ninio's hypothesis, a nearly identical (but clearer) model had been published in *Nature* by Antonio Lanzavecchia[14], and this time with strong supporting data. Lanzavecchia's model was referenced in the article in *Immunology Today*, and by 2010, had been cited 1027 times by various authors. Nevertheless, even now, 25 years after what is probably the greatest discovery in modern immunology, Lanzavecchia is still waiting for his Nobel Prize. And that is despite having a Hirsch index of 95 in 2010 (see Box 28 *How to measure the quality of science*).

Cattell's and Cloninger's weren't the only psychological questionnaires that we used to torture our test subjects. Starting in 2007, we began using the currently popular questionnaire known as the Big Five; before that, we used a Czech questionnaire known as N-70. Let's start with the second questionnaire. The N-70 was created by Czech psychologist Karel Vacíř as a shorter alternative to the better known SCL-90 questionnaire. Unfortunately, the N-70 is not used world-wide, so results obtained using the questionnaire are very difficult to publish in international journals. For this reason, we tried to replace it with the SCL-90, but it turned out that results obtained by the two questionnaires are not comparable, at least regarding the effect of latent toxoplasmosis on the human psyche. Phenomena we repeatedly observed with the N-70 could not be verified with the internationally accepted SCL-90 questionnaire. In a normal, healthy population, the N-70 measures tendencies towards certain psychopathologies, such as hysteria, neurasthenia, vegetative lability, and phobia. When testing several large groups of soldiers from the mandatory military service, we always saw differences between Toxo positive and negative people in several factors determined by the questionnaire. We weren't surprised to find differences, but we were surprised at the nature of these differences. Apparently, Toxo positives were psychologically healthier and more resilient. We repeated the studies on several groups of professional soldiers, but the results were not as clear as for those of the mandatory military service.

The Big Five, or rather its most popular implementation the NEO-PI-R, is a widely used psychological questionnaire. It primarily differs from Cattell's 16PF questionnaire in the number of factors it determines. As the name suggests, it distinguishes only five main factors (extroversion, neuroticism, agreeableness, conscientiousness, and openness to experience), whereas Cattell's 16 factor questionnaire, shockingly enough, determines sixteen. Nevertheless, this particular difference is not too substantial. Each of the main Big Five factors has several sub-factors (which is also true for six of the seven Cloninger's factors). Furthermore, the sixteen Cattell's factors can be used to calculate five factors quite similar to those of the Big Five (extroversion, emotional stability, self-control, self-reliance, and tension). The main advantage of the Big Five becomes apparent in practice; in comparison with most earlier psychological questionnaires, its results are not as affected by population type (male, female, nationality, etc.). And this was confirmed in our results. When we tested our students with this questionnaire, infected men and infected women had similar results (in contrast to the time when we used Cattell's questionnaire, and infected men and women were affected in opposite ways). Infected persons had greater extroversion and lower conscientiousness (Fig. 10). Today, we use the Big Five questionnaire more and more in our new studies. It's not because we consider it better questionnaire than Cattell's, but rather because most psychologists know the Big Five and can more easily understand our results. Consequently, our papers have a better chance of being published in good psychological journals.

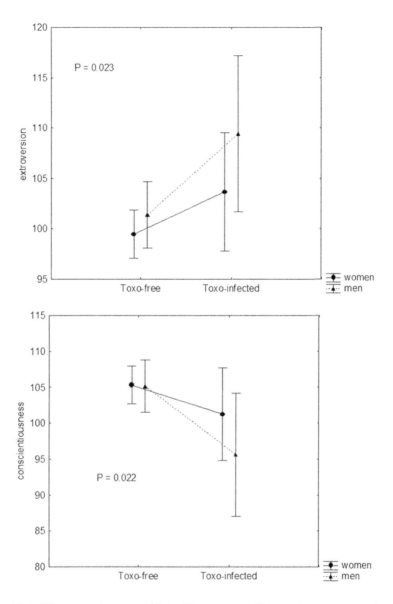

Fig. 10 Differences in two of Big Five personality traits, extroversion (a) and conscientiousness (b), in Toxo positive and negative male and female students. The groups consisted of 181 uninfected and 30 infected female students and 95 uninfected and 21 infected male students. Toxo positive persons have greater extroversion and lower conscientiousness. The graphs show the mean for each group with a 95% confidence interval.

III. What came first, the chicken or the egg? Toxoplasmosis, or a change in behavior?

From the beginning, I encountered the following problem: if there were differences in the psychological profiles of Toxo positive versus negative persons, then it wouldn't be clear whether *Toxoplasma* had caused the differences, or whether particular psychological traits made one more likely to be infected. And it's hard to decide between these two possibilities. Of course, if we were studying animals other than humans, then the solution would be quite simple. We could separate the animals into two identical groups – a control and an experimental group – and infect that latter with the parasite (see Box 15 *Popular mistakes when making a control group*).

Box 15 Popular mistakes when making a control group

When preparing experimental studies, we should always try to correctly set up the **control group**. Before the experiment begins, the individuals in the control group cannot be different in any way from those in the experimental group – the ones we expose to the studied factor, such as *Toxoplasma* infection. Otherwise, any differences we observe between the infected and uninfected animals might not be due to the parasite, but stem from differences that existed before the experiment. A good way to mess up your experiments is by setting up two cages, one for the infected and the other for the uninfected animals. Then we take twenty mice out of their crate, one by one, and set them in the control group cage; we repeat the process for the experimental cage. Because of our procedure, it now does not matter whether or not the parasite affects its host's behavior – in this experiment, we will undoubtedly find differences between the infected and uninfected mice. The control group consists of the first twenty mice we caught, so these animals will clearly have different behavior than the mice who escaped us longer. To avoid this problem, we should have alternately placed one mouse in the control cage and the other in the experimental cage. Another way to screw up your experiment is by placing the control cage on a different shelf than the experimental cage. This means that the mice in one of the two locations may be disturbed more often, or exposed to a greater draft, more noise, or bright light. A particularly effective way to mess things up is to expose the experimental group to different stimuli than the control group. In our case, it's enough to force-feed (using a feeding tube) the twenty experimental mice with brain from Toxo positive mice, and do nothing to the control mice. The correct procedure is to also force-feed the control mice, but in this case with brain from uninfected individuals.

Then we would observe whether the two groups differed in their behavior. If yes, then this would mean that the infection induces behavioral changes; if not, infection would not affect behavior. If the latter is true, then any differences seen between infected and uninfected mice in nature are probably because certain behavior increases their risk of infection. Of course, in studies conducted on humans, we cannot form two random groups and infect one of them with *Toxoplasma*. In these studies, our probands themselves "decide" who is and who isn't infected. As a result, we can't easily determine whether *Toxoplasma* caused the observed differences in psyche and therefore behavior, or whether these differences existed before infection and were the reason that some of the people became infected. For example, let's say that men who didn't respect social norms often ate raw meat or unwashed vegetables, and so more of them became infected (see Box 16 *A question of causality – what is the cause and what the effect?*).

Box 16 A question of causality – what is the cause and what the effect?

With statistical testing, we can estimate the probability that some association exists between two phenomena. But based on existence of a statistical association between two phenomena, we cannot determine which of the phenomena is the cause and which the effect – in other words, whether event A caused event B, or whether event B caused event A. And often there exists an event C that causes both A and B. To determine the **causality**, we usually rely on additional information. Sometimes common sense is enough. For example, if the statistical test shows us that a person's reaction time is related to his age, then we're not going to assume that worse reaction time causes a greater age. But even in this case, we cannot forget the distinct possibility that there may exist another phenomena C, which is related to both age and tested reaction time.

For example, younger people generally are better trained in rapid reactions (and especially in quickly reacting to stimuli on a screen and pressing buttons) from playing video games and texting. Sometimes it helps to use the criterion of temporality. If phenomenon A always comes before phenomenon B, then it's not very likely that B could be the cause of A. But even the **criterion of temporality** is not completely infallible (Fig. 11). Usually, we observe neither A nor B directly, but determine them based on other phenomena A' and B'. For example, we don't directly observe *Toxoplasma* infection (the presence of the parasite in the human), but determine it based on the presence of certain antibodies the immune system creates to fight the parasite.

But it takes a while for the body to create high enough antibody levels for us to detect them; so it might happen that we observe worsened reaction time in a person before we determine *Toxoplasma* infection, and base on the criterion of temporality, we might (erroneously) conclude that worsened reaction time increases the risk of infection.

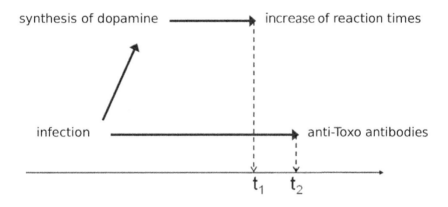

Fig. 11 An example of the failure of the temporality criterion. In a test, we may find that some people have longer reaction times before we detect (using the antibody test) that they have toxoplasmosis, even if/though the prolongation of reaction times is due to toxoplasmosis. This is a hypothetical and actually not too probable an example. It is more likely (but not certain) that specific antibodies appear before the infected person attains a longer reaction time.

Figuring out whether toxoplasmosis induces changes in the psyche, or whether psychological differences affect the risk of infection – in other words, determining cause and effect – wasn't an easy nut to crack. But again, we got lucky. In our department, we closely cooperated with the diagnostic laboratory of the Prague Hygiene station. The researchers of this lab kept long-term records of people who had been tested for toxoplasmosis. And these records contain not only the result of the toxoplasmosis tests, but also the addresses of the tested individuals. Back then, the Czech Republic didn't yet have laws about handling personal data, so we could afford to do something we probably couldn't (or at least shouldn't) do today. We looked up the addresses of the patients, and wrote them a letter under the name of the diagnostic laboratory requesting their cooperation in a research project regarding the relationship between toxoplasmosis and human behavior. I didn't tell them my suspicions that *Toxoplasma* changes human behavior, because I expected this might terrify a number of normal people. So most of the patients probably thought that we're studying how behavior impacts one's risk of infection. That was partly true, since we also included a couple of questions regarding risk factors, such as consumption of raw meat and unwashed vegetables, contact with soil, and the size of one's residence. In contrast, the university scientists and biology students (I was going to write "abnormal people," but finally changed my mind – there's no need to insult the reader's intelligence with overexplicitness) who served as subjects in the first study were usually excited at the possibility that a parasite manipulates human behavior, and therefore were happy to be guinea pigs in my study. Approximately 80% of the biologists I asked agreed to participate – even today, this seems quite incredible to me.

But back to the former patients we looked up in the records of the diagnostic laboratory. In cooperation with the researchers of this lab, we sent out about 500 letters. This first wave of letters went to men who had been tested for acute toxoplasmosis within the last twelve years and came out Toxo positive. I hypothesized that if *Toxoplasma* truly changes human behavior, then the psychological changes should become more profound over time: Superego strength (G), and maybe Self sentiment integration (Q_3) and Affectothymia (A) should be lower in long-infected men, and Suspiciousness (Protension, L) greater, than in recently-infected men. We sent the questionnaire only the men whose time of infection we knew. Fortunately, this can be determined according to levels of group IgM antibodies in the blood; these antibodies increase in infected persons, and usually peter out within half a year (see also Box 22 *Antibodies and myths about them*). We got back a good number of completed questionnaires, so in the end we had data on the psyche and time of infection of 190 men. The question we wanted to answer with this data was simple: Do the factors of suspiciousness and superego strength change with time after infection in the expected direction, that is, with suspiciousness increasing and superego strength decreasing (Box 17 *Checking and cleaning data*)?

Box 17 Checking and cleaning data

There is no data set so small that it does not hide at least one erroneous item. Perhaps there is or was an exception somewhere (probably at the edge of the world), but I haven't found it yet. When you finish collecting data and are getting ready to analyze it, you must suppress the curiosity to look at the results. Before seeing your results, it is imperative that you carefully check the correctness of the data. Otherwise you risk becoming enamored with the data, and become reluctant to check them – in which case, any observed association may be due to errors in the data. Besides, part of data checking is revealing and dealing with outlying values. You have to decide what defines an outlier, and whether you should leave it out or perhaps replace it with the average value, before approaching any sort of analysis. If you do it after the analysis, you risk eliminating "unfitting" extreme values and keeping only values which support your hypothesis. You must check the data for values that are too high or too low; negative values where data can only be positive (body mass, age); for text mixed in with digits (if you mix up the zero and O on the keyboard, a "number" like 1OO can cause you many a headache later on). There's probably no ideal way to check data. But you can't go wrong if you create a histogram of the distribution of each studied variable; and perhaps even an XY-graph of the relationship of each pair of quantitative variables. When looking at the histograms, you can not only find dubious data but also immediately recognize that some variables should be transformed before the analysis (for example, by taking their log), in order to obtain a symmetrical, and if possible, normal distribution (see Box 18 *Data transformation*).

Analysis of the data showed that two Cattell's factors, specifically Superego strength (Rule-consciousness G) and Self sentiment integration (Q_3), decrease with time after infection (Fig. 12)[15]. So we concluded that *Toxoplasma* changes a person's behavior, as opposed to a particular behavior increasing the likelihood of *Toxoplasma* infection. At the very least, this applied to the factors of Superego strength and Self sentiment integration; in this study, we did not prove a correlation between suspiciousness and time after infection. And I must admit that to this day I'm uncertain if there is a relationship between toxoplasmosis and suspiciousness. Whereas superego strength is almost always different in infected versus uninfected men, differences in suspiciousness can only be seen in a couple of subject groups.

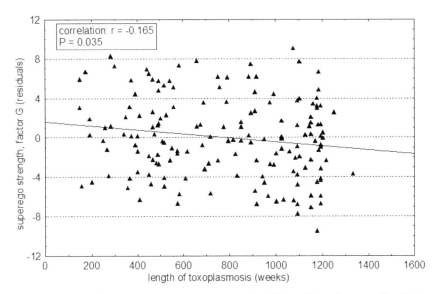

Fig. 12 The factor Superego strength (Cattell's factor G, Rule-consciousness) decreasing with time after infection by Toxoplasma. *The test subjects are male patients who were diagnosed with acute toxoplasmosis in the past. The date of acute toxoplasmosis was estimated on the basis of clinical symptoms and the transient increase in the levels of IgM antibodies against* Toxoplasma. *One hundred sixty-four patients participated in the study. Because one's psychological profile can change with age, we statistically filtered out the age of the subjects. The graph represents standardized residuals after this mathematical operation.*

Box 18 Data transformation

Most common statistical methods expect and more or less require a **normal (Gaussian) distribution** of values in the data set. A normal distribution has few high and low values; most cluster around the average. A histogram of a normal distribution is bell-shaped. Many values we measure in nature, such as body height, have such a distribution – or, more accurately, they do not differ much from it – but others do not. A common example is the **log-normal distribution**, an asymmetrical bell-shape whose right side (with the higher values) decreases at a much lower rate than the left side. A log-normal distribution can be transformed into a normal one by taking the logarithm of the measured values. If the measured values include zero, then we must add a small constant to all the values before taking their log, because the log of zero is undefined (Fig. 13). Sometimes, the histogram remains asymmetrical even after it been logarithmized, in which case we can logarithmize the values for a second (and maybe even a third) time. In general, you can make as many transformations of the data as you need. The results won't be distorted; rather, the statistical test becomes more reliable, the closer the data resembles a normal distribution. But when describing the results in the manuscript, you must keep in mind that differences in the logarithms of the heights – not the differences in height (of, for example, infected versus uninfected people) are statistically significant. There isn't a substantial difference, but the reviewer of your article might give you trouble over it. Even if you're using statistical tests to compare things like the logarithms (or perhaps arc sines) of heights, plot the axis with height in non-logarithmic units (such as centimeters). The graph should first and foremost be illustrative and clarifying, and height expressed in centimeters better suits this purpose than height in logarithmic values.

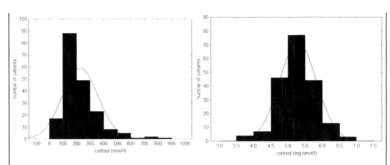

Fig. 13 An example of data (the concentration of the stress hormone cortisol in the serum of immunology clinic patients) that do not have a normal distribution (left), but which can achieve one through logarithmization (right). Data sets without normal distribution, particularly small ones, cannot be analyzed with common parametric statistical tests, for these tests may produce incorrect (usually false positive) results. Therefore, it is necessary to use nonparametric, randomized or exact tests. For large data sets, a non-normal distribution usually isn't an issue – in this case, applying parametric tests to our data did not produce biased results. Distribution type can be determined using the appropriate statistical tests. However, in small data sets, for which knowing the distribution type is especially important, deviations from normal distribution are often valued as not significant. In contrast, these deviations are almost always significant in really large sets of data. Therefore, it's better to always check the shape of the distribution visually.

While waiting for letters from the former patients, I continued collecting data at the university. I had already "picked through" most of the employees, so I now focused my efforts on the students – particularly the female students. The fact that I had originally not found statistically significant differences between infected and uninfected female students may have been because toxoplasmosis really doesn't affect them; or it could have been because there were too few women in the original subject group. After a year or two, our university subject group numbered 224 men and 170 women. When it was finally analyzed, it turned out that women with toxoplasmosis are likely to have psychological differences, which are primarily in the factor A, Affectothymia (Warmth). Affectothymia is actually the factor which most influences a human's personality profile. It accounts for the majority of differences among people in their psychological characteristics, coming just before intelligence. Women infected with *Toxoplasma* had a statistically significantly higher factor A than did uninfected women; therefore, they were more sociable and open, but also flightier. In contrast, uninfected women were rather closed-up and less sociable, but also more conscientious and responsible. Aside from this factor, there was a clear shift in Rule-consciousness (Superego strength, G) and Suspiciousness (Protension, L), which were the same factors that had been different in Toxo positive men. But what was interesting, was that these factors were shifted in the opposite way in women than in men – uninfected women had greater Superego strength, meaning that they were more willing to respect social norms and were less suspicious. This trend (the opposite relationship in men than in women) was seen in a number of other factors, including the factor Affectothymia, which in later subject groups was often lower in infected men. But most of the time, this was only a trend that did not prove to be statistically significant in women or men.

While collecting the new data, I managed to publish our first findings in an international journal[16]. It wasn't easy; many journals sent the manuscript back. It wasn't that the reviewers had found any glaring errors – but to most of them, the idea that some parasite might affect the behavior and psyche of a human seemed bizarre enough that they preferred to think we invented our data (Box 19 *Why not to mess with data and fabricate results*). Finally, the first article was published in the Czech, albeit printed-in-English journal *Folia Parasitologica*[16]; three years later, the second article came out in the British journal *Parasitology*[15]. The second article also contained the results from the former patients with acute toxoplasmosis.

Box 19 Why not to mess with data and fabricate results

Audits conducted by American officials on random samples of articles showed that about 7% of studies published after 1985 include fundamental violations of scientific ethics (falsified data or plagiarism). Before 1985, it was 12%. Surveys of researchers show that many of them at some point falsified their data. Usually this means that they "bettered" their results – for example, by omitting unfitting values or failing to mention the unfavorable results of certain analyses. An even greater percent of scientists – that is, 32% – believe that their colleagues sometimes "tweak" their results. So we should approach other people's data with a certain wariness. We cannot rule out even the unlikely possibility that all of the data is made-up, or fundamentally modified. So why not falsify our own results, instead of dealing with rebellious data that may be difficult and costly to obtain, and which oftentimes ruins our brilliant hypotheses? I won't delve into the ethical reasons; for example, that lying and cheating is wrong, and that people generally enter into science because they want to figure out how our world works – and clearly, falsifying data is the basest way to betray this calling. I realize that ethical reasons depend on the individual, and are not universally agreed upon; and so, for example, a PhD student or technician in a Japanese laboratory might see it as ethically more correct to please one's sensei and laboratory head by falsifying the results to obtain favorable data, rather than disappoint him with true results that refute his theory. No, the obvious reason we shouldn't falsify data is something else. If we published important and interesting results that were actually falsified, then other scientists would soon find

> out when trying to repeat our study. And falsifying
> unimportant and uninteresting data also doesn't pay off:
> it is easier and, from a career stand-point, more secure to
> collect unimportant and uninteresting data – there is
> tons of it available. (There's also tons of interesting data
> around us, but to find it, you must know how to look.)

In the first article, I managed to cram in an observation that I can't puzzle out even today. When looking at infected versus uninfected university employees, I saw one big difference. Among fourteen men with toxoplasmosis, there was only one who had some sort of a leadership position, such as the department head or dean. But out of 29 Toxo negative men, there were ten people with leadership positions. In truth, this corresponded with the results we obtained from the questionnaire. If someone isn't willing to follow social norms (has a lower factor G), then getting a leadership position in an institution like the university cannot be easy. That one outlying Toxo positive man was the department head for only two years, and had risen to the position by way of the revolution. Back then, department heads were still chosen based on personal and professional qualities, rather than progression through the social hierarchy and consolidating a position of power. I don't know if this dependency still applies. Many Toxo positive professors later became department heads. But even so, I expect that if we compared how many years Toxo positive versus Toxo negative men spent as department heads, then the difference would be perhaps even greater today than in the past. I knew that *Toxoplasma* apparently affected not only male behavior, as seen in the first study, but also female behavior, as shown in the second study on the students of the Faculty of Science. So I decided to supplement the first study with data from the former patients with acute toxoplasmosis – using data from the female patients. With the help of the workers of the diagnostic laboratory, I was able to amass psychological data from 230 female patients, who had had acute toxoplasmosis within the past 14 years. For this subject group, we plotted the factors of Affectothymia (A) and Superego strength (G) against how long the person had been infected. It turned out that the correlation with factor G is statistically significant – Superego strength increases with time after infection (see Fig. 14).

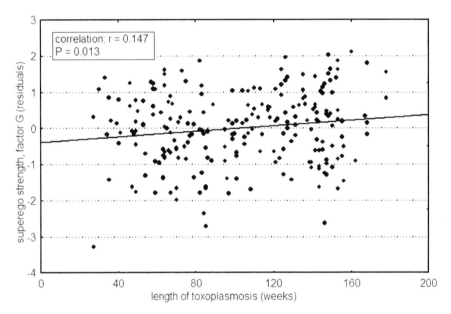

Fig. 14 The factor Superego strength (Cattell's factor G, Rule-consciousness) increasing with time after infection by Toxoplasma. *Subjects are female patients diagnosed with acute toxoplasmosis in the past. The date of acute toxoplasmosis was estimated on the basis of levels of IgM antibodies against* Toxoplasma. *Two hundred and thirty patients participated in the study. Because one's psychological profile can change with age, we statistically filtered out the age of the subjects. The graph represents standardized residuals after this filtration.*

On the other hand, Affectothymia – the factor which correlated most with Toxo positivity in female students – did not change with time after infection. Of course, just like in the previous study with male patients, I filtered out the effect of the person's age. It could be expected that women who'd been infected longer were, on average, older at the time of the study; and therefore psychological factors which normally change with age could have been higher or lower in longer and shorter-infected people. But with modern statistical methods, it's not difficult to filter out such confounding factors (see Box 20 *Dependent, independent, and confounding variables; fixed and random factors*).

Box 20 Dependent, independent, and confounding variables; fixed and random factors

When conducting a statistical analysis, we must first determine what is the independent and what is the dependent variable, because this usually determines not only how we interpret the results, but also the statistical method we select. An **independent variable**, also known as a **factor**, is a variable whose effect we wish to study. On the other hand, a **dependent variable** is a variable which is affected by the independent variable. So if we're studying how toxoplasmosis affects the suspiciousness of students, then toxoplasmosis is the independent and suspiciousness (based on Cattell's factor L) the dependent variable. Of course, there can be several independent variables which affect our dependent variable, including toxoplasmosis, gender, profession, age (age is a continuous variable, and independent continuous variables are also known as **covariates**). But let's say we're studying what affects the risk of *Toxoplasma* infection. In this case, Toxo positivity is the dependent variable and things like age, gender, consumption of raw meat, contact with cats, and nationality are independent variables. It's useful when we can include all our independent variables in the statistical test at once, because, among other things, it allows us to reveal any possible **interactions** – for example, toxoplasmosis may affect suspiciousness differently based on gender. Sometimes we're not actually interested in the effect of a particular independent variable, but we know that it affects our target variable, so therefore we must filter out its effect in order to reveal the (perhaps weaker) effect of the variable we are studying. To this end, we include it among the other independent variables. Such a variable is called a **confounding variable**. It's also important to know whether an independent variable is a fixed or a random factor. A **fixed factor** (such as gender) has a set number of possible values objectively determined, for example, by nature; whereas a **random factor** (such as profession or nationality) has a random number of possible values subjectively chosen by the researcher. A statistical program deals differently with these two types of variables.

Besides Superego strength, several other factors changed with time after infection. At this point, I'm not sure why there was no change in suspiciousness and Affectothymia in women. I may have just been unlucky with this data group. Statistical tests allow us to estimate the risk of a **type I error**, in other words the statistical test tells us the probability that the phenomenon we see in our data doesn't actually exist – that it's just the result of chance. Let's say that the difference in Warmth between infected and uninfected women is significant at the 2% level. So there is a 2% chance of obtaining this or a more extreme difference between two groups due to chance – in other words, because a different number of higher-Warmth-scaling women happened to get into the Toxo positive versus the Toxo negative group. Of course, a statistical test can never give us complete certainty, but if we obtain a sufficiently low P value (significance level), then we can lean towards the conclusion that the observed phenomenon is real – for example, that there exists some relationship between Affectothymia and toxoplasmosis. Generally, we can lean towards this conclusion if we get a P value lower than 5%, but this level is arbitrary, so its importance should not be overestimated. If you have observed an interesting phenomenon, such as the effectiveness of a new drug in treating cancer, then it's worthwhile to pursue it even if you get a P value of 10% – in other words, the probability that the drug doesn't actually have an effect, and that people who got the drug are just as well (or poorly) as people who got the placebo.

On the other hand, we'll probably abandon a trivial phenomenon, such as that the new drug lowers the frequency of blinking, even we get a P value of less than 5% (assuming, of course, that we aren't being paid by Formula One to find an anti-blinking drug). Similarly, if verifying the existence of a phenomenon is fast, easy, and cheap, we're more likely to pursue even a phenomenon with high P values. If such testing through an independent study is difficult or expensive, then we're likely to pursue it only if the P value is extremely low – maybe 0.1%. Beside the type I error, there also exists a **type II error**, which occurs when a statistical test refutes the existence of a phenomenon that actually exists. The probability of a type II error is determined by the **power of the test**. The greater the power of the test, the greater the probability that the test will reveal the phenomenon's existence. For mostly historical reasons, scientists are more afraid of type I than type II errors (maybe they would rather miss an existing phenomenon – nobody will ever know about their failure – than suffer the embarrassment of proving the existence of a non-existent phenomenon). The probabilities of type I and II errors are somewhat related, and statistical tests are set up so that when we require a type I error of less than 5%, then we'll get a high type II error, maybe around 20%. This means that in one out five studies, on average, the statistical test will refute the existence of a phenomenon that truly exists (see Box 21 *Analysis the power of a statistical test*).

Box 21 Analysis the power of a statistical test

If we're not interested in the probability of a type I error (the risk that the observed phenomenon is just the result of chance), but rather in the likeliness of a type II error (the risk that we incorrectly identify a real phenomenon as nonexistent, purely the result of a chance), then we must use the correct method of **power analysis**. This technique is primarily used for two things. The first is determining the extent to which we should trust the negative results of a study, which don't prove the existence of the phenomenon we expect. The second is related to the planning of the study. Power analysis allows us to estimate the size of an experimental group – i.e. the number of human subjects or lab mice – needed for us to have a good chance of proving an effect of a certain size (Fig. 15). Various statistical tests differ in their power, which means that they carry different risks of a type II error. For example, nonparametric tests usually have a lower power than parametric ones; whenever the data type allows it, we should preferably use a parametric test, or perhaps an exact test, which has an even higher statistical power.

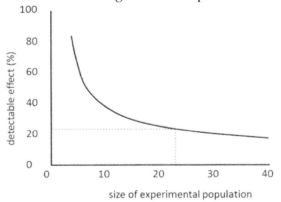

Fig. 15 Power analysis. If we had an effect that caused a 20% difference – e.g. if Toxoplasma *decreased the weight of infected mice by 20% – then 22 experimental mice would probably be enough to prove it. But if* Toxoplasma *decreased weight by only 15%, we would probably fail to prove the effect to be statistically significant, even if we had 40 mice.*

And this might have been what happened in the aforementioned study with the female acute toxoplasmosis patients. We expected that Affectothymia (warmth, openness and sociability) would increase with time after infection, but the statistical tests did not confirm it. So why do I suspect it was the fault of a type II error, i.e. a mistaken refutation of an existing phenomenon? Because immediately afterward we carried out another study with a somewhat different method and a completely different group of people, and this study did prove an increase in warmth and sociability with time after infection. One of my colleagues had, filed away in his desk drawer, data from a large group of women who had been screened for toxoplasmosis during pregnancy. We had no psychological data for these women, but on the other hand, the data set was very large – almost a thousand women. Next to each name was the woman's address, screening result, weight, and then two mysterious values marked Pm and Uz. I later found out that Uz was the duration of pregnancy based on an ultrasound – in other words, based on the size of the fetus – and Pm was the duration of pregnancy estimated from the date of the last menstruation. Both of these durations related to the time of the screening. Again, they were at first only mysterious values to me. I didn't expect that they might be related to toxoplasmosis. I entered all the data into the computer, including these three values: the weight, the duration of pregnancy according to ultrasound, and the duration of pregnancy according to menstruation. These three values proved to be quite interesting; their analysis led us to an entirely new area of studying *Toxoplasma*'s effect on the human organism – but that's a matter for a different chapter. We sent our ten questions mixed into Cattell's questionnaire to all the Toxo positive women, as well as to a random sample of Toxo negatives, and requested their cooperation in the name of the National Institute of Public Health.

This time fewer people responded and we obtained completed questionnaires from only 20-30% of the women. Partly, it was because the women now had children, and probably had little time for the questionnaire; and partly, it was because we intentionally refrained from discussing the goals of the study in the accompanying letter, to avoid needlessly frightening the women with the mention of a parasitic protozoan, *Toxoplasma*. I compared the psychological factors in infected and uninfected women; and using the subset of infected women, I tried to determine whether the psychological differences increased with time after infection. But of course, I didn't know how long ago these women had been infected.

I could have at least estimated it based on the levels of their *Toxoplasma* antibodies. This parameter is highly variable over time, and depends on the state of a person's immune system, so antibody levels cannot determine how long ago someone was infected (see also Box 22 *Antibodies and myths about them*). Some people have high antibody levels, and others have low ones. Furthermore, antibody levels in an individual change over time. Nevertheless, on average, they decrease with time after infection. So if we have two women with different antibody levels, we cannot definitely say which one was infected earlier. But if we have ten women infected five years ago, and ten infected two years ago, then it's almost certain that the average level of antibodies will be lower in the first than in the second group of women. So, statistically, there exists a relation between antibody levels and time after infection. And if we're looking for a statistical relationship, such as a relation between a psychological factor and time after infection, then we can look at the factor in relation to antibody levels, in place of time after infection. We can, on average, expect that the longer the time after infection, the lower the levels of antibodies; and the lower the levels of antibodies, then the greater the difference in the psychological factor. And the results of our study did show that antibody levels correlate with both factor A and G. In both cases, the factor changed in the direction that we hypothesize based on our theory and data we had obtained from students at the college. The factors of

Affectothymia (warmth, A), and Superego strength (rule–consciousness, G) increased with decreasing anti-*Toxoplasma* antibody levels. Several other factors also changed with decreasing these antibody levels: for example, Protension (Suspiciousness, L) decreased, Surgency (enthusiasm, heedlessness, F) increased, and Social boldness (H) increased. So we once more confirmed that changes in women's psyche occur after *Toxoplasma* infection, and therefore are induced by it[17].

Box 22 Antibodies and the myths about them

Antibodies are proteins whose biological role is to lock onto to foreign structures. These foreign structures, called **antigens**, often come from parasites. After an antibody binds to them, they are eliminated either directly by the antibodies or by specialized cells like **macrophages**, which detect and devour antibody-marked antigens. The antibodies are created in **B cells**, which are a type of white blood cells. Each B cell creates only one type of antibody to target one antigen (or more accurately, to target a small area on the antigen, known as the **epitope**). The body contains many B cells, and therefore can produce millions of different antibodies, capable of binding to millions of foreign structures with the individual has not yet encountered – including molecules created in the laboratory by man, and which weren't present in nature before. A healthy individual, or rather someone who doesn't have an autoimmune disease, doesn't make antibodies that would bind to structures found in his own body. The presence of antibodies against a certain microbe, usually a parasite, in the blood is commonly used to diagnose infection, since it's often much easier to detect antibodies than the actual parasite. According to the type and concentration of the antibody, it's often possible to determine the phase of infection. Soon after infection by a pathogen, class **IgM** antibodies appear in the blood. These decrease over time, and instead class **IgG** antibodies reach their peak. Once the acute stage passes, the amount of antibodies gradually decreases (but often they start binding more strongly to the antigens). If the antigen disappears from the body, then the antibodies disappear eventually, too. But a small number of the B cells that produced the antibody remain in the body as **memory B cells**, which create a person's immune memory. So in the future, if the body encounters the same antigen (for example, the same parasite), then the memory B cells can quickly divide and begin producing the respective antibody – in this case, they immediately release class IgG antibodies, which are capable of strongly binding to the antigen. This is called a **secondary immune response**. The parasite is eliminated by the antibodies and various white blood cells soon after penetrating the host body, and the acute disease is either much weaker or never happens.

A number of myths about the formation and function of antibodies are senselessly reprinted from textbook to textbook, even though modern immunology has long refuted them. For example, it's not true that antibodies serve to differentiate between foreign and self antigens. In reality, this function is performed by **T cells**, which do so based on the presence of unknown peptides (short amino-acid chains) from the proteins of a parasite, or from the antibodies that bind to the antigen. Antibodies serve to mark foreign structures, but the structures must first be distinguished as foreign by the T cells. It's also not true that the body has B cells capable of producing antibodies against all possible antigens ahead of time; and these B cells only need to start reproducing when an antigen enters the body. In reality, the B cell clones which produce antibodies that firmly bind to the foreign antigen but don't bind to self antigens, are "bred" by T cells in specialized immune organs only after the foreign antigen has entered the body. T cells do this in a similar fashion as a person breeding new variants of crops or farm animals. On their surface, B cells have molecules of the antibody they produce. These molecules constantly bind (sometimes not very strongly) to structures from both parasites and the self. These structures are then absorbed by the B cell, and if they contain proteins, then these get digested into small **peptides**. The peptides bind to strange transport molecules, known as **MHC proteins** (MHC antigens), which transport them to the surface of the B cell and display (present) them (see also Box 36 *On peptides, and why they should interest a parasitologist*). The B cells are constantly surveyed by T cells, which "feel" for the peptides presented on the MHC antigens. Each T cell recognizes a certain peptide, but these are only peptides not present in the body's own proteins. This is because young T cells which detect peptides present in the body are killed when passing through the **thymus** (this is where T cells get their name). So as soon as a T cell recognizes a peptide presented by a B cell's MHC proteins, it's clear that it must be a foreign peptide (it was not present in the **thymus**). And the B cell which just proved itself capable of binding to an antigen (a structure containing at least some foreign peptides), is given a dose of growth factor from the T cell, allowing it to reproduce. The "clones" of the B cell should produce the same kind of antibody as the original B cell.

But the gene coding for the antibody is subject to frequent mutation, so the offspring produces variations of the original antibody. Some bind to the antigen more or less strongly, some also bind to self-antigens, whereas others lose the unwanted ability to attach to them. Of course, the mutated B cells whose antibodies bind best to the foreign antigen and not to self-antigens (which would fill up their surface receptors, and thus limit their ability to bind to foreign antigen) are the most likely to bind to the antigen. So these B cells are most likely to absorb the antigen, present more respective peptides, and hence get more shots of growth factor from the T cells. The B cells again reproduce and obtain new mutations, some of which improve their ability to bind to the given antigen (or lower their ability to bind to self-antigens). And the B cells with these "good" mutations are again made to reproduce the fastest. Over several days and a couple of generations, the T cells will have bred a B cell clone which produces antibodies that bind very firmly to the foreign but not to self-antigens.

Later we confirmed our conclusions on results obtained using the more modern **Big Five** questionnaire. It turned out that the factor Conscientiousness (which is lower in Toxo positive humans, as mentioned in the previous chapter) decreases in infected men and women with time after infection. However, the decrease was statistically significant (and very significant, at that) only in men.

IV. Does toxoplasmosis account for why I'm weird?

What did I make of the results of that first study, of the answers of the students to those ten questions I put forth initially – could some of the characteristics not compatible with my personality type be somehow explained by an infection by *Toxoplasma gondii*?

The first couple of years my endeavor was not successful (an understatement, to be sure, since I know many colleagues who'd use a pithier and also more fitting expression in relation to my trials). As I already mentioned, some of the questions correlated with a *Toxoplasma* infection to a certain extent, but the strength of the correlation wasn't particularly striking. One of those questions even had an opposite correlation to that which I had originally predicted.

The main reason (or perhaps the main excuse?) for the many years I set aside the results of this study was my realization that it would be even more difficult to publish these results than to publish the results indicating changes in Cattell's Personality Factors. The results I acquired as by-products of the original study, while surprising, were at least obtained using a standard scientific method. Cattell's questionnaire is a published psychological tool of long-standing; psychologists presume the meaning of the individual factors measured by the questionnaire, or at least agree on the existence of these factors. There was therefore a possibility that if I proved that a certain biological factor (specifically an infection by *Toxoplasma*) influences some of these psychological factors, I would sooner or later succeed in publishing my findings. But if the observed changes were related to a hitherto undescribed psychological factor, whose existence I deduced purely from introspection (through a self-observation), then the chance of publishing my results was substantially lower. Mathematically speaking, the probability of publishing a study that explores an unusual phenomenon using hitherto undescribed factors ascertained by way of nonstandard methods approaches a limit of zero (see also Box 23 *Why to use established scientific methods*).

Box 23 Why to use established scientific methods

The answer is quite simple – because only by doing so is it possible to compare and therefore interconnect results obtained in different workplaces. Isolated results often don't mean much; they achieve their true value only when related to other results from different scientists, often from studies dealing with entirely unrelated problems. For this reason, wherever at all possible, it's best to use standard and preferably widely utilized methods. Scientists trained in former communist Czechoslovakia are often masters in the art of inventing new methods. Necessity indeed is the mother of invention – established methods were not available to them; they could not buy the appropriate standard chemicals nor tools, since funding for obtaining Western products was limited; and when funding happened to be sufficient, purchases from the outside had to be planned many years in advance, so that even if the long-desired instrument or chemical finally arrived, one had often forgotten, what he had needed it for. Under the communist regime the ability to improvise was the basic prerequisite for successful scientific practice, but today it is something of a two-edged sword. On one hand it allows the discovery of an oftentimes better, cheaper, faster or more effective method than that which is being standardly employed in a given field, but, on the other hand, results obtained through a nonstandard method are difficult to compare with results obtained in other workplaces (and of course also more difficult to publish in scientific journals). Newly developed methods often harbor unexpected obstacles. During my postdoctoral studies, for example, I tried to determine whether double-stranded RNA (dsRNA) present in *Trichomonas* cells floats freely in the cytoplasm or whether it is contained within virions. The standard method for isolating virions is separation of the cellular homogenate using the cesium chloride density-gradient ultracentrifugation. It is a time consuming method, the centrifugation itself spanning many hours; furthermore, cesium chloride is expensive, as is operating and maintaining the ultracentrifuge. I, however, discovered that I could obtain virions from the homogenate in less than an hour by precipitating them using the right concentration of cheap ammonium sulfate[5]. In addition, I discovered that when I isolated nucleic acids in the presence of high concentrations of ammonium sulfate using acidic phenol instead of neutralized phenol (so I reached into the fridge and grabbed the wrong bottle, nobody's perfect) all the DNA and single-stranded RNA disappeared – pure dsRNA remained in the resulting sample[3]. The problem was that the electron microscopy showed these virions to be empty, devoid of any nucleic acids (Fig. 16). I conceived daring hypotheses to explain this state of affairs, and tentatively allowed even for the possibility that the presence of virions might have nothing to do with the presence of dsRNA in *Trichonomas* cells. The reality was much more prosaic. During the nonstandard method of isolating virions by precipitation using ammonium sulfate, all the dsRNA escapes. Had I used the classical ultracentrifugation method, I would have saved myself a lot of trouble.

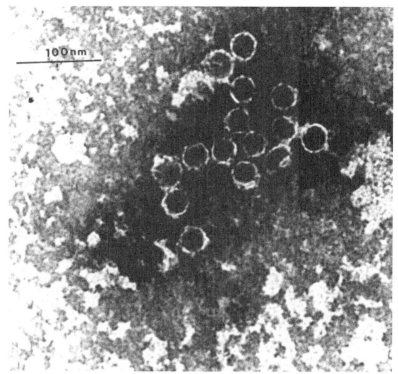

Fig. 16 Viral particles observed by an electron microscope in the cellular homogenate of Trichomonas. *When viral particles are precipitated by adding ammonium sulfate, all the nucleic acid molecules escape; therefore, the particles appear to be hollow. In reality, native particles contain double-stranded ribonucleic acid molecules. Photo by Jitka Štokrová.*

So I returned to those results only after fifteen years – and then actually just by chance. In the presence of my erstwhile PhD student Jitka Lindová, née Hanušová, I mentioned the beginning study of the effect of toxoplasmosis on the human psyche, and I admitted that at the onset of the study I observed that I let myself get duped by craftsmen. She didn't want to believe me, for even then my suspicious nature was widely known – some of my colleagues, for example, claimed that while other people may see around a corner, my perception extends past two or three. That in and of itself is not so surprising – as a Toxo positive person I have a high Cattell's factor Protension (L, Suspiciousness, Vigilance), and as a scientist skepticism is part of my job description. I explained to her that it wasn't just unbacked prattle on my part; I had stowed away tons of data that could be used to test my theory. And, if I remembered correctly, the results of the preliminary analyses certainly weren't uninteresting – in particular, some of the questions I had used to test my hypothesis seemed to correlate at least weakly with an infection by *Toxoplasma*.

At the time we were just beginning a new study and preparing to collect data from fresh 300-400 students. The main goal of the new project was to study people's behavior through the method of experimental games. It was clear, however, that this main trial would have to be supplemented with other tests, so that our test subjects would not sit idle during the course of the trial (a terrible prospect, to be sure). It was clear that we'd again give them some psychological questionnaires, and it occurred to me that it would be quite interesting to try to once more look at the results of the original toxo-questionnaire – the questionnaire of ten questions targeting behavior that could heighten the risk of capture by a felid – select those couple of questions, which might really be linked with a *Toxoplasma* infection, and present those questions to a new sample of students.

So over a weekend I looked up on the computer the old data obtained in the original study, and now, 15 years later, I analyzed them once more. The result was astonishing. It turned out not that more than just the answers to one or two questions were loosely linked with an infection by *Toxoplasma*. In reality almost half the questions were *Toxoplasma*-related. The correlation (statistical association) with toxoplasmosis was significant, sometimes even very significant. For some cases, the probability that the difference between the average answer of a Toxo positive person and that of a Toxo negative person could have been but a turn of fate was less than 1 per mille. Why had I not seen this 15 years earlier, when

I had that data at my disposal, and when I first analyzed it? Because then I was not yet particularly knowledgeable in statistics, and in evaluating the data I used an utterly unsuited method.

I posed my questions to the students in the form of direct statements (made up of many partial assertions), and the test subjects were to choose the most fitting of three given answers. One statement, for example, read as follows: "Unexpected personal conflict with a brazen, rude, crude or mean person generally distresses me; in such a situation I am often unable to effectively defend myself. When a craftsman asks me for money, I usually give it to him, even when I know that he doesn't deserve it. When I notice that a salesman is cheating me, usually I let it be." Students were to answer 1, 2 or 3. One meant *I agree*, two *I'm not sure*, and three *I disagree*. I originally compared the answers of infected and uninfected people using the method called Student's t-test. This method is decidedly not suitable for testing a variable that reaches only 3 values (1, 2, 3) – in other words a so-called ordinal type of variable (see Box 24 *Types of variables from the perspective of statistics*).

Box 24 Types of variables from the perspective of statistics

In "normal, everyday life" we differentiate between **quantitative variables** (temperature, body height) and **qualitative variables** (nationality, gender). But in statistics it makes more sense to classify variables as continuous and discrete. **Continuous variables**, such as the above-mentioned temperature and body height, are free to take on any value (but usually only within a certain range of accepted values). **Discrete variables** encompass two types of data. The first type are **ordinal variables**, which can be ordered from lowest to highest, though the individual values don't have to be equally spaced. One example of an ordinal variable is the level of education (primary, secondary, high); another is the degree of agreement with the statement in the questionnaire expressed on a given scale (strongly agree, mostly agree, not sure, mostly disagree, strongly disagree). The other type of discrete variables are **categorical variables** – these cannot be ordered by size. Among these are citizenship, the type of fertilizer or medicine used, etc. A special type of categorical variables are **binary variables** – these can take on only two values, like infected by *Toxoplasma*/uninfected by *Toxoplasma*, had a traffic accident/didn't have a traffic accident, male/female. Based on the type of variable we must select the right type of statistical test. If, for example, we're comparing the height of men and women, we'll most likely use Student's t-test; if it's the education level of men and women, we'll use some nonparametric test, like the Mann-Whitney U-test.

During the new evaluation I was already well aware of this, so in the new analysis I used a nonparametric test, specifically the Kendall correlation, which, like the more common Spearman's (rank correlation) test, fits that type of data (see Box 25 *Parametric and nonparametric tests*).

Using the new method, I discovered that the original ten questions had been very well selected, and that the relationship between the answers to these questions and toxoplasmosis was much stronger than in the case of Cattell's factors, which I had focused my studies on and because of which I had actually set aside these fascinating results for 15 years. But again it turned out that a more evident association could be observed in men than in women. This might have been due to not only the fact that we had more males in our group, but also that a man, on the basis of introspection, came up with the questions. The strongest correlation with toxoplasmosis was held by the statement: "My instinctive (reflexive) behavior in situations of imminent personal danger is rather disproportionately slow or passive. In situations when other people would likely be frightened and, without looking around or deliberating, jump back, I react more slowly or belatedly. When a car surges towards me or when a honking sounds behind me, there is a greater chance that I won't react and let myself get run over, than that, without looking around me, I'll jump in front of another car."

Box 25 Parametric and nonparametric tests

In practice, statistical tests are divided into **parametric** and **nonparametric tests**. Parametric tests, when used for the right type of data, are said to have more statistical power (that is, when they are used there exists a greater probability of a justified rejection of an unvalid null hypothesis) than corresponding nonparametric tests (see Box 21 *Analysis of the power of a statistical test*). This is understandable, since a parametric test uses a greater part of the information contained in the data: for example, it directly compares the body height of individuals in a group, whereas a nonparametric test uses but a small part of the information, most often the **information about the order** of the individuals according to their arrangement from tallest to shortest. In practice, the difference in the power of tests doesn't tend to be great, usually under 10%. Parametric tests, however, are intended for data with a particular type of distribution, generally for continuous variables with a normal distribution. If our data has a different type of distribution – for example, if we're dealing with ordinal data – a parametric test may yield a false result. In such a case it's necessary to use a nonparametric test, or, where possible, a more powerful **exact test**, or at least a **randomization test** (see Box 83 *Randomization tests*).

If we're comparing, for example, the average value of continuous data (like average height) between two groups (males and females), we'll most likely use a parametric **t-test**; for multiple groups (Czechs, Germans, Chinese, English, Japanese), we'll use the **ANOVA** (an analysis of variance). If we're comparing paired continuous data (such as the body mass of the same mice before and after infection, see Box 67 *What is the difference between the paired and unpaired t-tests, and why is the paired one better?*), we'll use a **paired t-test**. If we're studying the effect of a certain factor taking on two or more levels (gender or ethnicity) and simultaneously the effect of another continuous variable (such as the age of the person) on a continuous variable (such as body mass), we'll use an **ANCOVA** (an analysis of covariance). If we're studying the effect of multiple independent factors, we'll use the **MANOVA** instead of the ANOVA and the **MANCOVA** (multivariable analysis of variance and covariance) instead of the ANCOVA. If we're simultaneously studying the effects of continuous and discrete variables (age, gender, size of residence) on binary variables (infected by *Toxoplasma*/uninfected by *Toxoplasma*), we'll use a **logistic regression**, whereas for an ordinal variable we'll use an **ordinal logistic regression**. If we're studying the relationship of two continuous variables, we'll use a **correlation analysis**, and if we also know or have decided beforehand which of the two variables is dependent (target) and which is explanatory, we'll use a **linear regression**; if we're studying the dependence of a continuous variable on multiple continuous variables, we'll use a **multidimensional linear regression**. If we're studying the relationship between two categorical variables, we'll use **contingency tables**; if it's between great numbers of categorical variables, we'll use **log-linear analysis**. In all the above-mentioned cases we can also use the more universal **GLM** (General Linear Model) method, and, if needed, the even more universal **GLZ** (Generalized Linear Model method, often also noted as GLM to make the orientation in the method more difficult for non-statisticians). A nonparametric analogue of the common (unpaired) t-test is the **Mann-Whitney U-test**; an analogue of the paired t-test is the **Wilcoxon test**; an analogue of the simple ANOVA is the **Kruskal-Wallis ANOVA**; an approximate analogue of the two-way ANOVA is a **Friedman test**; and an analogue of correlation analysis is a **Spearman's rank correlation test**, or a **Kendall's Tau test.** Aside from hypotheses of the location (average, median value), we often test a hypothesis of the equality of the empirical and theoretical frequency distributions (most often using the **Chi^2-test**); or we test a hypothesis of the equality of distribution of values in two or more sets (using the **F-test**); or a hypothesis of outlying values (using **Grubbs'** or **Dixon's test).**

In this case the correlation became statistically significant for both genders, which together had a P value of 0.001 and for men alone less than 0.00001. (Repetition is the mother of learning: P value of 0.00001 in layman's terms means that there is a probability of only about 1:100,000 that such a large or even larger difference in answers of *Toxoplasma*-infected and *Toxoplasma*-free subjects can be observed just coincidently, it means, if toxoplasmosis has no effect on the subjects.) In men, there was also a highly statistically significant (P = 0.001) association of toxoplasmosis with the statement: "When I'm attacked, physically or otherwise, or if I am to fight for something important, then in some cases or from a certain point I stop defending myself or fighting. It has nothing to do with a rational decision not to fight, for in reality I know that I should continue in the fight – and I'd like to continue – but my own subconscious betrays me and my will to fight is used up."

Agreement with the following statement was also statistically significant (P = 0.012): "Diplomacy is not one of my strong suits; I am not particularly adept in dealing with people. I often unintentionally spoil dealings requiring a measure of diplomacy with an inadvisable comment that irritates a person I'd rather like to win over to my side. If I have a negative opinion about someone and I don't want them to know it, usually they can tell anyways. When I try to flatter someone, it often comes out sounding more like an insult." as with the statement "I believe that there are people able to impose their will on others using hypnosis or persuasion." (men: P = 0.02, all together: P < 0.001). In women, the most significant association of toxoplasmosis was with agreement with the statement: "I don't have a strong sense of self-preservation: in situations, when others would probably be scared, at night alone in the woods or in a deserted house, I am not particularly afraid." (P = 0.029).

We subsequently included the same questions, or at least some of them, in other questionnaire-based studies. We never again accomplished such strong associations with so many questions, yet even here the significant effect of toxoplasmosis on the subjects' (blood donors, pregnant women) answers to some of these questions was apparent. Most often the test subjects mentioned that they have slower reflexes and that they believe that some people are able to impose their will on others using hypnosis or persuasion[18].

The statements which I set to our test subjects were relatively complex, each made up of multiple partial assertions. In the study which I carried out in the years 2007-2011, aside from the original ten complex statements, we also gave the students individual partial and specifying assertions. At the start of the 44-point questionnaire we presented the original ten statements, followed by 34 partial assertions, such as: "My instinctive (reflexive) behavior in situations of imminent danger is disproportionately slow or passive." or "At night alone in a deserted house I'm not particularly afraid." The students filled out the questionnaire on the computer, which recorded not only their answers, but also the time they needed to select each answer (this time on a 5-point scale). The final results of this more detailed study are not yet available.

I already mentioned that publishing a description of an unknown phenomenon studied using a nonstandard method doesn't tend to be exactly easy. Nevertheless, I succeeded that time, and, what's more, right on the first try[18]. Apparently my results were clear and convincing, and my argument bullet-proof enough, that neither the editor nor the reviewers were able to raise any substantial objections. But we cannot bar the possibility that a certain role may have been played by the fact that the editor of this particular special journal number, and therefore also the person who selected the reviewers, was I.

V. Casual contemplations about scientific luck, mistakes, and an experiment I am truly embarrassed of

So the start of our study on the effect of toxoplasmosis on human behavior looked something like this. In some things I started off with bad luck, in some things with good, but I must objectively conclude that I had more good luck than bad. I did a couple of clever things and a couple of foolish ones, but I guess that's how it goes in anything, not just in science.

My great fortune was that when I returned to the faculty and began looking around for a fitting parasitological subject, I came across toxoplasmosis, and that this happened precisely in the period when I was musings over my own psychical characteristics – by that I mean those strange elements of behavior and feelings which I was unable to explain to myself. When these two circumstances were put together, there resulted the idea that I was later able to develop.

But the greatest fortune came to me right at the beginning, when I was given room to grow. It wasn't just me – when the communist regime collapsed unexpectedly, crumbling like a house of cards, many young people just stepping into science got the opportunity to begin researching completely independently. This usually doesn't happen in an established system, where continuity of research teams exists. There a young person generally starts his career working for a long time on someone else's projects – planning and picking his own projects usually begins only when he's past the prime of his creative (and sometimes also physical) strength. People of my generation and often even younger were very lucky, that they lived in the Czech Republic (at that time still Czechoslovakia) and were starting their scientific career in the period when science was undergoing a resurrection, when new functional scientific teams were being built, often nearly from scratch.

Most scientific teams under the communist regime were not functional, because they were led by entirely incompetent people whose primary and often only premise for carrying out a leadership function was being a member of the Communist party. The competent people were usually "weeded out" of prestigious scientific institutions and definitely couldn't lead their own team. Of course there were exceptions – in some cases a communist could even be a skilled scientist – but that happened only rarely. The leader of a research team was almost never chosen based on scientific ability, but generally according to his servility, his ability to "brownnose" and say out loud that black is white and two plus two makes five. All that, and a sufficiently thick skin, formed the main requisites for the person in question to carry out a career in any field, and hence also in science.

By career I mean obtaining a leadership position, money for a study, a laboratory and so on; scientists who held informal prestige were often entirely other people. I do not claim that all this happened only then, and only in communist countries, but likely in hardly any other time and place did possessing professional qualities lower one's chance of a successful scientific career. It was so in communist Czechoslovakia – the head of the team basically had no interest in producing quality research, and so when he was free to, and when he could distinguish it, he chose of two job applicants the one who was less capable, who posed less of a threat of growing beyond him. Interestingly, for the very same reason he'd rather pick a nonmember than a member of the communist party for his team; but unless he had a very high position in the party hierarchy himself, other comrades often commanded him to take on a party member.

All this ended in the year 1990, or soon after. Communists were stripped of their long-standing leadership functions, a few individuals were even forced to leave the faculty, and new research teams began to form in workplaces. Only rarely was some continuity maintained. I don't know how it was in other institutions, but in the biological section of the Faculty of Science in the year 1989 there were only two or three functional research teams that were operating truly on a top level. I was very lucky that I grew up professionally in one of these teams. In the Laboratory of Physiology and Biochemistry of Parasitic Protozoa, informally led by Jaroslav Kulda and Jiří Čerkasov, I worked on my undergraduate thesis and later even my doctoral dissertation.

After the revolution, Jaroslav Kulda became the head of the department of parasitology. He took several young people, who he expected were professionally capable, into his department and gave them the opportunity to build their own teams and, above all, to devote themselves to topics, which they themselves chose. I was also given this freedom, and for this reason I was able to begin dedicating myself to the emerging field of manipulation hypothesis.

That certainly would not have been possible if I had already been a part of a functional work team, which annually produces several high quality publications. There it is expected that each member of the team devote himself to projects already underway, which regularly bring publishable results – they won't be allowed onto an uncharted field, where there exists a serious risk that nothing interesting will come of the study. And if something does come of it, then the first results suitable for publication will be obtained only after many years.

My third great fortune has to do with the risk I was just talking about. The probability that *Toxoplasma* influences human behavior, and that it has a strong enough effect that we could detect it using such simple methods as a psychological questionnaire, was in reality quite small. When I was starting up my project, I expected rather to prove no effect of toxoplasmosis on human behavior. The chance of "winning" was very low, but, on the other hand, the enormity of the prize seemed very great. The idea that I'd be the first on earth to prove that the manipulation hypothesis doesn't just apply to animals, but that a parasite can also influence the behavior of a human, was tempting enough to me that I took that risk and dedicated my time to this uncertain project. An important role in my decision was also that work on the project, in comparison to the usual work going on in the molecular biology laboratory, was much more exciting. And why not admit it: I always try to do in the laboratory first and foremost that, which I enjoy. Of course, I had it easy in that I enjoy whatever promises to bring interesting results (see Box 26 *What is to be done?*).

Box 26 What is to be done?

I don't know what is contained in Chernyshevsky's original *What is to be done?*, nor in Lenin's treatise of the same name. Not that I'd wish to brag about it, or to even build my career on it (I'm a veteran opponent to communism – I fearlessly paid no attention in classes of Russian Literature and Marxism-Leninism!). In any case, after a meeting last year of the Faculty Academic Senate, at which a certain formerly high-ranking comrade, now a properly elected member of the Academic Senate lectured me about morals – I even got the impression that such bragging would bring me harm. The truth is that aside from the contents of the Marxist-Leninist treatises, I unfortunately also forgot most of what was poured into my head in high school and later in college. In any case, I am almost certain that the contents of my box are entirely different from the writings of my more famous predecessors. Here I'd like to deliberate the criteria, according to which it is appropriate to choose a topic for scientific research. Be warned that this is my purely subjective opinion, which I definitely don't wish to impose on anyone (although, in years to come, I will be diligently checking the knowledge of said opinion in exams of my course Practical methodology of science!).

The main criterion, which I applied always and before anything else, was whether the research question interests me. Our life is too short and (intending no offense to Buddhists) only one, so it is the height of folly to waste it searching for answers to questions that don't really interest us. Sure, it might be nice to tell yourself and others that we're able to find the answer to the given question before our competitors, but competition can also be carried out solving interesting questions (and one also attracts more spectators). Secondly, I applied the criterion of the probability that I could solve the given problem. That was related to the difficulty of the project, as well as (first and foremost) to whether I had the necessary materials and prior knowledge to solve the given problem. I'd really be interesting in researching the validity of string theory, but when I see an integral (I'm ashamed to admit it, but even a derivate is enough), I cannot help but shudder. Nor do we momentarily have an appropriate particle accelerator in the department. The third criterion is practical. I don't think that I exactly need to save or at least nourish a "suffering mankind," but it would definitively bring me joy, if something useful came of my discovery. The fourth and, admittedly, at once the most important criterion, is that I must enjoy the research of the given topic. I definitely enjoy it more when I'm inventing ways to find, using an ethological experiment, whether *Toxoplasma*-infected people are more suspicious, than when I was inventing or rather used trial and error to find how to best separate out virions from homogenized trichomonad cells.

The cleverest thing that I did lies in that I realized that testing my hypothesis from the aspect of methodology is easy, that it could be carried on material I had at my disposal – that is to say on patients we were testing in the department for toxoplasmosis, or on people, who we could ask to let themselves be examined for the purposes of the experiment. In addition, this was a low-cost study. At the start of the 90s we had very little money and this was one of the cheapest studies, perhaps with the exception of the modeling, possible to carry out in the circumstances of the Faculty of Science (see Box 27 *Why to model in science, and what can and can't be modeled).* In retrospect, it became clear that the inexpensiveness of the study was something of a two-edged sword. On one hand, it made our research easier, on the other hand it made it more difficult to publish the results and dissuaded established laboratories from verifying our study, and perhaps picking it up. I'll explain right away.

The reason it's difficult to publish the results of low cost studies is all in all obvious – expensive studies can't be done by just anyone, so expensiveness is a certain guarantee of the seriousness of the study. Why it's hard to continue inexpensive studies today is more difficult to explain.

Box 27 Why to model in science, and what can and can't be modeled

In engineering, we model primarily to replace a difficult or expensive study of the behavior of certain systems with a much cheaper and easier study of the behavior of their models. Usually we try to make it so that the behavior of our model corresponds as closely as possible to the behavior of the modeled system, and we're glad when we succeed in this. In science, however, we usually model for a completely different reason. With the help of **a model** we generally try to show what the mechanism of a certain process isn't like, and so we're happy when the behavior of the given model is substantially different from the behavior of the real system. The model is actually the realization of our hypothesis as to what the mechanism of a certain process is like – what elements the given system contains, and what relationships are applied between these elements. When our model behaves differently than we imagined, it means that our hypothesis likely wasn't true, which means that we have to discard our hypothesis or more often modify it. We'll embody the new hypothesis in another model, which we'll again subject to our test. When we discover a model whose behavior corresponds very well with the behavior of the real system, meaning that we observe in it processes analogous to those in the real world, we should actually feel disappointed (usually we aren't, because men are vain creatures and dislike their proposals being rejected). When the model's behavior corresponds with that of the system, it signifies that we couldn't disprove the given hypothesis, and therefore that the hypothesis could be true. But we won't be certain, because the same behavior can produce many very different models.

Modeling is a tremendously powerful tool. It enables us to quickly and cheaply refute (more accurately, to make improbable) a large number of hypotheses, and thus to concentrate on testing those more likely to succeed. Additionally, creating models allows us to specify and elaborate our often somewhat vague hypotheses. An intuitive visualization that something should work like this and this achieves a defined outline only after conversion into a mathematical or numerical model; and often we still have to alter it during the very creation of the model (frequently we must decide on very significant details, which we didn't tackle during the verbal construction of our hypothesis). For example, in my book *Frozen Evolution: Or, that's not the way it is, Mr. Darwin*, I expressed the hypothesis that sexually reproducing species with an inability to fit the model of natural selection may have a paradoxical advantage in quickly changing environments. Evolutionarily plastic asexually reproducing species are in a serious danger of opportunistically adapting to a short-term variation in environmental conditions, and after a return of the conditions to normal, they won't manage to adapt to the original conditions quickly enough, thus dying out. Precisely this could be the reason why most known species reproduce sexually. Only during the modeling, which was conducted by Petr Ponížil, did it become apparent that I must decide whether plastic and non-plastic species compete directly for a common resource, or whether they just coexist independently. The results consequently showed that apparently only in the second case could the evolutionarily non-plastic species win over the plastic species. They also showed that it is more advantageous for the success of the non-plastic species when the changes in environment are cyclical (this I did not expect); and that jump changes are more favorable than continuous changes for the success of the non-plastic species (this I expected, but it pleased me anyway).

We can model any processes (phenomenona, properties). One must realize, however, that we never model an object or system, but always only the certain specific behavior of the given object or system. The command "Model the watch!" is nonsensical – it isn't clear whether we're supposed to model how the watch will behave after a crash from a speed of 200 km/h into a brick wall, or after being placed into 70% sulfuric acid, or whether we just want to know why its hands tick regularly. All of these processes would require completely different models. Technically, we can study the behavior of mathematical models, either analytical or numerical or perhaps even mechanical models (for example in aerodynamic or hydrodynamic testing). In science the mathematical models are most applicable, and for a biologist, whose qualification prerequisites almost inherently include mathematical illiteracy, numerical modeling is useful above all. Modern computers and modern programming resources are immensely powerful and allow even modeling amateurs to model. Nevertheless, to this end I'd recommend to taking up cooperation with a professional. Modeling on your own harbors one serious hazard – it's addictive.

When one leads a research team, he needs money not only for the material necessary for the experiment and the general running of the laboratory, but also to pay the salaries (rather stipends, in our case) of his coworkers. Today this money is raised by asking for scientific grants. The researcher will write out a project: "I want to study such and such a topic, which could make such and such a finding, and I need this amount of money to carry it out." And in the instance that we're talking about an inexpensive study, he can't write that he needs a couple of cents for postage, writing paper and envelopes, in addition to half of million for the salary and health insurance of his coworkers. To put it more accurately, he can write it, but the evaluators will see the budget as dubiously imbalanced and reject the project. So it is more favorable to enter the grant arena with a more expensive project, which requires costly equipment and chemicals, because then I need half a million for the actual material and equipment and a similar amount for the pay of coworkers, lab technicians and students. And that is enough to ensure the functioning of a smaller-sized laboratory. Since our project didn't require anything aside from "pencils and paper," which today actually means a computer and some statistical software, for many years no one else followed up on our experiments. Colleagues from abroad assured me that our results are interesting and that they understand the necessity of someone else repeating our study. But for a long time no one else tested it, and most likely for the reasons I just mentioned.

To a certain extent, that was an advantage. Thanks to it we had enough time at our disposal, so we could discover most of the interesting things on our own. If several other research teams were simultaneously working on the same project, then we probably wouldn't have discovered as much; in the best case scenario we'd often come out in second place. Not because many of the world's top laboratories have better equipment and more money for research – the problem, as I already mentioned, wasn't in that. The problem lies in something else. Established laboratories in top world universities, which Charles University, unfortunately, is long not a part of, can publish their results more easily. So even in the case that we discovered something before our competitors, it is very likely that the researchers of another laboratory would overtake us in publishing the results of their study, which might have not been as thorough, but bore the glorious name of a famous institution.

If a certain university or even laboratory has produced a number of quality studies, then the editors and reviewers look upon its manuscripts much more favorably than when similar results are sent in by a researcher from a practically unheard of laboratory and, what's more, from a university which, after the forty years that the communists cut us off from the world, certainly isn't among the world's top (see Box 28 *How to measure the quality of science*).

Box 28 How to measure the quality of science

It's hard. The value of a scientific discovery is usually seen only in retrospect, and just for an individual discovery it's often difficult to determine who contributed to what extent. The quality of science produced by certain researchers, by a certain research team or institution, can be weighed based on the examination of individual scientific papers, the response to these papers and the scientific reputation of the researchers (according to awards received, invitations to be a plenary speaker in conferences, and so on). But such individual evaluation is pretty demanding and in the conditions of a medium-sized country would require the formation of an international team of evaluators. On the other hand, this approach would be hardly objective. For example, in our small Czech pond we all know each other too well, and personal ties would likely have a greater effect on the evaluation than did the objective quality of the study. In most cases we must therefore rely on auxiliary, indirect criteria, which we take to at least approximately reflect the quality and quantity of the research. A simple criterion is the **number of publications**, which the evaluated scientist (team) produced in a certain period. Another indirect measure reflecting the quality of research is the **number of references** of the article of the given author in the articles of other authors. This value reflects, above all, the author's age (this can be avoided by counting only the references of articles published in a particular time period); as well as the extent of his social network (this cannot be helped, but it is questionable, whether it would even be desirable); and finally the significance of the published papers for other authors – nobody would reference unimportant works (unfortunately, they would reference erroneous ones, albeit in a negative context, but we wouldn't differentiate this during the evaluation).

When evaluating the number of publications, it is possible and fitting to take into account also the quality of the journals in which the papers were published. A simple criterion of the quality of a journal is its JIF, or **Journal Impact Factor**, the impact which is the average number of references to one article within its first two years of publication. Of course, in individual fields there are different procedures for referring resources; so basically one can't compare the quality of journals nor certainly of researchers from different fields; but that isn't necessary very often. Today the most popular indirect measure of the quality of a researcher is likely the **Hirsch index** (h-index). We obtain it by ordering the papers a scientist published in a given time period, from most referenced to least referenced. We determine the h-index as the number of papers h cited at least h-times. An h-index of 20 was achieved by a researcher who, in a given time period, published 20 papers, each of which was referenced at least twenty times. An advantage of the Hirsch index is that it is little affected when an author references his own publications in his other papers (auto-reference) or when, among many low quality papers, he somehow manages to publish one high quality, or rather highly referenced, paper. Nevertheless, a highly referenced and scientifically valuable paper doesn't have to be one and the same. For example, my most referenced article is a study describing a new computer program for molecular phylogenetics. The program is definitely useful – for this reason others use it and reference the article – but the scientific value of the article is relatively low. Indirect measures for evaluating science, offered to us by today's **scientometrics** (a field which pursues the measuring of scientific quality), are imperfect, but we have no better ones, so thank goodness we have at least these.

And the mistakes that I made? For example, twenty years ago, because I wasn't very skillful in statistics, I overlooked an interesting result regarding my ten-question toxo-questionnaire. As a consequence of this stupid mistake, for fifteen years I didn't know that the clearest proof of the effect of toxoplasmosis on the human psyche was brought by just the first study – the one which came out of my own introspection. (I probably shouldn't mention this too much. When a former PhD student of mine recently found out about my school-boyish mistake, I think he was considerably wounded.) Maybe it's just as well, that I don't know how many similar, hitherto undetected mistakes I've made during my scientific career.

What I'm really ashamed of is my first ethological study on animals, which I conducted sometime in the first half of the 90s. I attempted to verify whether infected animals have a greater tendency to give up a yet undecided fight. I asked this directly of people in my toxo-questionnaire, and, as it turns out, Toxo positive men truly reported this tendency. I had to ask the question of the animals using an experiment. I conducted my experiment on bank vole (*Myodes glareolus*, a small vole often found in the forest), captured on the Ruda research field station. From previous studies we knew that about half of the bank voles on this field station were infected by the protozoan *Frenkelia*, a parasite which subsequently must get to its final host, a bird of prey. *Frenkelia* is related to *Toxoplasma*, but, unlike *Toxoplasma*, its cysts can be recognized on brain tissue slides prepared using the squash technique. To find out whether the vole is infected, we need only two slides, between which we gradually squash the brain of the freshly killed animal and look under the microscope for round cysts. Therefore we don't need to conduct any laboratory tests, which in the case of some wild animal species may have a lower specificity and sensitivity (see Box 7 *The specificity and sensitivity of a diagnostic test*).

I brought about 15 voles from the Ruda field station. Around my laboratory I laid out fifteen aquariums filled with water, placed a vole in each one, and watched how long they would swim before giving up fighting for their life, and sink their head into the water. At that moment I planned to take them out of the water, kill them and examine the presence of cysts in the brain. The reason I am so ashamed of this experiment today isn't even so much that I harmed the voles – that I let them swim to utter exhaustion, though that bothered me greatly about the experiment. Yet if exhaustion was the object of my study, then I didn't have much of a choice. I am most ashamed that I prepared my experiment badly, and so tormented the animals needlessly (see Box 29 *Planning and preparing experiments* and Box 30 *Animal testing*).

Box 29 Planning and preparing experiments

The most important part of a research project is its preparation. One must first resolve what he actually wants to determine during his study, or **what question he wants to answer**. We're dealing with perhaps the most important phase of project preparation, during which the researcher must decide whether the given question is even worth being pursued, whether there isn't already a known answer and whether he is the right person to pursue it. Always in this phase it's necessary to conduct a thorough **literature review**, to find what's already been written about the given topic. In the next preparatory phase one must choose an **appropriate**

method for answering the given question and **plan out the project**, making clear when and where the study will be carried out, as well as who will work on it and how. The project must address not only how the data will be collected, but also how they will subsequently be pre-processed (what will be done, for example, about missing or outlying values) and how the pre-processed data will be assessed. It is an unforgivable error, which can definitely come back to bite you, if during the project preparation you don't decide ahead of time how specifically you'll evaluate the data. For it can easily happen that we neglect to record some important information and finally won't be able to correctly evaluate the data. Next is the phase of the project's **technical preparation**, which involves procuring all the necessary material, learning to work with the equipment and preparing the protocols. The **protocols** contain tables used to record data during the experiment, and are prepared ahead of time by the researcher; afterwards he records the actual progress of the research in his **laboratory notebook**, whether it's a paper or an electronic lab notebook, e.g. an Excel or Open Office spreadsheet. The latter is easier to navigate, namely in the case that one is working on multiple projects – using an automatic filter he can easily control all the recorded data related to a particular project. For a more complicated project it is often appropriate to first carry out a **pilot study** and test whether it's possible to carry out the project as planned originally, or whether it's necessary to modify or entirely scrap our plans – as would happen, for example, if we found using a study power analysis that the studied effect is so weak that to prove it we'd require too many experimental animals.

What follows is carrying out the **actual study**, **pre-evaluating and controlling the obtained data** and finally **evaluating the data**. For more complicated studies the pre-evaluation and evaluation of the data often involves as much or even more work than taken up by the experiment itself. Usually it's also the most challenging phase for the expertise of the respective scientists.

Above all, I could have realized beforehand that fifteen voles is not enough to detect a difference between the infected and uninfected individuals. Considering that it was a group of animals of various ages and both genders, there was definitely a large variability in the studied value, i.e. the amount of time they tried to swim. Therefore the probability that I would successfully prove using fifteen animals a statistically significant difference between the infected and uninfected individuals was very low; even in the optimal case that this difference was very substantial, and that half of my sample of animals was infected and the other half uninfected. Such an optimal case could not be expected; it was much more likely that in a small sample of fifteen animals there were, for example, five infected and ten uninfected individuals, or vice versa.

Another problem was that I underestimated the preparation of the experiment. That became clear, for example, in that the animals in aquariums closer to the door gave up their struggle before the animals nearer the center of the room. Apparently there was some sort of gradient in that room, most likely a temperature gradient, and as a result the voles who gave up first were those in aquariums with the worst conditions for survival – where, for example, the water was coldest.

The last problem was that for subjective and objective reasons I was unable to remain focused during the entirety of the experiment; so some of the voles drowned, and in some cases I didn't even record the exact time that a certain individual gave up his struggle. It would have been better for two observes to switch off every half hour during the experiment.

I originally intended the experiment as a pilot study to verify whether such means could be used to find if infected individuals give up more easily. In this aspect the study was actually successful, for it gave me a fairly unambiguous answer. Technically, after certain modifications, the given topic could be addressed using this method. However, I would have to use a more genetically and physiologically homogenous group of infected and control animals, and carry out the experiment under better controlled conditions – for example, in thermostat-equipped water baths. Moreover, the course of this experiment convinced me that I don't have the "proper" disposition for this kind of study, and that it would be better that similar experiments never again be performed in my laboratory. That promise I was able to keep, so perhaps those fifteen voles didn't die entirely in vain (Box 30 *Animal Testing*).

Box 30 Animal Testing

Unfortunately, biomedical research can never entirely do without animal experiments. Moreover, it often cannot even do without testing on humans. If the effectiveness of a new drug or medical procedure is to be verified, it is clear that eventually there must come the final phase of testing on human volunteers. Some animal testing can be replaced by testing on tissue cultures (if we want to know how a certain substance or physical factor influences the viability of individual cells). In most cases we have to conduct the experiment on animals in the end anyway, because there exist many factors which have an entirely different effect on the functioning of cells and the functioning of multicellular organisms. In the same way, it is not possible to replace an animal experiment with a mathematical model. The model can only serve a didactic purpose – using the mathematical model we can "painlessly," inexpensively and quickly demonstrate to students the course of certain processes. The model can also sometimes reveal that conducting a certain experiment is useless, that the pursued effect is so weak that we basically cannot prove it in the laboratory. In some cases, it is possible to replace an experiment with observation in the wild. There it's not necessary to infect reindeer with *Echinococcus* tapeworms and observe whether the infected individuals become the prey of wolves; it's enough, using a suitable serological technique, to find what percent of the reindeer in a normal population and what percent of reindeer that become wolf prey are infected. During animal testing, even with the best intent, we cannot avoid more or less harming them. That we're doing it in the interest of science or mankind, and that it was approved by the respective Institutional for Animal Care and Use Committee, may be an extenuating circumstance, but it doesn't diminish the guilt. As my colleague Jan Zrzavý says, science cannot do without animal testing, but those who do that testing should perhaps know that they'll finish in the fiery pits of hell. Before any experiment, one must deeply consider whether its possible outcome is important enough to justify our carrying it out; whether it really enables us to obtain the expected results; whether there exists another way to obtain them; what is the smallest number of animals we must include; and how to minimize the animals' suffering.

VI. How science was (also) conducted in the 90s

So what was my research team actually like? Probably like most of the teams forming in our university in the 90s. It's reminiscent of a passage from Šimek and Grossmann's *A visit to the circus*: "The orchestra may not have been the most numerous, but both of the musicians, the accordionist and the conductor, did what they could." As was practically a rule in our departments at that time, the majority of the studies were carried out by my own efforts and those of undergraduate students. When the first generation of undergrads "grew up," some of them went on with graduate studies – only then could they systematically devote themselves to independent research. Until then, the majority of their time was taken up by lectures and training, but, unlike today, almost none of them had a job during the course of the year. They likely got money for their studies and vacations abroad from their parents, from summer jobs and a few of them also from merit-based scholarships.

At first I hunted down experimental subjects on my own; I went around the biological departments, trying to convince students and my colleagues, both those I knew and didn't know, to participate in the study. Testing for toxoplasmosis was conducted by Jaroslav Kulda, and if he wasn't available, then Ivan Hrdý, one of his graduate students, filled in. Hrdý Ivan I convinced to continue the testing even after we stopped receiving patients. That was around the year 1993. I don't know why the testing stopped; I suspect it was because of the recent interest of medical diagnostic laboratories to test patients themselves, because it held a financial interest for them. Then there hung over our head the threat that someone would complain of being tested by a someone who is not a qualified medical person. A somewhat laughable state of affairs – whereas a nurse fresh out of high school is acceptable, a professor of parasitology with over thirty years of work experience poses a problem. This state of affairs – that only a physician, and not a biologist, can give people injections – is the successful result of physicians' efforts to monopolize through bureaucratic means a certain part of the scientific field. In reality, a biologist with a long-time experience will certainly manage an injection better than a freshly graduated nurse. That it's not, in fact, a matter of protecting a patient against untrained incompetent biologists, but merely an effort to achieve a monopoly, is apparent in that phytopathologists, "plant physicians," are purportedly attempting to achieve the same. With their efforts, the phytopathologists have shown the physicians' true colors, and if they also succeed, it will be clear to any discerning person that similar practices aren't in the interest of the patient, but are about a certain guild's display of power, by which it ensures itself a monopoly. Oftentimes I've told myself that it'd be nice to push into some law the provision, that any experiments with live organisms can only be provided by the graduate of a Faculty of Science. Then I'd be interested in a lawyer's arguments on whether some medical studies aren't illegal, because their research team lacked a natural scientist-biologist, permitted to work with, let's say, sea urchins (or with primates of the genus *Homo*).

But back to the beginnings of our study. My colleague Hrdý, a fresh postdoc in those days, was happy to conduct the testing, mostly because I brought in pretty female students as test subjects; and because acting as his secretary was Štěpánka Zitková, his future wife, who at the time was an undergrad. Her main topic was testing the manipulation hypothesis using laboratory mice as a model. She tried to find whether infected mice also have delayed reactions. As I mentioned previously, I introspectively observed that I react more slowly than do others to sudden stimuli, that I don't get frightened and flee instinctively from a dangerous situation. For this reason, I invented the experiment that should prove similar manifestations of infection in mice. During this experiment Štěpánka Zitková placed the infected and uninfected mice onto a metal hot plate heated to 60 degrees Celsius, a temperature which did not endanger the mice, but was uncomfortable for them. We watched to see how soon the mice would realize that something wasn't right, and jump off of the hot plate. Indeed, we discovered that infected mice react more slowly; however, these differences in behavior were only transient and disappeared after four months (Fig. 17). The back-up plan for Štěpánka Zitková's undergraduate thesis, prepared in case the main subject brought no reasonable results, was the study of the effect of toxoplasmosis on human, so she was also involved in the studies on people.

Along with Štěpánka Zitková, another of my students, Jan Votýpka, was working on his undergraduate thesis on manipulation hypothesis. He compared how different species of parasites, with different types of life cycles, affect the behavior of a host. We were interested in whether the respective behavioral changes in the infected animals would also occur when the given parasite wasn't transferred by predation from prey to predator. Unlike Štěpánka, he wasn't examining the development of the respective behavioral changes over time, but was rather observing these changes at only one point in time – on the other hand, he did it for about five different parasites.

He used a set of several simple ethological methods. Among them were definitely the hot plate and the so-called open arena. In the latter test a mouse is thrown into a meter by meter arena with a square grid drawn on the floor, and one follows how many squares the mouse visits during the course of ten minutes, how often it perches on its hind legs and looks around, and so on. This method actually follows the animal's spontaneous action. If I remember correctly, Jan Votýpka wasn't involved in the studies on humans, but only in those on animals.

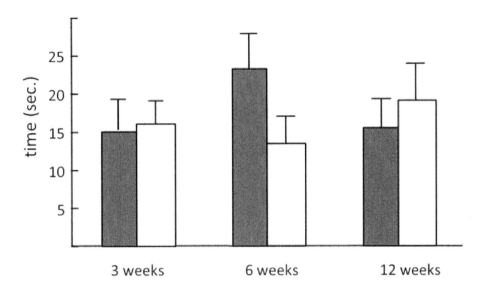

Fig. 17 A bar graph demonstrating the difference in reaction time between Toxoplasma-*infected (shaded bars) and uninfected (unshaded bars) mice. Six weeks after infection, mice jump off the warm platform substantially later than uninfected mice. Three months after infection, there is less of a difference; the infected mice even jump off sooner than the control animals. But it is important to realize that few mice survive three months in nature, therefore the situation so long after infection is not relevant to* Toxoplasma's *chances of transferring to a cat. The graphs show means with standard errors.*

Box 31 What our British competitors discovered on animals, and how we will soon beat them

Probably the most interesting discovery regarding the effect of latent toxoplasmosis on the behavior of animals was achieved by our British competitors in the laboratory of Joanne P. Webster. If you google "**fatal attraction**" and *Toxoplasma*, then the search engine won't come up with the new release of the famous thriller, but many links to the research of this British team. In the year 2000 they were able to describe that brown rats with latent toxoplasmosis no longer avoid places rank with the smell of cat urine, but, to the contrary, they seek them out[19]. Neurophysiologists from Stanford University later showed that this is a highly specific phenomenon[20,21]. Infected brown rats (and mice) have an unimpaired sense of smell and avoid other dangerous stimuli; but the scent of cat truly attracts them. This study, which even I was initially skeptical of, has been repeated many times, in at least three different laboratories. So the described phenomenon is most likely real. It is, however, quite difficult to imagine how *Toxoplasma* can affect the nervous system of its host so specifically, that the switch from repulsive to attractive occurs only with the scent of cat. So how do we Prague scientists plan to beat them? It's probably better that I keep it to myself. Otherwise, our students might realize the identity of these samples, whose odor they've been evaluating for our experiments for last two years[22].

A while later Jan Havlíček, who conversely devoted himself exclusively to studies on humans, joined my laboratory; he didn't, however, test our students, but blood donors in the nearby blood donation center. His primary object of interest were the reaction times of these persons. Initially, the questionnaire studies – whether those applied to the first batch of students, to the former patients with acute toxoplasmosis or to pregnant women – were primarily carried out by me. I remember very well, copying from the barely legible index-card files in the Center for Disease Control and Prevention the necessary data regarding the former patients. A brief digression – it was good that I did so, because in the year 2002 the flood swept out the center, and the filing cabinet with this valuable data was mostly destroyed. It was fortunate that at the last minute I extracted something beneficial for science from this gathered data.

When conducting the second study on women, former patients with acute toxoplasmosis, I had already obtained a moderate research grant and could afford to pay the laboratory technicians in the Center for Disease Control and Prevention to enter the data from the filing cabinet into the computer for me. Nevertheless, completed questionnaires continued to come to our department, and I or my students had to transfer this data into the computer by hand. I usually fulfilled such mechanical work at home, watching TV while pounding away at the keyboard of a primitive PP-06 computer. I made myself a nifty program which checked for specific types of mistakes made when I entered in the answers. At the time I also used a modified version of this program in the department for testing students. Unlike the paper questionnaire, this program not only made filling out the questionnaire about thirty percent faster, but also immensely simplified processing the test results – it wasn't necessary to transfer the data from paper to computer, nor was it necessary to manually convert raw data using tables into age-standardized values. But the program additionally recorded how long it took the test subject to select an answer for individual questions. I expected that toxo-positive persons would answer some types of questions more slowly than toxo-negative persons – though the answer might not differ. Yet I never got to actually processing the data regarding the time to complete the questionnaire. It's one of the many arrears tucked away in my desk drawer, or rather somewhere on the hard drive of my computer. From my experience, I've realized that when research really takes off, results pile up much faster than it is possible to continually process them – and, above all, faster than it is possible to publish the processed results (Box 32 *How and why a scientific publication is born*).

Box 32 How and why a scientific publication is born

Officially, scientific publications ensue from research projects. A researcher writes a project whose purpose is to answer a certain scientifically interesting question. If he succeeds with his project in the grant competition and obtains financial resources, he'll implement the planned studies and glean an answer to the questions he laid. He subsequently publishes this answer as a scientific article in a journal, so that the results of his study might be shared with as much of the scientific public as possible. I don't insist that my experiences are universally applicable, but, on the other hand, it doesn't seem to me likely that they would differ dramatically from the experiences of my colleagues. What I am sure about, however, is that my experiences and the official process of scientific publication are like night and day. Most of the results that we finally published were obtained as the by-product of other studies. Even when the results were directly related to the project from which they arose, they were most likely obtained long before the respective project was proposed for a grant. For only a completely irresponsible person submits to the grant competition a project that's not at least half-way done. A careful person, like I, generally enters a project at least 80% complete (and for the duration of his proposal's evaluation, crosses his fingers that the publications not come into the press before he is given the grant). But the institution giving money for an already completed project is not defrauded – the funds are used for another project, usually a follow-up, which becomes the subject of the next grant proposal. Publications don't usually come about so that other researchers in the field can use them, but in spite of the fact that other researchers can use them. Other researchers in the field are first and foremost competitors, and the ground must be cut from under their feet – i.e. they must be overtaken in solving questions. Yes, overtaking competitors usually means publishing a discovery before they do, but only a small percentage of articles actually publish a discovery – most of them show how it is and isn't possible to achieve that discovery in the future. Many publications come about so that a researcher can display a scientific feat to the grant agency and thus heighten his chances of later obtaining another grant. Many publications come about because a certain number of one's own publications are required of an applicant for a scientific or teaching degree or position (a PhD, associate professor or professor). But most publications arise from vanity. Like a gunfighter notches his pistol, a researcher collects his publications, delighting late at night in how his list is steadily growing. Yet today this proclaimed honorable competition, which in many cases resembles the manner of amateur sport until the 50s, is critically endangered by intensive commercialization (but then again, what isn't?). The taxpayer began to care about what he's getting for the billions that go to science, and an educated taxpayer even begins to wonder whether he's getting the same number of publications for his taxes, as is a taxpayer in the U.S. or Great Britain (which he likely won't get anytime soon). So the respective government agencies don't waste time in motivating their researchers to the highest production of scientific articles in top journals. The number of articles is strictly observed, and based on their number and the ranking of the journals in which they were published, the respective scientific institutions and sometimes even teams are financed (see also Box 28

How to measure quality of science). In some countries this effort of the government bodies is carried out to an extreme. For example, in China, publishing an article in a prestigious journal brings the team and specifically the researcher such a great financial award that researchers there are supposedly willing to pay foreign teams a more than decent sum for being added to the list of authors on their publication.

As I already mentioned, the entire time I actually led two teams, which ceaselessly produced more and more data. For one, I led a team studying manipulation hypothesis, whether it be on humans or on animals (Fig. 18), and then I led a team studying the molecular phylogenetics of parasitic protozoa. In addition, I collaborated very closely with a team studying human ethology in the Faculty of Humanities, led by my former undergraduate and graduate student Jan Havlíček (see Box 33 *How engaged women sniff out good genes*). Only the students researched on animals, whereas both I and the students did so on people. I must confess that the studies on humans interested me more, but a number of my undergrad students who began researching in the department and eventually even in my laboratory were interested in working with animals, and not in convincing students or blood donors to participate in experiments, sending out questionnaires or transferring data from questionnaires into the computer.

I myself have never considered the method used particularly important, but have always been fascinated by the given problem. The question whose answer I was seeking had to be interesting; but the method with which I sought the answer, whether it be the mechanical entering of data from questionnaires into the computer, or DNA-sequencing, or catching mice in the wild and observing whether more Toxo positive or Toxo negative individuals were caught in the mouse-trap, was not important to me. But it was important to some of my students, so I carried out at least part of the studies on animals, even though I was much more interested in the results obtained on humans.

Fig. 18 The Toxo-team, in its strongest lineup to-date (2003). From the left: Jitka Hanušová-Lindová, Petra Kolbeková, Martina Vitáková-Novotná, Mirka Pečálková-Berenreiterová, Jaroslav Flegr, Jan Havlíček, Šárka Kaňková, Romana Vavřinová-Křivohlavá, Anna Skallová-Fialová, Hana Hodková-Šturcová.

Box 33 How engaged women sniff out good genes

I don't know whether my colleague Jan Havlíček would agree, but I think that the most interesting result so far came from his project studying the differences in women's olfactory preferences for men's scent during the menstrual cycle[23]. He was able to convince 48 men, students, to first complete a commonly used psychological questionnaire revealing dominance, and then to wear cotton tampons under their armpits for 24 hours, for the tampons to absorb their body odor. Then he placed the scent samples in brown glass containers and convinced 65 female students to evaluate how attractive they found each scent. It turned out that women in the fertile period of their menstrual cycle found more attractive the scents of men evaluated as dominant by the questionnaire.

This result corresponds with the evolutionary psychological theory, which presumes that women choose their sexual partners according to the level of dominance. Dominance is hard to fake and a pretty expensive mark for its bearer, which honestly shows how good his genes are and how many resources he probably has. A man can dissemble for some time, and try to look witty and intelligent, but if he's trying to fake dominance and "doesn't have it," he'll eventually be put in his place. A more detailed analysis of our data showed something even more interesting. The effect pertained only to women with long-term partners; women without long-term partners preferred the scent of dominant men only minimally (Fig. 19). This goes to show that women who chose dominant men were seeking above all the man's "good genes," as opposed to his resources; they were interesting in only a short-term sexual partner. Women seeking a long-term partner, with long-term access to resources, did not put dominant men first. It seems evolution programmed women to follow a sort of mixed reproductive strategy. They would prefer the dominant man (her sexual partner during the fertile period of her menstrual cycle) as the genetic father of their children, whereas her choice of a social partner was subject to different criteria. It also works like this with other animals – for example, studies on swallows have shown that attractive males are often poor social partners and are not as involved in feeding the young as are less attractive males. Females have it hard – they'd like to be faithful to their husbands, but nature ruins it for them. And those backwards vegetarians would like to stone them for it! Or was it the Shintoists or Lutherans? I'm not very good with religions, for in school the communists only taught scientific atheism…

Note: By backwards I only mean that they haven't yet read my book, don't search for any other meaning. It was explained to me that I must be politically correct in the English version of my book and avoid joking about certain topics. It's something I'm well-trained in; I had to practice auto-censorship for half my life.

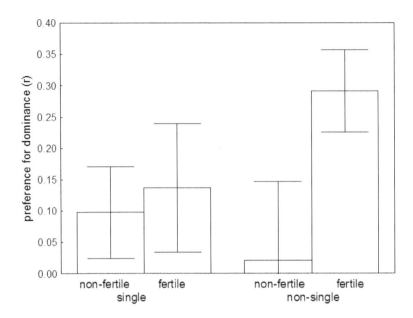

Fig. 19 The preference for the body odor of dominant men by engaged and not engaged women in different phases of their menstrual cycle. Preference for dominant men was expressed as the value of the correlation coefficient (r) between the dominance of the man based on a psychological questionnaire, and the average pleasantness of his body odor according to a given group of women. The graph demonstrates that all women preferred the odor of dominant men; however, the greatest preference was expressed by women in the fertile period of their menstrual cycle.

It's interesting that women were able to sniff out the dominant males so well. The modern obsession with body hygiene and the use of deodorants may even be one of the causes of the high divorce rate. A number of studies show that, in seeking their partner, mammals (including humans) follow olfactory cues. When comparing, for example, the MHC proteins of couples, there are more differences between them than could be attributed to chance. At the same time, it has been safely proven that the effectiveness of the immune system, and thus also the resistance against infectious diseases, depends primarily on the optimal heterogeneity of the

MHC proteins of individuals (Box 34 *Is sexual reproduction related to defense against parasites?*). If through the use of deodorants we prevent that couples smell each other when getting together, we cannot be surprised that a large percent of them discover only after the wedding that the other person "stinks"[24].

The main reason I had to constantly lead two teams occupying themselves with entirely disparate subjects was actually financial. As I already mentioned, in the case of the study of manipulation hypothesis it wasn't possible to ask for that much money for projects, and there also wasn't a good chance that the given project would be successful in the grant competition. In the typical grant competition in the Czech Republic, the researcher writes out a project and hopes that it will appeal to three anonymous reviewers, that they will all evaluate it fairly positively, and thus that the given grant agency will be willing to finance him. The problem arises when the project has a controversial subject – which the study of manipulation hypothesis on the model of *Toxoplasma*-human most certainly is. Then, it is very likely that among the three reviewers at least one won't like the project and, under whatever pretext, will reject it. There was nearly always at least one reviewer evaluating my projects directed towards the study of the effect of toxoplasmosis on human behavior who found the idea that a parasite could alter human behavior completely absurd (and maybe even offensive).

Box 34 Is sexual reproduction related to defense against parasites?

> The origin of sexual reproduction is one of the greatest evolutionary mysteries. At first glance (as on second and maybe even third), it would seem that when competing with an asexually reproducing species, which for one doesn't throw out half of its reproductive potential in the production of useless males, the sexually reproducing species should quickly lose. Yet the opposite is true – the

vast majority of known species reproduce sexually. Evolutionarily biologists have gradually suggested a whole range of possible explanations. One of these, which is reasonably supported by a number of studies, is called the **Red Queen Hypothesis** and presumes that sexuality evolved and is maintained in nature as one method of defense against parasites. The evolution of parasites is usually faster than that of their hosts; thus they are able to quickly adapt to the most frequently occurring form of the host species (i.e. the individuals with the most frequent genotype). If there are individuals with a combination of genes (genotype) most resistant against parasites, they're asking for trouble in the next generation. They'll leave behind the most offspring, and the new generation of parasites will adapt precisely to these offspring. Biological fitness in a world full of parasites, i.e. in our world, actually has a **negative heritability**; individuals who have the most offspring in one generation have the least offspring in the next. But this applies only to asexually reproducing species, where the gene combination of the parent passes to the offspring unaltered. With sexually reproducing species, in every generation each offspring has a random combination of genes, half from the father and half from the mother, so that the offspring differ genetically not only from their parents, but also from each other.

Sexually reproducing species present a sort of moving target to parasites – as soon as the parasites adapt to gene combinations in one generation of hosts, these old combinations disappear in the population, giving way to entirely new ones. An immensely important role in defense against parasites is played by **MHC proteins**. As described in Box 22 *Antibodies and myths about them*, these proteins transport parasite protein peptides from cell interior to cell surfaces, and so determine what signals (which peptides) the immune system will recognize to conclude the presence of a parasite. In a host species, each gene for an MHC protein occurs in many variants, meaning that it has many different alleles; these variants can be differentiated by which peptides they bind and transport to the cell surface. For the species an also its members, this is highly advantageous. If each MHC gene had but one variant, all the members of a species would recognize the presence of a parasite by the same peptides in its proteins. A parasite capable of rapid evolution, such as a virus, could remove these peptides from its proteins and become invisible to the host's immune system.

Because the individuals of a host species differ from each other in the variants of their MHC proteins, they also differ from each other in the peptide sets they use to recognize the presence of a given parasite. When the proteins of a parasite are cleaved, they form the same (enormous) set of various peptides; but the MHC proteins in each individual choose from this fundamental set a distinct subset of peptides they bring to T cells to look over (see Box 22 *Antibodies and myths about them*). Thus parasites cannot adapt to a host species by removing from their own proteins the peptides the host uses to recognize their foreign nature – in each individual of the host species the peptides used are different. For a member of a host species, it is also advantageous to have a sufficient number of MHC protein variants; in that way it will be able to recognize a large spectrum of peptides, and thus also the foreign nature of a large number of parasitic species. This is apparently the reason why women, in choosing their sexual partner, prefer men with different variants (alleles) of MHC genes than they themselves have[24]. How women recognize these out of all the other men isn't entirely clear, though it's likely that they sniff them out – peptides have a relatively low molecular mass and after being loosened from MHC proteins may spread through the air. In a number of mammal species, a so-called **vomeronasal organ** is designated to detect them; but in humans this organ is not functional and it seems that the peptides are detected by a population of specialized cells in the olfactory epithelium. Signals from these cells go directly to the brain stem, as opposed to the cerebral cortex, so a woman's conscious mind is never clued in – to her the given man just suddenly seems so inexplicably and irresistibly attractive...

Yet I was able to gradually carry through a number of projects. Either I, or later my students, managed to get several grants from the internal Grant Agency of Charles University, and four from the Grant Agency of the Czech Republic. Nevertheless, I had to submit overall about 12 to 15 grant applications on this subject to just two grant agencies. Maybe this rate of success isn't that much lower than the average at these grant agencies, but the fact remains that our molecular taxonomy projects were more successful.

Still, the main problem lay in that the projects related to *Toxoplasma* brought the laboratory substantially less money than did projects in the field of molecular taxonomy, so it was difficult with the former to finance lab equipment and the pay the salaries of all the grads and undergrads. It was especially necessary to ensure pay for graduates in their fourth or higher year of study, when then no longer received a stipend. This funding could be easily obtained from the molecular taxonomy projects. For these purely practical reasons, I had continue to also lead a molecular taxonomy team; although I admit that when the studies on the effect of toxoplasmosis began clearly producing very interesting results, molecular taxonomy projects weren't that exciting to me. Fortunately, I had a number of clever students who took charge of these projects and were able to achieve many interesting results. Our molecular taxonomy papers were published in top journals and abundantly cited; and, above all, many were written. That was another reason why I devoted a substantial chunk of my time to these projects, even though my heart was elsewhere. Scientific productivity is measured – and not just in my country – according to the number of published papers, as well as how often those papers are cited in the works of other authors.

Fig. 20 The team of molecular taxonomy, at the time of its strongest lineup (year 2005). From the left: Vladimír Hampl, Ivan Čepička, Magdaléna Uzlíková, Dušan Kolár, Martin Kostka, Martin Kolísko, Jaroslav Flegr.

Namely the amount of published papers grew faster in projects studying molecular phylogenetics than in projects pertaining to the effect of toxoplasmosis on behavior. Our molecular taxonomy projects weren't controversial, and we had the advantage that there were people in our department able to acquire the necessary protozoa from nature. In our case it was mainly Jaroslav Kulda, who not only brought us a vast amount of vital knowledge and experience, but also managed to pass on this knowledge to students; so after a while our team had many such people (Fig. 20).

By these I mean my colleagues Vladimir Hampl and Ivan Čepička; Martin Kostka and Martin Kolísko were also very good. Plus we had at our disposal a unique collection of frozen isolates of parasitic protozoa. At the time a number of them had no known gene sequences, so often we only had to select a couple of interesting protozoa species, whose placement in the protozoological classification was unknown, and then fish around in the container of liquid nitrogen. We hit upon an opportune time, because the phylogenetic system of unicellular organisms was just being radically re-evaluated, so there was great interest in our results. So it wasn't all that difficult to publish them. Whereas work pertaining to the effect of toxoplasmosis on behavior was mostly rejected by the editors of three to four journals, until it was finally accepted by the fifth; our molecular phylogenetic papers were usually accepted by the first, and at least by the second journal we sent it to. That was important to me, because thanks to the molecular phylogenetic publications our laboratory didn't in any way performance-wise fall behind the other research teams in the department (and even less so in the university), so I could defend projects regarding toxoplasmosis, which brought publications much more slowly.

And finally it must be said that the molecular taxonomy projects enabled me to achieve habilitation, to obtain the teaching position of associate professor and later even full professor. While my inaugural professorial thesis was dedicated only to manipulation hypothesis, a large part of the publications and citations also evaluated by the promotion committees were actually related to molecular phylogenetics, and sometimes evolutionary biology, another field that I studied for a long time. I worked independently on evolutionary biology, sometimes cooperating with colleagues in different workplaces; but that's another chapter, which I don't wish to discuss too much in this book – perhaps just here and there in some box (such as Box 35 *How I refuted Darwin*).

Box 35 How I refuted Darwin

Darwin's theory of evolution presumes that **advantageous traits** evolve in species as a result of the effect of **natural selection**. If stronger individuals are more likely than weaker individuals to survive to maturity and reproduce, then the average strength of the member of a species should increase each generation. For with each individual there are always mutations, some increasing and others decreasing the fitness (viability and fertility) of their bearer. Individuals bearing mutations which raise their fitness are more likely to reproduce than individuals without such mutations, and even more so than individuals with mutations that lower their fitness (this is the majority of mutations). Because mutations are passed down from parent to offspring, the fraction of individuals with advantageous mutations should steadily grow, and the average fitness of the member of a population should thereby increase each generation. The vast majority of biologists sees Darwin's theory of evolution as entirely satisfying and doesn't believe it necessary to change anything about it. But in reality this theory can explain evolution only for asexually reproducing organisms (such as bacteria or plants reproducing vegetatively, through tubers or rhizomes). In sexually reproducing organisms, mutations can also be passed down from the parents to the offspring, but because the genes of both parents are mixed to form the genotypes of the offspring, then in each generation the same mutation occurs in the presence of different genes, changing its effect on the traits of the organism. A mutation (or, rather, a gene variant – allele) which raised fitness in one parent may, with a combination of genes with the other parent, actually lower the fitness of the offspring (or raise the offspring's viability, but lower its fertility). In asexually reproducing organisms, the parents' gene combination passes down to the asexual offspring unchanged (at most enriched by some new mutation), so the parents' traits are inherited by the offspring of the next generation. Unlike this, in sexually reproducing species new combinations of alleles arise in each generation, mixed from alleles of both parents. As a result of this, the parents' traits are not inherited and the classical Darwinian mechanism of evolution cannot work here. This corresponds with the findings of modern paleontology, a science studying fossils.

Paleontologists have shown that species change very little over the span of their existence, and when their time comes to die out, they often look entirely the same as they did when they were formed. Of course, here and there an old species branches off a new one, which from the start is distinct from the ancestor species. If Darwin's theory were also applicable to sexually reproducing species, the paleontological picture would be very different – above all in that species would have the capacity to change at any time during their existence, not just in the beginning. To explain how evolution can work in sexually reproducing organisms (which, by the way, is the vast majority of known species present on Earth), and simultaneously to define the picture of the species evolution provided to us by modern paleontology, sometime in the later 90s I created the **frozen plasticity theory**[11,25,26]. According to this theory, sexually reproducing species really cannot evolve through the effects of natural selection, firstly because their traits are not inherited unchanged (see the above), and secondly because the advantage or disadvantage of individual gene variants often depends on their numeric representation in the population. So species don't act plastically (as Darwin imagined), but elastically – at first they happily react to natural selection, but as the numeric representation of individual alleles grows further from average, the individuals respond less to natural selection, until they finally stop reacting entirely. When natural selection is interrupted, the numeric representation of individual alleles (and thus also the average traits of the member of that species) returns to previous levels. But under certain conditions the species can switch over from an elastic to a plastic state, and, through the effect of natural selection, began evolving just as Darwin imagined. This happens, for example, when a small number of species members colonize an island far from the continent, where their offspring survive many generations as a small colony. During this time, chance (biologists call this genetic drift) erases almost all the alleles – from each gene there ideally remains but one. When the population increases sufficiently, there arise ideal conditions for Darwinian evolution. The population is large, so the fate of an individual is determined by natural selection, instead of chance, like in small populations. But at the same time, the individuals are genetically similar; therefore the mutations in each generation will occur in the presence of the same alleles – despite the fact that each individual gets new gene combinations mixed from two parents. Because both parents have nearly identical gene combinations (aside from maybe a few mutations), their genes can combine in whichever way but always achieve the same result. Therefore a species re-establishes evolutionary plasticity and can begin evolving. Yet over time the new species accumulates more and more alleles, often because the benefit of these alleles decreases as they spread throughout the population.

The fate of such variants is determined by the so-called negative frequency dependent selection. So long as alleles remain rare after they're formed, they are advantageous and spread throughout the population through natural selection; but when they become abundant, their merit decreases. Due to their frequency dependence, they can never become prevalent nor entirely disappear from the population (see Box 70 *Genetic polymorphism: what it is, where it comes from, and how it's maintained in nature?*). A new species loses its plasticity and becomes more and more elastic. Paleontological data shows that a species persists in a plastic state only about 20 thousand years (less than one percent of the usual length of a species' existence), which is a fairly long time for it to substantially change from its ancestor species, but also a short enough period of time in paleontological record that the formation of the new species looks like a sudden jump. The extension of frozen plasticity theory, the frozen evolution theory[27], further presumes that over time different evolutionary branches accumulate characters which could become plastic only with great difficulty even during the formation of a new species. The accumulation of these eternally frozen characters is thanks to the process of **sorting on the basis of stability** (what is unstable comes and goes, and what is stable remains). This accumulation of eternally frozen characters may explain why the rate of evolution over the course of Earth's history has been slowing, and why the greatest evolutionary innovations in animals were formed over a relatively short period of time, half a billion years ago (in the Cambrium) – and why, since that time, no radically different body plans have appeared.

That I was capable of turning out a sufficient number of publications additionally increased the chance that I'd gain resources for projects regarding *Toxoplasma*. When one requests a grant, he also presents a list of his past publications (at some grant agencies only those from the last five years). The reviewers don't usually peruse the topics of these publications, but observe their number, and how prestigious the journals. When I had a sufficient number of papers, there was a decidedly greater chance that I'd obtain a new grant, even one for a completely different project – related, perhaps, to toxoplasmosis. So that I could successfully pursue myself to the study of toxoplasmosis, I had to dedicate my time and energy to other projects, which, as I already admitted, were not as dear to me. Although, to be honest, I exaggerate a bit. I enjoyed molecular biology projects too. Probably I was one of the first in our country to start seriously studying the topic, and in the time when molecular phylogenetics was just developing as a scientific field. Only at the end of the 90s was it definitely established, and at that moment the subject lost a great deal of its magic for me. I wonder what problems I would have pursued in the new century had I not hit upon the effect of toxoplasmosis on human behavior. I expect that it would not have been molecular phylogenetics anyway. Rather, I'd bet on genomics, particularly in relation with immunology – most likely I'd be testing my hypotheses concerning the adaptation of the peptide repertoires of parasites to the peptide repertoires of hosts (see Box 36 *On peptides, and why they should interest a parasitologist*).

Box 36 On peptides, and why they should interest a parasitologist

Proteins are generally considered to be the most interesting and varied molecules in modern cells. (Time will probably show that RNA molecules are even more interesting and varied, but so far not much is known about them.) **Proteins** make up the definite majority of enzymes, regulatory and signaling molecules, molecular motor and pumps, as well as a large part of cells' molecular building-blocks. They therefore are the main component of a modern organism's "hardware."

A protein molecule is chemically formed by a linear chain, in which twenty kinds of **amino acids** alternate in an apparently random pattern. The order of the twenty amino acids (relatively small organic molecules, which have in common only the fact that on one end they have a carboxyl and on the other an amino group, allowing them to unite using peptide bonds into a linear chain) is determined by the respective genes. This order decides the shape the chain will fold into, and thus what function it will perform. Yet the same shape and thereby similar function can be attained with different, though generally similar, amino acid sequences. Proteins are the main molecules used by the immune system to recognize the presence of parasites, whether they be viruses, bacteria or even *Toxoplasma*. A certain amount of each protein synthesized in the cell (intracellular) or brought in from the outside (extracellular), is cleaved using special enzymes into small pieces about 7-14 amino acids long. These **peptides** are, by the means of **MHC proteins** (MHC antigens), transported to the cell surface and there presented. Peptides from intracellular proteins are bound to and presented on **MHC class I proteins**; peptides from extracellular proteins, on **MHC class II proteins**.

All cell surfaces are continuously examined by a type of white blood cell called **T cells** (or T-lymphocytes). Each T cell has on its surface a receptor with which it is able to recognize a certain peptide. In the body there are many groups of T cells clones, with different receptors and thus recognizing different peptides. Unless an organism suffers from an autoimmune disease, it has only T cells that recognize "non-self" peptides, peptides not present in the proteins synthesized by its own body. The body does produce T cells that recognize any type of peptide, but all "immature" T cells, which recognize a "self" protein, commit cell-suicide (apoptosis) while passing through the thymus. There are many types of T cells; at this moment we are interested in cytotoxic and helper T cells. **Cytotoxic T cells**, or "killer" T cells, recognize only peptides presented on class I MHC proteins, peptides which come from intracellular proteins. True to their name, cytotoxic T cells kill the unhappy cell presenting the foreign peptide – since the presence of a peptide that a cytotoxic T cell can recognize signifies that "non-self" proteins, which most likely come from a parasite like *Toxoplasma* or a virus, are being synthesized in the presenting cell. **Helper T cells** recognize peptides presented on class II MHC proteins, peptides from proteins brought into the cell. While class I MHC proteins occur on almost all types of cells, class II MHC proteins are present only on certain cell types defending against parasites, such as B cells or macrophages. (Dear reader, I simplify greatly, but believe me when I say it is for your sake.) If a helper T cell recognizes the presence of "its" foreign peptide on a cell, then it's proof to the helper T cell that the cell presenting the peptide is capable of ingesting a foreign intruder or proteins from a foreign intruder. The helper T cell provides such a cell with growth factor (see also Box 22 *Antibodies and myths about them*). It would be particularly advantageous for a parasite to succeed in removing from its proteins (gradually by evolution, through mutations in the respective genes) all the peptides not present in the proteins of its host. If the parasite could adapt its own **peptide repertoire** to that of its host, then the host's immune system could not detect it. Similarly, it would be advantageous for the parasite to cut down its peptide repertoire as much as possible, getting rid of all the peptides it can afford to. This would eliminate of a large part of the target the T cells in the host body use to recognize an invader, so the parasite could target a wider range of host species. It would likewise be advantageous for the host organism to cut down on its own expendable peptides, for then it could recognize a greater number of peptides as foreign. But all this is only a theory – my theory, to be perfectly clear. Seemingly, it shouldn't be difficult to prove it. Potential hosts like mammals and birds, with an immune system based on the presentation of peptides, should have a sparser peptide library than potential hosts without such an immune system – hosts such as plants and free-living protozoa. Parasites should have a sparser peptide repertoire than their non-parasitic relatives; a specialized parasite, targeting but one host species, should have a similar peptide repertoire (containing the same peptides) as its host. Hybrids of two host species should have a richer peptide repertoire than both the parent species and should also be more susceptible to parasites (this has actually been confirmed).

> But surprisingly enough, over time it became clear that proving or disproving the existence of these (and other) phenomena stemming from my theory was extremely difficult. I threw in the towel over 20 years ago, followed ten years ago by my undergraduate and later graduate student Pavel Cindr. Five years ago not even my colleague Martin Mokrejš got very far, and currently my graduate student Michaela Zemková continues to wrestle with the problem. It seems there's nothing to do but cross our fingers and hope.

Or I would have dedicated myself to cytology and tried to experimentally prove that the eukaryotic cell carries out isoelectric focusing of molecules in its cytoplasm, and thereby determines and regulates its biochemical processes. Those were two other problems, which *Toxoplasma* actually lured me away from. Whether this was a good or a bad thing, I don't know. I think that a scientist should do what he knows and what interests him, but that he should also tackle problems whose study he is equipped in the technical respect, and thereby has an advantage over others.

The study of isoelectric focusing in the cell requires fairly sophisticated technical equipment (namely in comparison with the equipment needed for the study of the effect of toxoplasmosis on human behavior). I expect there are laboratories much better equipped for the testing of this hypothesis of mine, so sooner or later someone will confirm or refute it. If only because I sneak descriptions of my hypotheses under the most varied contrivances into all of my books, whether the book is related to evolutionary biology or toxoplasmosis (see Box 37 *Does a cell conduct isoelectric focusing?*).

Box 37 Does a cell conduct isoelectric focusing?

Most biologically significant molecules, including proteins, carry both positive and negative charges on their surface; we call them **amphiphatic molecules**. In an environment with a high pH (a basic environment) where there are few free protons, positively charged protons loosen from the amphiphatic molecules and the molecules' net charge becomes more and more negative. But in an environment with a low pH (an acidic environment), where there are many free protons, there these positively charged particles bind to amphiphatic macromolecules, whose net charge thus becomes positive. In an electric field, positively charged molecules move towards a negative electrode, while negatively charged molecules towards a positive electrode – a process called **electrophoresis**. If the electrophoresis of proteins or other molecules carrying both a positive and negative charge occurs in an environment with an existing **pH gradient** (in which the pH gets higher approaching a positive electrode and lower approaching a negative electrode), then proteins move towards a positive or negative electrode, depending upon their surface charge. When molecules with a positive initial charge reach an area of high pH, they gradually lose protons, and thus also their net positive charge. For this reason, in a certain area of the pH gradient, their movement stops. The same is true for molecules with a negative initial charge. At first they move towards a positive electrode, approaching an area of low pH, gaining more and more protons, and so gradually losing their negative charge – until they lose it entirely and their movement in the electric field comes to a complete stop. Each amphiphatic molecule (and thus every protein) has a pH at which its net charge and movement in an electric field are zero. We call this pH the **isoelectric point** and abbreviate it as **pI**.

If we form an electric field in an environment with a pH gradient, then the proteins concentrate (focus) in certain locations based on their pI, separating different proteins from each other. When we have many types of ampholytes, with different isoelectric points, in solution, we don't have to create a pI gradient ahead of time – it will form in the solution on its own due to the voltage between the electrodes. Biochemists use isoelectric focusing to separate complicated mixtures of proteins occurring in the cell; as well as to isolate a protein they're interested in, or at least to detect its presence. In the year 1990, I published in the journal *Biosystems* the hypothesis that isoelectric focusing is also carried out by a living cell. I calculated that only a fraction of the energy the cell has at its disposal is needed for the cell to focus its macromolecules into different areas of its interior, accelerating and streamlining its metabolic processes. In the year 2009 I published in the *Journal of Molecular Evolution* an article in which I showed that evolutionary "invention" of intracellular focusing could have prompted the **origin of the eukaryotic cell** – it could have made possible the existence of cells with a volume ten thousand times greater than that of typical prokaryotic cells (the cells of bacteria and archea)[28]. In a small prokaryotic cell, molecular transport can be managed by diffusion; but molecular transport spanning a large cell would take dozens of minutes by diffusion, which would intolerably lower the rate of all metabolic processes in the cell. In order for the cells to get bigger, they had to invent alternative mechanisms to transport molecules, and one of these mechanisms could have been intracellular isoelectric focusing. Incidentally, isoelectric focusing can explain even the usual way intracellular processes are regulated. When a cell is to switch on or off a certain chemical process, such as a metabolic pathway (perhaps a sequence of reactions leading to the synthesis of various carbohydrates), it often phosphorylates or dephosphorylates a key enzyme of the metabolic pathway (by binding a negatively charged phosphate group to the enzyme, or removing it). This necessarily changes the enzyme's isoelectric point, and results in the enzyme moving to a different part of the cell, somewhere the metabolic process can (or can't) be carried out. Additionally, all enzymes of individual metabolic pathways can be concentrated through isoelectric focusing into certain parts of the cell, so that the respective metabolic processes can proceed simultaneously and yet independently.

VII. How *Toxoplasma* slows a person down, and throws him under the wheels of cars

Along with the study on the effect of *Toxoplasma* on human personality and behavior, I tried to observe whether *Toxoplasma* has an effect on human performance, particularly reaction time (how quickly one can react to simple stimuli). I expected that since *Toxoplasma* lengthens reaction time in mice, thus increasing their risk of being captured by a cat, it could similarly influence a human.

The very first project didn't work out, but I often joke about it. A high school peer of mine, who worked as a doctor in a Prague hospital, agreed to supply me with sera from patients who had suffered a car accident, as well as from patients hospitalized for different reasons. These sera I had examined for toxoplasmosis. Since blood testing is carried for almost all patients, I obtained samples from the blood routinely withdrawn – I needed at most half a milliliter per sample of blood for my studies. I predicted that among victims of various accidents, there would be a higher percentage of Toxo positives, because these would be less coordinated, more likely to be run over by a car or to crash a car as a driver. As I mentioned, this project didn't work out.

The sera samples accumulated slowly, and it wasn't always clear how the patient came to the accident – whether he wasn't, perhaps, just the unfortunate passenger who had nothing to do with the crash. Mainly I wasn't sure whether the control sample of people who did not suffer an accident came from the same region as the sample of people who did. For this reason, after about half a year I ended this project.

Why do I say the results were amusing? They'd likely appeal to any black humor enthusiast. I received the sera anonymously, marked by only number codes. But one time, when I arrived in the hospital for the samples, my doctor friend told me that I might know one of the patients and that maybe I should stop by him. Which I did – only to find laying on one of the hospital beds my colleague Petr Kodym, who two days before had nearly cut his leg off with a chain saw he'd enlisted in an attempt to cut limbs up in a tree (this is a likely a new, hitherto little used method in pomology, which he evidently picked up in one of his frequent expeditions to the Balkans). For many years Kodym had been examining all the sera samples for toxoplasmosis, and both of us knew he, just as I, was Toxo positive. At the time I believe he was already head of the National Reference Laboratory for Toxoplasmosis, and he'd always been pretty skeptical of my studies. I think that in this particular case I showed him pretty clearly that there was probably something to my theories on increased risk of accidents in infected subjects.

This unsuccessful study was basically an analogy of the predation experiment, in which manipulation theory is tested on animals. The predation experiment observes a parasite distribution in the hosts which became the prey of predators (the final hosts of the given parasite), and this occurrence is compared with the parasite's total prevalence in the host species in the studied locality. These studies were carried out, for example, on *Frenkelia*, a parasite related to *Toxoplasma*. Its intermediate hosts are rodents such as common voles (*Microtus arvalis*) or bank voles. The parasite forms typical round cysts in the rodent's brain, and its final hosts are birds of prey. So one can collect prey (common and bank voles) from the nests of predatory birds, determine what percentage of prey individuals are infected by the parasite, and finally set out traps for voles in the same area to determine how many of them are infected (Fig. 21). By comparing the frequency of infection of the prey and that of the animals in the traps, one can calculate whether the parasite increases the probability of being captured by the predator.

The predation experiment was carried out by my former undergraduate student Jan Votýpka[29]. The results of this very carefully conducted study showed that infection by *Frenkelia* significantly raises a rodent's risk of capture by a buzzard. Votýpka and his colleagues supplemented the study with laboratory experiments – the predation experiment isn't really an experiment, but an observational study (see Box 38 *Experiments and observational studies*).

Fig. 21 A field predation experiment. The investigators placed wooden frames with nets over the nests of predatory birds (in this case, nests of the common buzzard, **Buteo buteo***). Parents bringing food to their nestlings have to put it on the net, where it was regularly collected by investigators and analyzed for the presence of parasites. In the same location, the prevalence of parasites in trapped rodents was analyzed. The prevalence of parasites in rodents caught by birds of prey was compared to the prevalence in rodents trapped by the investigators to determine whether infected individuals are more likely to be the prey of the definitive host – the bird of prey. I can assure my soft-hearted readers that the nestlings didn't starve during the study – the investigators returned all analyzed rodents to the nests, so the birds were successfully raised. Photo by Petr Voříšek.*

Box 38 Experiments and observational studies

Empirical studies are primarily classified as **experiments** and **observational studies**. Both types of studies have their advantages and disadvantages. In an experiment, the researcher should have everything controlled; he himself decides which individuals are subject to the observed factor and which serve as the control (see also Box 15 *Popular mistakes when making a control group*). If he discovers that the individuals of the control group behave differently than do those of the experimental group, then he can conclude that this difference was caused by the observed factor. The disadvantage of experiments is the risk of experimental artifacts. In a laboratory (or in an experimental field), individuals are subjected to fairly different conditions than those freely in nature. For example, the natural infection method and dose of a parasite are often completely different from those a researcher will use in the lab. Therefore in the lab we can sometimes observe phenomena which basically don't exist in nature; and in the lab we might sometimes not observe phenomena, which do occur in nature.

In the case of observational studies, the researcher should ideally not interfere with the course of events; so control over the happenings of the study, including, for example, which individuals will and won't be infected, is entirely up to the study subjects (and, of course, chance). This is the fundamental problem in **causality studies**, which ascertain what is the cause and what the effect. If we find that men infected by *Toxoplasma* tend to disregard social norms, then without additional information we cannot rigorously determine whether the observed behavioral characteristic arose as a result of infection, or whether it was conversely the reason why they got infected. A great advantage of observational over experimental studies is that they carry a much smaller risk of experimental artifacts, so the phenomena which we prove through them usually have biological significance – they really occur in nature. From a practical standpoint, there is one more difference between typical experiments and observation. Because a researcher has no control over the course of an observational study, he must generally use much more sophisticated statistical techniques during the evaluation of collected data.

In observational studies, it's usually impossible to distinguish whether infected rodents have an increased risk of capture by a predator, or whether they have a decreased risk of us capturing them in a trap (but sometimes it is possible, see Box 72 *You can't expect miracles, even from a prospective cohort study*).

Votýpka and his coworkers infected 21 mice with the coccidian *Sarcocystis dispersa*, and when they stopped exhibiting signs of the disease's acute phase, he shut them along with 21 uninfected mice into a room with lots of hiding places as well as a predator – a long-eared owl *Asio otus* (affectionately christened Bubeek) (see Fig. 22).

For the next nineteen days he followed how quickly the infected and uninfected mice disappeared from the room. Again it turned out that the infected mice were devoured by the predator first[29].

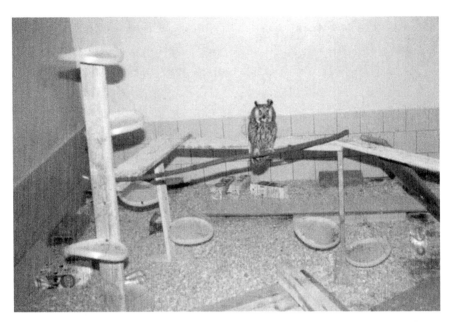

Fig. 22 A laboratory predation experiment. The long-eared owl (Asio otus), *christened Bubeek, was placed in a room of 42 mice, half infected and half uninfected with* Sarcocystis dispersa *at the start of the experiment. Overall, Bubeek caught infected mice earlier than control mice. Photo Petr Voříšek.*

Over the years I have conducted three experiments on humans, which I at first jokingly labeled as pseudopredation experiments. Rarely will a predator catch today's human, whether *Toxoplasma* tries for it or not, but characteristics which should make prey more liable to get caught by a predator should similarly predispose a person, for example, to get run over by a car. With my undergraduate student Jan Havlíček, for the first time I successfully finished this study, in which we followed the prevalence of toxoplasmosis in the victims of car accidents in a Prague hospital emergency room. It was a long-term study, in which we collected data for over three years. Fortunately, at the time we already had a control from the data of the aforementioned Petr Kodym, who discovered from epidemiological surveys how *Toxoplasma* often occurs in healthy men and women in the center of Prague. We could therefore compare the prevalence of toxoplasmosis in various age groups of men and women in the normal population with the prevalence of toxoplasmosis in the age groups of 146 people involved in a car accident, whether as the drivers who caused the accident or as the pedestrians who were hit by the car. The results were interesting. It turned out that Toxo positive people, both drivers and pedestrians, men and women, really are 2.65 times more likely than Toxo negative people to be involved in a car accident[30]. This study was immensely difficult to publish, most likely because it has quite a substantial practical impact. Even I, were I to receive a manuscript for review, especially one from a similarly exotic country like the Czech Republic (Where is it? In former Yugoslavia?), I'd probably also view it with skepticism. According to the World Health Organization, about 1.4 million people died every year as a result of traffic accidents at the end of the last century. If we assume, for simplicity's sake, that the occurrence of toxoplasmosis in the world is the same as in the Czech Republic – about 30% – we find that just in traffic accident hundreds of thousands of people die as a result of toxoplasmosis (see Box 50 *How many road traffic victims does the "harmless" toxoplasmosis have on its conscience?*). This would mean that latent toxoplasmosis, assumed to have no practical significance, is actually the second deadliest protozoan killer after malaria.

We sent our article to several journals, at first to the most prestigious, and then to the less prestigious. Finally, after two years we were able to publish it in the fifth or sixth journal. This was still in those idyllic times, when the majority of editors sent almost all the manuscripts to be reviewed. Today editors likely have such an overabundance of manuscripts (perhaps from India, China and post-communist countries), that they send a large part of them back to the authors without review. It's not unusual for a controversial manuscript to go through ten editorial boards, until it reaches its first reviewers (Box 39 *How I outwitted unwelcoming editors and reviewers*).

Box 39 How I outwitted unwelcoming editors and reviewers

From personal experience I can confirm that the game of ping-pong which a beginning author is forced to play with the editorial boards of scientific journals, whenever he tries to publish a manuscript that's even a little controversial, is a quite frustrating event. A researcher sends his carefully pampered manuscript to a journal's editorial board, which in a couple days sends him a formal email. The editor regrets to say that lately they have received such an overabundance of quality manuscripts that they can published only the very best of them, and the rest, like this certainly very valuable manuscript, must be rejected without review. In any case, the editor thanks the researcher for choosing to publish his article in specifically this journal, and looks forward to working with him in the future. Sometimes a member of the editorial board will write an additional brief rejection statement, concluding that the article likely wouldn't have made it through the reviewing process anyway. About half the time the manuscript is forwarded to reviewers, and rejected based on two to three reports. Approximately every third review is valuable and the reviewer gives useful recommendations for modifying the manuscript. Unfortunately, in the case of controversial results, just one negative review out of three is enough, and the editor feels it's safer to reject it. Then there is nothing to do but rearrange the manuscript to fit the format of another journal, send it to another editorial board, and hope that finally in some journal it will get three rational reviewers and an editor that's in a good mood, and finally be accepted. Nevertheless, if an author doesn't give in to disgust, but perseveres, all quality (as well as most not quality) manuscripts will finally make it into some journal. There are a lot of scientific journals and the law of probability works reliably – sooner or later the manuscript must get a favorable editor and reviewers. So the main thing is to not get discouraged and find a way to make waiting for a fortuitous event more enjoyable. For myself I discovered a completely suitable method. I carefully follow how many editorial boards the manuscript went through before it was accepted for publication, and look forward to one day, based on this data, write out a study on the relationship of the number of citations, and thus the quality proven post-publication, and the number of boards which originally rejected the article. When today I get an editorial board's rejection of a manuscript (and recently I got three such rejections within two days), I certainly won't be too happy about it. But at the same time I'll tell myself – hey, I got new data for my future study.

About four years after we did, a team of Turkish researchers obtained and published the same results[31]. I was one of the reviewers of this manuscript and must admit that I had rather mixed feelings about their work. The usual prevalence of toxoplasmosis in Turkey is relatively high, but in this case the prevalence of toxoplasmosis in the controls turned out suspiciously low.

I was glad that someone else had confirmed our results, but to this day I am not sure whether this study was completely sound. In 2009 another Turkish team published results of an analogous study, which once more confirmed that latent toxoplasmosis heightens the risk of traffic accidents[32]. In this case the prevalence of toxoplasmosis in the control population fit the expectation. In the same year we also published further results of a broader pseudopredation study[33]; but I'll describe these in the chapter dedicated to the protective role of the RhD antigen.

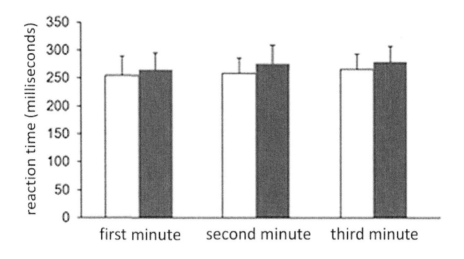

Fig. 23 Toxoplasma-*infected blood donors (dark bars) have a longer reaction time than do uninfected blood donors (white bars). The increase in reaction time was most pronounced during the second minute of test, and accounted for 7% of the variability in reaction time.*

We observed the effect of toxoplasmosis on the accident-related behavior of infected persons not only using the pseudopredation tests, but also by measuring the reaction time of infected persons under laboratory conditions. We sat the test subject before a computer and let him complete two tests. In one we projected the image of a square white frame into the middle of the screen, and had a small white square appear in the frame in irregular 1 to 8 second intervals. The test subject was to click the mouse the instant the small white square appeared. The second performance test was a bit more complicated. At regular intervals a three-digit number appeared in the middle of the screen and the person was to click the mouse whenever the current three-digit number shared at least two digits with the previous. This was more difficult for the test subjects, for now they had to analyze information, not just react to a simple stimulus.

This experiment was carried out by my colleague Havlíček on blood donors in a blood donation center near our department. While the blood donors were hooked up to a platelet separation machine, he convinced one after another to take our two performance tests after finishing their blood donation. In his undergraduate work, Jan Havlíček proved that Toxo positive persons really perform significantly worse in the first, simpler test than do Toxo negative persons[34]. The differences between the two groups, however, were apparent primarily in the second minute of the three-minute test. In the first minute the performance of both Toxo positive and Toxo negative persons was fairly high; in the second minute the Toxo positives got tired and their performance went down; and in the third minute the performance of the Toxo negatives also went down, so then the performance of the infected and uninfected pretty much evened out (Fig. 23).

Professor Andrew Smith of Cardiff University helped us out a lot in this study, providing us not only with the program for measuring reaction time, but even sending us the devices with which we carried out the measurements. Thanks to his technical support we were able to successfully finish this study. The second, more complicated test showed no difference between Toxo positive and Toxo negative persons. It might have been because fewer people took the test, or maybe because the effect of toxoplasmosis on processing information is more complicated and some of its manifestations in this test mutually canceled each other out (Box 40 *What all influences the results of a performance test?*). In any case it would probably be worthwhile to eventually go back to the results of this test, and once more try to analyze the data which Havlíček and, in the past few years, Martina Vitáková-Novotná have gathered.

Box 40 What all influences the results of a performance test?

When testing simple reaction time, we want to measure how quickly the test subject is able to reaction to a simple stimulus. Unfortunately, the performance of the test subject is influenced not only by his actual reaction time, but also by a number of other factors. It's clear that test subject's performance is highly influenced by his motivation. When the person tries, he reaches a significantly better reaction time than when his approach to the experiment is rather casual. Similarly, the test results are also influenced by how experienced the person is in such exercises, how little or well rested he is during the test and what instructions he received before the test itself. Therefore, the test must be carried out under the same conditions, the test subjects addressed under the same situations, in the same manner, and, if possible, by the same person. Even so it can easily happen that the same factor, such as *Toxoplasma* infection, can shorten the reaction time of one type of person but lengthen it in another. For example, men infected by *Toxoplasma* have, among other things, a heightened level of the hormone testosterone[35]. Yet testosterone heightens the motivation to succeed as much as possible in performance tests, particularly when an attractive female student is giving the test. *Toxoplasma* infected men may have slower reactions, but in tests they may appear faster. By all accounts, toxoplasmosis directly or indirectly influences a number of psychological and physical characteristics in infected persons. The results of individual tests may depend on multiple characteristics, so the results, especially whether the infected subjects perform better or worse than the uninfected subjects, depend largely on which effects of toxoplasmosis are prevalent in the given population. A practical suggestion is to independently test various and, if possible, homogenous groups of people (such undergraduate students, blood donors, military drivers), and to analyze the results for each population separately.

We later tested the effect of toxoplasmosis both on undergraduate students and on soldiers. Again it turned out that toxoplasmosis significantly influences performance in tests of simple reaction time. The fact that we originally tested reaction time on blood donors later proved to be a crucial and immense advantage. In the first phase of the experiment, it was very helpful that we didn't have to take blood from the blood donors to inspect for toxoplasmosis. We only had to persuade them to allow an examination for toxoplasmosis, and agree that scientific studies could use their results. These results included those from further examinations (in blood donors, routinely conducted), along with the results from reaction time tests. The main advantage of the blood donor subjects, which became apparent only much later, lay in that we had available the results of other hematological examinations, including data pertaining to their blood groups. That we even had data available about the presence or lack of Rh factor in an examined person, finally led to perhaps the most surprising result of our study. But that will get its own chapter (Chapter XVI).

VIII. Treasures buried in my desk drawer
– someday, perhaps, I'll get the time…

As I already mentioned, I began and never finished a number of studies; more often, I finished them but didn't analyze the data, which were left lying somewhere in my desk, and eventually passed from even the back of my mind. They never got a high enough priority for me to dig them out again; there was always more important data to analyze. Sometimes this other data was more important from a scientific stand-point, meaning that I was particularly interested in how a certain study would turn out. Other times for practical reasons, when a study was part of the undergrad or graduate thesis a student had to defend, I had to give priority to this student's study. Therefore, it is possible that the most interesting discoveries lay unrecognized, buried at the bottom of my desk drawer.

When I think back on my unanalyzed data and unfinished studies, I envision a sort of comparison. Doing science is most similar to walking through an unknown rugged landscape. One sets out on a path, sees various paths branching off, and tries to pick the most interesting of these. But the landscape is rugged, so he doesn't know – if he'd turned on an earlier path or continued on the original – where he might find, perhaps, a spring or an enchanted valley, more beautiful than the landscape he's currently traversing. This comparison has one flaw: the scientist himself makes these paths, as he asks himself questions. So there is some difference between roaming a real and scientific landscape; in the end, though, it's still aimless wandering. When one chooses a path, he must accept that he won't get to the others and will never know what he might have found at their ends. Maybe the reason I found several interesting things during my studies on toxoplasmosis, and the reason the members of my lab made a number of compelling discoveries, was that I was intuitively able to choose those paths which led to something exciting. Or it might have been just good luck. Of course it's also possible that we narrowly missed things that could have been much more interesting. One such path, whose results I never really analyzed due to time constraints, was the longitudinal study that my colleague Havlíček and I carried out on the university students (Box 41 *Longitudinal and cross-sectional studies*).

Box 41 Longitudinal and cross-sectional studies

To observe the effect of a certain factor (such as age) on the characteristics of an organism (for example, on reaction time), we can organize our study in two different ways – as a longitudinal study, or as a cross-sectional study. A **longitudinal study** is more difficult in regards to time, organization and generally finances. One must test the abilities of the same individuals at least twice: for example, measuring the reaction times of the same students now and five years later, to look at how these individuals' reaction times changed. A longitudinal study is hard to use when only some of the individuals are exposed to the studied factor. Such is the case with the study on the effect of toxoplasmosis on reaction time. Then it becomes necessary to include a large number of individuals in the study, so that enough of them get infected during the course of the study. On the other hand, paired statistical tests can be used to analyze such data (see Box 67 *What is the difference between the paired and unpaired t-tests, and why is the paired one better?*). These tests are generally more sensitive and allow us to detect even weaker effects (each individual is his own control, eliminating the effect of possible interfering variables, see Box 20 *Dependent, independent, and confounding variables; fixed and random factors*). In a **cross-sectional study**, each individual is tested only once, but the study encompasses people of various ages (or infected and uninfected persons), and one looks for the variation in reaction time among individuals of different age (or status of infection). The disadvantage of a cross-sectional study is that its results must be analyzed with a less sensitive unpaired test; as well as that it doesn't allow us to determine cause from effect (whether infection leads to worse reaction time, or whether slow reaction time increases the risk of infection). In addition, the results of a cross-sectional study can be systematically distorted by the **cohort effect**. If, for example, we're comparing the reaction times of twenty- and forty-year old men, the twenty-year-olds will probably have a distinctly better reaction time. But it's questionable, whether this is a result of their age, or because today's twenty-year-olds have a substantially greater training in computer games than today's forty-year-olds.

During this study we sent each student a letter with the same psychological questionnaire they'd completed five years ago. We expected that differences in psychological factors due to infection would have intensified in Toxo positives, over those five years between the first and second questionnaire. In the Toxo negatives, we expected on average no change. Hence we expected that Toxo positive women would have an increase in warmth (factor A) and rule consciousness (factor G), while in Toxo positive men, these factors should decrease. I don't remember anymore whether the results were even statistically significant, but in any case they were opposite of the direction we expected. In infected men, factor G increased instead of decreasing; in infected women, factor A decreased instead of increasing. The reason we obtained such unexpected results could have been trivial, a mistake in the data or an error in the statistical program (Box 42 *Errors in statistical programs*).

Box 42 Errors in statistical programs

Unfortunately, even statistical programs aren't perfect. And some errors are very subtle and hard to find. I remember that some versions of my favorite program Statistica switched the labels of the two groups being compared, so the correlation, which was supposed to be positive, came out negative. Even the newest version 9.0 of this program makes an error in Kendall's Tau correlation analysis – it usually calculates a significance about twice as great, i.e. a p-value two times smaller than it should be. One must reckon with the possibility of errors in statistical programs. It's good to verify the results with a number of different tests, and, if possible, conduct parallel calculations of the same analysis with two independent programs from different manufacturers.

We carried out only perfunctory analyses on data that was not checked carefully enough (Box 17 *Checking and cleaning data*). Therefore, it is possible some people's data had unreasonably high or low values; these errors might have completely changed the results of the analyses. But the study could have had results opposite of those we expected for nontrivial reasons. The values for Toxo negatives could have shifted because a part of them got infected during those five years (for obvious technical reasons, it was not possible to retest students for toxoplasmosis after five years). The values of both Toxo positives and negatives could have shifted due to the so-called ceiling effect. For example, Toxo positive women already had a very high factor A (warmth) in the first testing, so stochastic changes over the five years were more likely to be decreases than increases in its value. Cattell's psychological factors take on values from 1 to 10. If a Toxo positive woman were to get a 9 for factor A, it would be much more likely that a second testing would give her a lower number (1-8), than a higher number (10). Women who got a 10 for factor A in the first testing reached the "ceiling" of this factor; in another test they can only get an equal or lesser value, for they can't get any higher. Conversely, Toxo negative women who got a 3 for this factor in their first test had a greater probability of having the value increase than decrease, due to a random change, mistake, or a mood swing during the repeat test. Of course, these are just theories, and I expect that modern statistical methods could eliminate the ceiling effect.

It is also possible, I think, but not very probable, that the opposite shifts in Toxo positive subjects are real. For example, the personality changes could be only transient and begin returning to their original values after five years. However, our studies on male and female patients who have passed the stage of acute toxoplasmosis do not show any such return (see Figs. 13 and 14). It's possible that I'll eventually get back to the old data, or even try to add to it. It would definitely be interesting to send this questionnaire to the same people after another five years and see how the personal profiles of Toxo positive and negative people develop in such a long period of time.

Something else that surprised me, and is worthy of note, regards factor G (Rule consciousness). So long as we used the original version of Cattell's questionnaire, Toxo positive male students had a significantly lower G factor than did the Toxo negative males. But over time, new versions of the questionnaire appeared, and some of the reviewers of our manuscripts criticized us for using the outdated version. So finally, for practical reasons, to one-up the reviewers, we decided to switch to a newer questionnaire. When we used it to test a large group of soldiers, about 400-500 in total, it turned out that Toxo positive and negative men still significantly differed in factor G, but this time Toxo negative men on average reached a lower value than did the Toxo positive. In other words, the new version of the questionnaire showed *Toxoplasma* as having effects on men, as did the old questionnaire on women.

Of course, I don't know why this happened, but two possibilities seem most likely. The first relates to the change in Cattell's questionnaire – that the new version measures men differently than does the old. The second is based on the change in people – that students and employees of the college react differently to latent toxoplasmosis than do soldiers of the mandatory military service. We can test the possibilities by either testing the students with the questionnaire's new version, or giving the soldiers the old version. Seeing as the original study with the new version of the questionnaire was conducted on these soldiers, and in the meantime mandatory service was abandoned, we could only test the students using the new questionnaire. In a bit, I'll explain what happened.

If it was true that the new questionnaire measured factor G (rule consciousness) differently than the old, then psychologists who habitually used the questionnaire would not be too happy, since it would mean that one the versions measured something other than it should. The other possibility, that reaction of soldiers and students to the same factor (toxoplasmosis) was different, wouldn't be all that serious nor surprising (see also Box 40 *What all influences the results of performance tests?*). It's actually a common problem of most observational studies, which we encounter quite often in those with questionnaires. It's an issue of the representativeness of a sample.

In our studies, we generally aren't interested in just a particular study group, but in what happens in the entire population. For example, we don't want to know how the 2001 students of the Faculty of Science react to toxoplasmosis, but how people in general react to it (or maybe men in general). Of course we can't test all the people infected by toxoplasmosis and observe them along with all the uninfected people. Instead, we must use a smaller sample of the population, like 300 students or 500 soldiers; and then extrapolate the differences between the Toxo positive and negative people in the group to the whole population. The problem with conducting a study on a truly random population sample (so that it includes all age groups, usual professions and social and economic classes), is that the sample will be very heterogeneous. Thus the effects we measure in the sample – such as psychological traits – will have an enormous variability in the trait being studied. The group will have individuals with extremely high and extremely low values of this trait. As a result, if there is a difference between Toxo positive and Toxo negative people in this group, there is a good chance our tests won't discern it as statistically significant. Statistical tests usually determine statistical significance by finding to what extent the variability in our group explains the studied factor (such as toxoplasmosis). Of course, when we're analyzing a very heterogeneous group, then the contribution of even a fairly strong factor to its variability is relatively small. Consequently, these tests offer only negative (statistically nonsignificant) results. One way to limit this risk is to make the group as homogenous as possible – like using only the students of the Faculty of Science. In many ways, these students are quite similar to each other, for they all got into our group, already passed through several "sieves," apparently have similar interests, are all about the same age, passed the entrance exam for the Faculty of Science, and were willing to volunteer for our tests (Box 43 *Where have all the brown-eyed students gone?*).

Box 43 Where have all the brown-eyed students gone?

Aside from the psychological questionnaire, one of the methods we used to find whether Toxo positive and negative students differ in suspiciousness was based on asking the students whether we could photograph their face, and observing how willing they were to agree. So another byproduct of our studies was a collection of hundreds of photos of our students.

For some time, my colleague Karel Kleisner studied the human eye as an organ through which the individual sends out information into his social surroundings. Using our photographs, we looked whether brown- and blue-eyed individuals differ in their psychological traits, behavior and even in what their photograph conveys to their surroundings. The results of our studies were very interesting, but that's discussed later, in Box 64 *Are brown-eyed men more dominant than blue-eyed, and is it because of their eyes?* We discovered one unintended result almost immediately: there were substantially fewer brown-eyed than blue-eyed men in our photographs, yet no such thing occurred with women. There were several possible explanations of this phenomenon. First we looked towards the most interesting – that is, that eye color in the Czech population could be related to gender. For example, the same variation of a gene for eye color would bring about brown eyes in women but blue eyes in men. I was quite interested to know whether generations of our ancestors had overlooked such a fascinating phenomenon.

Unfortunately, this working hypothesis turned out to be false. When we looked at the eye color of children in several kindergarten classes, we found no difference in the occurrence of brown eyes in boys and girls. The second, less interesting, but more likely hypothesis was that Prague's Faculty of Science had more brown-eyed students (the ratio of brown-eyed female students matched the ratio of brown-eyed girls in the kindergarten classes). I sent out an e-mail to a couple hundred students who attended lectures given by me and one of my colleagues, asking them their eye color. It turned out that even the second hypothesis was false – the ratio of brown-eyed students was about equal between males and females. So we were left with the third possible explanation – that we attracted more blue-eyed than brown-eyed male students to our tests. So far we have only indirect proof of this hypothesis. First off, there are very few brown-eyed men that came to be tested twice (to give blood samples and take experimental tests); there are almost no brown-eyed men among those who came three times (blood samples, psychological tests and experimental games). Secondly, our results show that the personal profiles, based on a psychological questionnaire, of blue-eyed versus brown-eyed men are really somewhat different. Therefore, it's likely that their willingness to participate in our tests is also different.

As a result, the variability (dispersion) of our students' characteristics is much lower, than had we chosen a typical representative sample of the general population. Theoretically, a sample of soldiers of the mandatory military service should also be representative of the masses. In reality, this is far from true. When we conducted our studies, it was well known that the mandatory military service in the Czech Republic would soon be cut. Therefore, the only people who went to the military were either those who didn't mind it, those who looked forward to it, or the people unable to get a note from the doctor to excuse them until it would no longer be required.

But a homogenous sample has at least two disadvantages. Firstly, things we discover on such a homogenous study sample cannot be entirely generalized to the whole population, for it's possible these discoveries fit only the sample group. Secondly, the sample group may be missing some characteristics present in another sample group, or in the general population. This second problem can be partially addressed by studying our particular phenomenon in several very distinct sample groups. But then one can get the situation we had with soldiers and students examined with Cattell's questionnaire – in terms of the factor of rule consciousness, the relationship between Toxo positives and negatives was different in the student group than in the soldier group. In the male student sample, the infected people had a lower rule consciousness than the uninfected – but in the soldier group, the uninfected had a lower rule consciousness.

One explanation would be that the phenomenon of compensation, more strictly overcompensation for psychic change, might play a role in this. When the infected soldiers or students felt that something strange was happening with their behavior, they may have consciously or subconsciously tried to suppress or at least "cover up" the changes from themselves and those around them. They may have overdone this cover-up to the extent that, though they really had a higher rule consciousness, it showed up on the psychological questionnaire as lower. Something similar could have also happened in the case of warmth (factor A). For a long time, it was how we explained to ourselves why men and women have opposite reactions to toxoplasmosis. This happened not only with warmth, as well as rule consciousness, but with many more psychological factors. Once I sat down and counted up the factors with a shift that wasn't statistically significant, but only suggested a trend; or where the shift was statistically significant just in one of the genders, while the other gender had an opposite trend. It turned out that out of sixteen Cattell's factors, twelve had an opposite toxoplasmosis-associated shift in men to that in women. Eventually, it became apparent that the explanation based on overcompensation of toxoplasmosis-induced changes was false; and that there was a number of simpler explanations for the opposite shift of psychological factors in men and women. But this realization came to us only with the results of our study on testosterone levels in Toxo positive and negative people; but these results will be discussed in a later chapter.

As I already mentioned, we can no longer test soldiers of the mandatory military service (hopefully, so long as mandatory military service isn't reinstituted). However, we did analyze data obtained from blood donors with the old version of the questionnaire. It turned out, that even in this group infected men behaved the same as infected women – they had a higher rule consciousness (factor G) and a lower vigilance (factor L)[36]. Therefore, it seemed that our students, not the new questionnaire, were at fault. To confirm this possibility, (with a heavy heart) we began testing our students with the new version of the questionnaire. Try and guess the results that we got. Are you ready?

An experienced scientist certainly would guess correctly that this study turned out completely differently than the previous two. In men, the differences between infected and uninfected weren't statistically significant; though this time infected students had a lower instead of a higher factor G. In women, the differences were statistically significant; but now infected women's factor G was statistically lower. It's hard to decide, how we should determine these new results (which came out completely opposite to the results on students over 10 years ago). However, it's most likely that the students of the Faculty of Science today are quite different from the students 10 or 15 years ago. Even without the questionnaire, it's clear that our students change over time. (Of course, they get worse. Each teacher agrees that the department had its best pupils when they were students – whether the teacher was a student 5 or 50 years ago.) We'll never put together the exact same group of students that we tested 15 years ago. So we'll never definitely know, whether each population's different results of Cattell's questionnaire were really due to distinct personal profiles in each group, or differences between the new and old questionnaire versions. It's true, we could let our students take both the new and old version of the questionnaire, but I probably won't dare to do that any time soon. I'm almost afraid to think what our test subjects would say to us, and I couldn't print it in this book, if they had to fill out two nearly identical about 200-question questionnaires.

By the way, the fact that we have different students than before is one of the paths I'd like to explore, had I the time. Since 1992, every year I go to the lectures of my colleagues and convince students to take part in our trials, and each time a fairly large number of students succumbed to my persuasion. And so far all these victims have, among other tests, completed the Cattell's questionnaire. Though we didn't systematically follow the changes in our students' psychological profiles, we noted some differences anyway.

Cattell's questionnaire has about twelve questions which can be used to roughly estimate intelligence. Sometime in 2006, we compared how the intelligence of our students changed over the years. We found that intelligence of the male students stayed about the same; in women, however, it was slowly decreasing. I hardly think that this is due to a decrease in general intelligence in the female population, and a steady-state of intelligence in men. It's almost certainly because, while we test about the same amount of students each year, over 17 years the number of female students has dramatically increased (about three times the original number). The increase in accepted applicants is due to the fact the college gets money from the state primarily based on number of students, so it has a tendency to increase the number of students each year. In general, I see this as good thing: the more people aged 18 to 22 we put in classrooms, the less of them will be in the streets setting cars on fire and throwing Molotov cocktails at the police. Plus, we'll teach them to learn – whether by training their minds on the classification of sawyer beetles, theology or macroeconomics. Knowing how to learn (anything) is a skill that will almost be useful in finding a place in today's changing world. But raising the number of students also has its dark sides. Namely, the workload of teachers is increasing. As a result of the increasing number of applicants, already many years ago we abandoned oral entrance exams. In my opinion, this is a grave mistake, and the greatest failure of us teachers.

I have no solid data to support this opinion, but I have the feeling that statistically women, unlike men, do much better in written than in oral exams. Additionally, oral exams also looked at the motivation of applicants, so our college got these enthusiastic young biologists, both men and women, who had wanted their whole life to study, for example, the behavior of Przewalski's horse in the Prague Zoo, or collect rove beetles.

To a disinterested bystander, this may seem like a silly occupation, but our experience shows that precisely such "enthusiastic fools" grow up to be the most interesting students or scientists with the most original ideas. The majority sooner or later moved on from Przewalski's horses or rove beetles, and, with no less enthusiasm, turned to studying things like the characteristics of cancer cells. But because today we only give written exams, these people are much less likely to get in than before. They studied exciting Przewalski's horses, not boring high school textbooks. For this reason, they don't make up the same proportion of the increased amount of students; instead probably about the same number gets in as before. And among "normal" high school students, i.e. in male and female students who were never interested in rove beetles nor Przewalski's horses, females score better in written exams than males do. This, I think, is the reason that average intelligence decreases specifically among female students. More and more female students are accepted, so there is a greater fraction of them who, while not that creative and motivated, were able to cram for the high school material we test in our written exams. I guess that in comparison with studying Przewalski's horses and collecting beetles, the ability to excel in written tests over high school knowledge is a relatively poor indicator of success in university studies – and probably does not correspond with formal intelligence tests.

Using written exams to test biology is a questionable method anyway. Yet even I must do so, because annually about 400 hundred students apply for evolutionary biology classes. If I had to give each person an oral exam, then I couldn't be a scientist, but would spend half the year testing undergraduate students. So, I was forced to switch to written exams; in other words, I made myself a sort of compromise. All students take a written exam, and if they aren't happy with their grade, then they can request an oral exam, in which their previous written score is not looked at. So the written exam is actually a test they can retake orally. The truth is that most students are content with their written exam grade and never come in to improve it. I don't know, whether it's because my grading is overly lenient (maybe because I don't want too many students taking an oral exam), or because our students don't really care what grades they get. I'm afraid that many students only care about completing their study requirements, not about how they do so or with what results.

Giving exams to hundreds of students and grading them is an annoying business anyway (I am certainly happier giving lectures and researching). To make this duty more enjoyable, I usually try to carry out an experiment along with the written exam. Participation in the study, of course, is voluntary; and I always stress that it has nothing to do with the grading. Most students usually take part in it, and after the test for example complete some questionnaire. Recently, during a written exam, I observed how the hormone levels in the saliva of students changed in relation to how they did in the test. I found that the level of testosterone rose in "victors" and decreased in "losers," verifying that in this regard students behave the same as bucks fighting for a doe. Furthermore, I unexpectedly discovered that a student's subconscious may understand evolutionary biology better than his conscious mind (see Box 44 *Does a student's subconscious understand the material he's learning better than his conscious mind?*).

Box 44 Does a student's subconscious understand the material he's learning better than his conscious mind?

It's well-known that the level of testosterone increases in the animal who left a battle victorious, and decreases in the animal who came out defeated. This is probably so that the successful individual be emboldened to engage in further battles, and that the defeated be discouraged from them to avoid being wounded (during that season). In humans, this rule has many exceptions, even though it's often true. For example, it was observed that the fans of a victorious soccer team experience a surge in the testosterone in their saliva after the game, while the fans of the defeated team experience a decrease. That human hormone levels often behave differently than we'd expect might have to do with the fact that we generally don't examine the participants of an actual battle, but e.g. a simulated game in the lab. To see what happens with the hormone levels of people in real situations, we measured the level of testosterone in the saliva of students before and after a written exam. We looked whether the increase or decrease in the level of testosterone correlated with the number of mistakes they made in the test, or with how many they thought they made after the test. While some of the results of this study could have been expected, others were pretty unexpected[37]. In students who performed well in the test and answered most of the questions correctly, the level of testosterone in the saliva increased; in those who performed badly, the testosterone level decreased. Surprisingly, the change in the level of testosterone correlated much more with how many errors the student actually made in the written exam, than with how many errors he thought he'd made (Fig. 24). I would not be surprised if our subconscious mind, which is responsible for manipulating hormone levels, were better able to discover than we are, for example, whether a fight won us the girl (or, more often, whether we successfully impressed her with our penetrating wit and intelligence). The subconscious, unlike the conscious, doesn't have a reason to convince itself of anything; and the more objective it is in guessing the result of a fight (or any other form of intrasexual competition), the better our ability to pass on our genes to the next generation. But it seems strange that the subconscious of the students would understand the subject of evolutionary biology and estimate the number of errors made in the test better than the students themselves. Although, why not – as Sigmund Freud teaches, we can't see into all the corners of our unconscious mind.

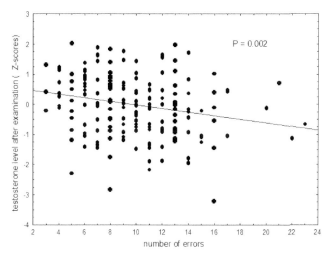

Fig. 24 The relationship between testosterone levels after a written examination on evolutionary biology, and the number of errors made on said test was statistically significant. Neither the relationship between testosterone levels before the exam and the actual number of errors, nor the relationship between testosterone levels after and before the exam and the number of errors the student thought he made was statistically significant.

But back to *Toxoplasma* and toxoplasmosis. We hit upon another potentially interesting mystery already in the first years of our study on the effect of latent toxoplasmosis on human behavior. Latent toxoplasmosis is diagnosed using two independent tests: the complement-fixation test (CFT) and the enzyme-linked immunosorbent assay (ELISA) (*Box 45 How science, using the ELISA test, once again saved mankind*).

Box 45 How science, using the ELISA test, once again saved mankind

Sometimes a taxpayer (generally through his solicitous elected representative) wonders if there's any sense in putting millions and billions into science, and whether it wouldn't be more effective to put money into applied research. (I don't know how it's elsewhere, but in my country this means directing the funds in the form of subsidies into the pockets of companies owned by friends). It is safely proven that resources spent on science have the greatest return. For example, just the invention of hybrid seed, through the increase of agricultural yields, has long since paid for all the resources mankind ever put towards science. But it's a little-known fact the discovery of monoclonal antibodies and their use in diagnostic ELISA recently saved mankind from one of the insidious pandemics it had ever encountered – the pandemic of AIDS. This disease, caused by HIV, a retrovirus, is most deceptive in that the time between infection and when the disease breaks out is very long, generally a period of many years in which the infected person, unsuspecting, spreads the virus to others. Another trick of the virus is that it damages the host's immune system, so the victim finally dies of a number of apparently unrelated diseases.

Fortunately, when AIDS began to spread in the 80s, molecular biologists already had at their disposal several complementary approaches from basic research studies. One was a technique for producing monoclonal antibodies (antibodies produced by cell clones formed by the fusion of a B cell producing antibodies for a certain antigen, with an immortal cancer cell). Another was a method for detecting a virus based on the ELISA, a technique which uses monoclonal antibodies. Thanks to these advances, scientists were not only able to find the etiological agent of the new deadly disease, but also to work out a relatively cheap and quick method to identify the presence of HIV in a human years before the person got AIDS. Had the AIDS pandemic started thirty years earlier, we wouldn't be worrying at all about overpopulation today; looking back on the Black Death in Europe, we'd nostalgically recall it as a peaceful and beautiful period of human history. Each species dies out sooner or later, and parasites (first and foremost, probably viruses) are the most common cause of extinction of species formed by large dense, interconnected populations. Today's human population is a very good candidate for extinction, and I think only investing in science can at least stall this fate.

An ELISA test recognizes class IgG antibodies in the blood (see Box 22 *Antibodies and myths about them*). A complement-fixation test detects class IgG immunoglobulins, but only some of their several subclasses, and also detects class IgM immunoglobulins. The ELISA is more sensitive in the case of a fresh infection, and can more precisely distinguish whether a person has acute or latent toxoplasmosis. A complement-fixation test is less sensitive, but its results fluctuate less and based on them one can estimate when the person was infected. In some people, the results obtained with each method differ. A person may be Toxo negative based on the ELISA and Toxo positive based on the CFT, or vice versa. In most cases the results of the two tests agreed; nevertheless, in our groups there were always several individuals (in large groups even a couple dozen people), whose results did not match. Sometimes we solved the problem by not including these people in the final analysis, counting only the people who had the same results for both tests.

What is surprising – when we split the people into Toxo positive and negative based only on the CFT results (and didn't rule out those with opposite test results obtained by ELISA), we almost always found a little stronger correlation between toxoplasmosis and psychological factors. Conversely, when we divided them into positive and negative based only on the ELISA results, we usually found a stronger relationship between toxoplasmosis and reaction time. I don't really know how we're supposed to explain this observation. Our working hypothesis presumes that the CFT is less specific and detects not only toxoplasmosis (infections by *Toxoplasma gondii*), but also infection by a related protozoan – and that both these protozoans cause the same psychological changes. Furthermore, the ELISA method might be more specific and only detect infection by *Toxoplasma gondii*, not by the other hypothetical protozoan which causes no changes in performance. It is even possible that both tests detect only *Toxoplasma gondii*, but that the CFT detects a wider range of strains, whereas the ELISA detects only the most widespread (Box 46 *There's no Toxoplasma like Toxoplasma*). Recently, it was discovered that different strains affect the behavior of infected rats differently. Whether we presume that the differences in our two tests for Toxo are caused by the occurrence of another parasite, or by the distinct characteristics of *Toxoplasma* strains, it'll probably be necessary to someday focus on the matter more closely. The two parasites (or different *Toxoplasma* strains) don't have be different in only how they affect the human psyche and reaction time; they may also be distinct in other, clinically much more important characteristics.

Box 46 There's no *Toxoplasma* like *Toxoplasma*

Toxoplasma gondii has many genetically distinct strains, so it can be expected that these strains may be different biologically, as well as in the way they affect the infected host organism. The three most widespread strains of *Toxoplasma* are closely related (see Fig. 25). The members of the other strains are found mostly in wild animals, and some of these probably only occur in the region with the greatest biodiversity of this parasite, in South America.

It's quite likely that the parasite evolved on this continent, and that only a couple successful strains were able to spread to the rest of the planet. Even today, *Toxoplasma* in South America behaves a bit differently than *Toxoplasma* in Europe or North America. Not only is it more widespread in the human population there, but the course of toxoplasmosis is often worse. This is probably because some of the strains are "meaner" (more virulent) to their host.

There are results which show that *Toxoplasma* strains differ in both how much and by what means they affect their host's behavior. While changes caused by one strain of *Toxoplasma* subside fairly quickly in a mouse, those caused by another strain may last much longer[38]. The effect of different *Toxoplasma* strains on the psychological manifestations of toxoplasmosis in humans has not yet been studied.

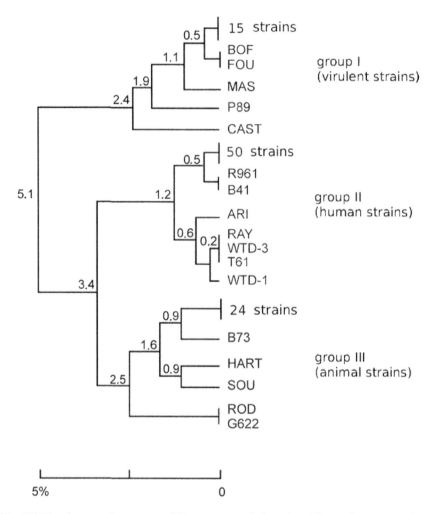

Fig. 25 The three main groups of European and American Toxoplasma *strains. Molecular taxonomic methods demonstrate that in Europe and North America these three closely related and biologically similar* Toxoplasma *strains are prevalent. The three groups branched from a common ancestor, and each group into several strains, relatively recently. In contrast, South America is home to several strains, which are not related to these groups; they branched from Toxo's common ancestor much earlier. It is likely that most of the evolution of* Toxoplasma gondii *occurred in South America. The numbers on the graph show genetic distances. Adapted from Sibley and Ajioka, 2008.*

Of course, our hypothesis, which suggests that each diagnostic test has a different specificity, isn't the only possible explanation. Perhaps one of the tests overlooks fresh infections, whereas the other overlooks those that happened a long time ago. It's possible that psychological changes develop more slowly than the changes in reaction time (or vice versa). In this case, the different risk in each test of falsely negative results, for someone freshly or long infected, could explain why the correlation between toxoplasmosis and psychological factors comes out stronger when we use the CFT to diagnose toxoplasmosis; and why the observed relationship between toxoplasmosis and performance comes out stronger when we use the ELISA.

IX. Toxo's effect on the performance of our soldiers and pilots

Working with the psychology clinic at the Central Military Hospital in Prague, we tested in much greater detail the differences in performance between Toxo positive and negative people. Over the years, thousands of recruits in this workplace went through our hands, because those who were supposed to be military drivers in garrisons near Prague, part of patrol service or the Prague Castle Guard, had their psychological examination in this hospital. The psychologists of the army hospital gave them a number of tests, which determined psychological profile, psychical endurance and performance in stressful situations. Through the medical personnel we asked the studied recruits for permission include their data in our study. Those that agreed were examined for toxoplasmosis, and then we only had to compare the results of the psychological and performance tests of Toxo positive and negative people (Box 47 *Informed consent*). We used performance tests similar to those we used on the blood donors, as well as more complicated tests. The latter tests used not only data on reaction time, but also on several other physiological and psychological parameters, like short-term memory, resistance to fatigue, etc.

Box 47 Informed consent

When conducting research on people, we first need to get their **informed consent**. We need to familiarize them with the goal of the study, as well as with what we will ask them to do and how the results will be used. We must further inform them how and when they can withdraw their agreement to participate (usually it's possible at any time, until the data is made anonymous). If experimenting on children or people with limited legal competence, we must obtain the consent of their legal guardian. These rules, established in the Czech Republic through routine scientific practice and adhere to the Convention of Human Rights and Biomedicine adopted by the Council of Europe, must be strictly followed; especially when the studies might disturb or endanger the test subject's rights to integrity or dignity. If there is no such danger, like if we're only observing how people behave in natural or constructed situations that don't put them at risk, then the requirements for the informed consent aren't as strict – but the ethical committee of the respective institution should always decide this, not the individual researcher. In some cases, a strict request for informed consent could take away the value of the entire study. For example, if we're studying how trusting people are, and have them drink an unknown liquid or sign a blank sheet of paper, we clearly can't tell them about the purpose of the experiment beforehand. If it's drinking water, the danger is minimal, and the people can be informed about the purpose of the experiments in general terms "you will participate in a set of ethological experiments studying the effects of toxoplasmosis on human behavior and psyche" (so that the test subjects won't spend half of their time studying a detailed form, and to limit the risk of revealing the experimental purpose to other participants). But if we're filming experimental subjects in a similar experiment, we must subsequently inform them of this and offer the choice to delete the recording. If we're uncertain about any ethical aspects of our work, we shouldn't base our judgments solely on the recommendations of the ethical committee (though it's good to bear them in mind). Rather, we should consult Immanuel Kant's categorical imperative: *"Act only according to that maxim whereby you can, at the same time, will that it should become a universal law."*

We were a little surprised by the results of the simple reaction time tests, since the soldiers reacted differently than the blood donors. It was most likely because the blood donors were persuaded one at a time to take part in the experiment, and we stressed to each that they should react as quickly as possible to the stimuli, that we are interested in their top, not usual, performance. In contrast, the soldiers of the mandatory military service were always examined in groups of up to 20, and their motivation to perform their best may have been substantially lower than that of the blood donors. Nevertheless, there were differences between the Toxo positives and negatives, though mostly in the first 30 seconds of the test. The test was set up to start with a 30 second practice section, followed by 2 minutes of the actual test. We expected that the first 30 seconds would allow each experimental subject to become familiar with handling the computer, and that we'd see true differences in performance only in the latter two minutes. Basically we weren't wrong, but only underestimated the reality, that the main thing our recruits would learn in the training phase would be how to cheat our test. While analyzing the data, we saw that nearly a third of them clicked the mouse before the stimulus appeared on the screen, or even held it down during the entire test. As a result, we had to rule out a large part of the data. Perhaps for the same reason, the differences measured in the main portion of the test weren't statistically significant. The results of the first training part turned out better – there we proved a worse performance in Toxo positives (Box 48 *One can never be too careful…*).

Even worse were the results of professional soldiers, whom we began testing when mandatory military serve was abandoned. As the professional army was being built, a psychological department examined possible professional soldiers, as well as various participants in foreign military missions, such as the SFOR or KFOR. We expected that the motivation of these would be greater, so our results on the effect of toxoplasmosis would be much better.

Unfortunately, the greater motivation of these test subjects showed itself mostly in a greater motivation to cheat, so we found no stronger differences in simple reaction time between the Toxo positives and negatives.

We had a similar problem with yet another group, which we initially had great hopes for. It included the military and civilian pilots, as well as the ground crew and students of flight school, which had to routinely undergo performance testing in the Institute of Aviation Medicine. We managed to begin cooperation with this workplace too, but the collaboration wasn't nearly as close or productive as it was with the psychological department of the Central Military Hospital.

Box 48 One can never be too careful…

Human experimental subjects, unlike lab mice or bacteria in test tubes, are happily inclined to cheat. When filling out the questionnaire, they often intentionally or unintentionally lie, to make themselves look better (to the evaluator or themselves) than they really are. If cheating and lies are not the topic of our study, we must try to make both very difficult. We will never completely succeed in preventing them, so we should at least have an idea of how much the test subjects are lying and cheating. Some psychological tests, for example, allow one to calculate their lying score, to determine how much the person, when filling out the questionnaire, tried to improve their image. At the least, we must ensure that cheating on the part of the test subjects does not distort the answer to our given question. Most important is that the cheating not give a false positive result. To prevent this from happening, the test subjects cannot know what group (experimental or control) they belong to when being tested; and the researchers must treat both groups of test subjects entirely the same. During the tests, we made sure that neither the subjects nor the person administrating the test knew who was or wasn't infected (known as a **double-blind study**).

Even so, cheating could have distorted the result of the study, usually by increasing the variability of the results achieved by the test subjects, thus preventing us from revealing the existing effect. It couldn't, however, lead to a **false positive result**, i.e. that we'd prove an effect that doesn't really exist. Not only the test subjects, but also our coworkers, are capable of cheating. For example, if a nurse is paid according to the number of patients whose data she enters into the computer from index cards, she might invent part of the data. Usually we can discover this using the right statistical test. For example, if one invents a list of ones and zeros, such as when making a list of Toxo positives and negatives, then the ones and zeroes alternate much more regularly than if the order were determined by chance. This can be easily found out using the **runs test**. Similarly, if one invents multiple digit numbers, then usually certain numbers repeat more than others, in a way that is not random. Usually we can reveal this easily, by having the computer draw us a graph of the frequency of individual digits (i.e. a histogram, see Fig. 26). In everyday life there exists the well-known saying, "Trust, but verify." But in science it pays off to hold to the saying, "Don't trust, and verify."

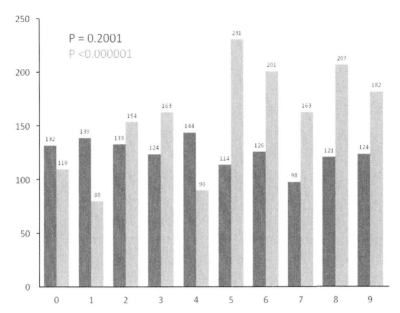

Fig. 26 The difference in frequency of the digits in real (dark-colored bars) and in invented data (light-colored bars). The real numbers were created from averaged, standardized results of measuring the attractiveness of tiger urine odor and then removing the first significant figure. The invented numbers come from the attention test, in which tested persons were presented with a list of randomly alternating digits. Over the course of three minutes, they were to mark all pairs of subsequent digits that added to 10. The chi-squared (χ^2) test demonstrates that the numbers from the real data have a homogenous distribution of digit frequency, whereas the invented numbers show a strong bias towards certain digits.

None of our projects reached the publication phase; nevertheless, we obtained several sets of data from people examined there. We found basically no difference between Toxo positives and negatives in the performance test. However, we did obtain one interesting result. In one examined group, numbering about 200 people, the total frequency of toxoplasmosis was only about 3%. In a normal population we would expect around 15-25% to be infected (depending on average age). Unfortunately, we were never able to obtain further information about them, for the data we got was anonymized. We can only guess that they may have been students or fresh graduates from flight school, rather than pilots or flight crew. We expect that these people recently took performance tests, and that those who didn't pass either weren't accepted into the school or didn't finish it. In this way, a large part of the Toxo positive people would be eliminated, and so would have been missing in this group. In groups of pilots and airline dispatchers taking regular performance tests, the frequency of Toxo positive people was no longer significantly decreased – apparently, a number of them became infected since graduating flight school. Yet even in these groups, the differences between the infected and uninfected people were not significant.

Our explanation is that the pilots' motivation to perform well in the test to maintain his prestige and a well-paid job was high enough, that individuals with a worsened performance trained harder for the tests, perhaps even took it repeatedly. At a weak moment, the employees of the psychological department of the Institute revealed that almost everyone, if not the first time then in the retake, is able to pass even these very difficult tests (hence the Toxo positives weren't removed from the test group, as was most likely the case with the flight school students). So if we couldn't know whether a person was taking the test his first or second time, after intensive training or just "offhand," it isn't surprising that we couldn't discern possible differences in performance of the infected and uninfected people.

Our experience from the Institute of Aviation Medicine, among other things, showed that the system for testing pilots probably doesn't work as well as it should. Aside from this practical conclusion, which should probably be important to the people and institutions responsible for air transportation safety, our experience is also noteworthy to scientists with research projects similar to ours. It is a reminder that we cannot ever forget that our test subjects often pass through a variety of "sieves" before they get to our laboratory. So if we don't find a difference in the observed parameters between the two test groups (be the subjects humans or animals), it doesn't have to mean that there is no such difference within the general population. Thanks to a "sieve," our experimental group may get a different ratio of individuals from each group we're comparing. For example, we get only the people who scored at least a hundred points in the entrance exam for flight school, which could mean only the fastest 10% of the Toxo positives, and the fastest 50% of the Toxo negatives that applied. We may not find any difference in reaction time between the two groups, even though a large difference exists within the general population. So how much does *Toxoplasma* affect people's performance? For a moment, let us look away from the above-mentioned problems of varying motivation and reaction speed, along with the unmentioned problem of distinguishing reaction speed and the ability to maintain maximum concentration over long periods of time. Apart from these, we can calculate the strength of Toxo's effect on human performance in our simple reaction time test quite easily (Box 49 *How to determine the effect size in statistics*).

Box 49 How to determine the effect size in statistics

Laymen, and unfortunately some scientists, often inaccurately believe that **effect size**, which measures the strength of the relationship between two variables, is indicated by the P value, i.e. **statistical significance**. This value, however, only (indirectly) reflects the probability of a **first order error**, the probability that the effect we observe in the data (such as the worsened performance of Toxo positive people), is only a result of chance. The lower the P value obtained from the statistical test, the greater the probability that the observed phenomenon isn't merely a turn of fate, but really exists. Statistical significance (P), however, says almost nothing about the effect size. For the P value is influenced not just by the strength of the studied effect (such as by what percent toxoplasmosis lowers one's performance), but also by the number of subjects in the test group and the variability of the dependent variable. When we have a large test group of several thousand individuals, we can prove even a very weak effect, which may not have any practical significance for a person's life. Conversely, in a small test group, we may not find even a large effect to be statistically significant. The effect size of the studied variables is decided by other characteristics, such as the **coefficient of determination** in the ANOVA (how much of the target variable's variability is explained by the studied factor); **eta²** in the GLM (something quite similar); or **Cohen's d** in Student's t-test (the difference in the target variable's means in the experimental and control groups, divided by the target variable's standard deviation from all the data).

Our studies showed that in blood donors toxoplasmosis is responsible for about 7% of the differences in reaction time among individuals in the human population. In other words, people differ amongst each other in reaction times – some are faster, others slower – yet toxoplasmosis is responsible for only 7% of the differences. On first glance, 7% may seem like a small number. In reality, an effect of this size in biology is already considered to be of medium strength. The thing is, the strength of biological effects accumulates from generation to generation. If we measured the same size effect in engineering, for example, finding that the effect of the outside temperature causes 7% of the observed variability in manufactured screw size (the remaining variability due to the diligence of the workers, the quality of the material, etc.), then we might disregard such a small effect. But dealing with biological phenomena constitutes an entirely different situation. Let's say that in the natural *Toxoplasma* population there appears a mutant, a protozoan able to manipulate its host's behavior. In lowering that host's reaction time, the parasite increases the probability that the host will be captured by a cat, the so-called final host of *Toxoplasma*. Even raising the probability of capture by just 1% is enough for this parasite to prevail in a couple dozen generations (a blink of an eye from an evolutionary stand-point) over the parasites unable to lower host reaction time. So 7% is fairly substantial – many of the effects we observe in evolutionary biology are responsible for 1-2% of total variability, which is quite enough for such an effect to manifest in evolution, for the organisms with the respective characteristics or abilities to prevail in nature. Hence even a 1% effect is strong for evolutionary biology, though most likely insignificant for the manufacturer of a screw.

The 7% effect that toxoplasmosis has on reaction time may be responsible for the fact that Toxo positives have a 2.65 times greater odd of traffic accidents, as we discovered in our pseudopredation studies. It's clear that latent toxoplasmosis influences driving ability much less than, for example, alcohol or just the common flu. However, a person gets drunk only occasionally, and even then rarely gets behind the wheel in such a state. Similarly, the flu worsens our cognitive abilities and reaction time much more than does latent toxoplasmosis, but we catch the flu at most once or twice a year. In contrast, once infected by *Toxoplasma*, we're stuck with latent toxoplasmosis for life. Whenever a Toxo positive gets behind the wheel or decides to cross the street, that person has a greater chance of becoming part of a traffic accident than does someone uninfected. And when the average person has a generally low risk of traffic accidents, a high prevalence of latent toxoplasmosis can add up to hundreds of thousands of deaths

It seems that subconsciously the infected person does learn to allow for his worsened reaction time. In our experiments we discovered that though reaction time worsens with time after infection, and those infected the longest have the worst reaction times; the probability of a traffic accident gradually decreases with time after infection. When tracking the reaction times of soldiers, blood donors or students, we of course didn't know how long a Toxo positive had been infected. Nevertheless, we found the worst reaction time always in people with low levels of antibodies – apparently infected long ago. On the other hand, people with the greatest risk of traffic accidents had the highest levels of antibodies, and so had apparently passed through acute toxoplasmosis relatively recently. In my opinion, infected drivers simply got used to their worsened reaction times. They discovered that they have a longer reaction time, and adapted their driving accordingly. Of course there exists a less optimistic explanation, that infected drivers who were already not very careful, got killed or at least had their driver's license taken away. But as a Toxo positive person, I prefer to reject the second explanation ahead of time, and categorically spurn it as entirely absurd and definitely improbable.

Box 50 How many road traffic victims does the "harmless" toxoplasmosis have on its conscience?

If we knew the percent by which toxoplasmosis increases the risk of a traffic accident, as well as the number of people who die each year from these accidents, we could approximately calculate how many traffic victims would be spared were it not for toxoplasmosis. This value is generally known as the **population attributable risk**, and this parameter which we can calculate by plugging into the respective formula. The problem is that mankind doesn't form a single population with the same incidences of toxoplasmosis and traffic accidents throughout. In some countries, the prevalence of toxoplasmosis is low, and that of fatal traffic accidents is high (for example as result of poor transport infrastructure and an outdated make of vehicle); in different countries, it's the other way around. Furthermore, data from various countries have different levels of reliability, and change from year to year. When I looked for data on the number of traffic fatalities ten years ago, the website of the WHO showed that were 3 million yearly[39]. The same source indicates that there are currently 1.4 million yearly. While it's not impossible, I'm not convinced that traffic fatalities decreased so much in 10 years. A further complication is that our data on the heightened risk of traffic accidents for infected people concerns only traffic accidents in which a participant was injured. It's possible that the heightened risk of fatal accidents is lower or higher than this value. Hence, I prefer to stick with an approximate estimate of traffic fatalities which can be attributed to *Toxoplasma* – several hundred thousand of dead each year[30].

And what about the other way around? Shouldn't Toxo positives enjoy some advantages; for example, if they cause a traffic accident, shouldn't their Toxo positivity prove a mitigating circumstance? I think not. One should always adapt his behavior, including how he drives, to his current ability. The problem is that in Rh-negative people, the worsening of reaction time due to toxoplasmosis can be very sudden, so the driver may not find out until the accident itself. Maybe I'm re-inventing the light bulb, but I think a good solution would be to install in every car, aside from seat-belts, a system to measure simple reaction time. The driver could only start the car if, for example, he pressed a button within 300 milliseconds of an auditory signal or a light in the dashboard turning on. The system could record the measured reaction times, so the driver could be immediately alerted if his psychomotor abilities are deteriorating over a long period of time, or if he is suspiciously indisposed just that day. In comparison with similar existing systems that monitor the presence of alcohol in one's breath, this system would be significantly cheaper, and I think even more useful. The possibility of using Toxo positivity as a defense has apparently already occurred to some clever lawyers. Very soon after we published our results, I received a letter from Germany from a lawyer, asking for additional details regarding Toxo's effect. It seems to me that he was trying to dig out one of his clients who may have caused a traffic accident. In any case, the knowledge whether a person is or isn't Toxo positive could be important in the insurance industry. On one hand, insurance could give benefits to its uninfected clients, for apparently successfully avoiding possible sources of infection; on the other hand, the insured could select an appropriate insurance policy according to whether or not he's Toxo positive, and thus whether or not he has a heightened risk of traffic accidents. If I know that as a toxoplasma infected subject I statistically have much higher probability of a crash than an uninfected person, I will most likely consider a better, though maybe more expensive insurance.

Years ago I tried to patent such a use for our findings, but my first attempt, as well as further appeals, was unsuccessful. I'm not sure whether the decision of the patent office was justified. It is clear that usage of the patent, especially by insurance companies, could be seen as ethically controversial. Nevertheless, I regret neither my unsuccessful efforts nor the expenses I invested. At least, when dealing with the good woman of the patent office, I understand why the Czech Republic is so far behind the rest of the world in number of awarded patents.

X. Of mice and men – why men are better (models)

We tried to test the original hypothesis that Toxo positives give up earlier than Toxo negatives in a struggle not only by using questionnaires given to people, but also by experimenting on animal models. However, when planning the latter, we committed a basic error. We planned to put together two male mice, one Toxo positive and the other Toxo negative, and observe which one of them first surrendered the fight. When two male mice, thus far kept separate, are put in the same cage, they begin fighting almost immediately. If we don't separate them in time, the stronger will literally stress out the other male to death in a matter of days. We, however, selected male mice which had not been raised separately, but in large groups. If a mouse's group is large enough, no hierarchy forms between the males. The males don't fight among themselves, not even when we pick out two and place them in a separate cage. Hence, when we put these Toxo positive and negative mice together, they pretty much ignored each other. As a result of this unpleasant mistake, our otherwise carefully prepared experiment didn't work out. Seeing as it was only one of many parts of Štěpánka Zitková-Hrdá's undergraduate work, we never repeated it. Sustaining 60 males, each in a separate cage, is an expensive matter. It's another of the topics we should get back to. Especially since it's a fairly simple experiment, so long as we avoid the mistake we made the first time.

Aside from the experiment with the hot plate, we also used the so-called tail-flick test to study the effect of acute and latent toxoplasmosis on the reaction time of infected mice. This standard test observes how quickly a mouse pulls away his tail when its base is subjected to heat. The mouse is kept in a short polypropylene tube, and a ray from a heated light bulb is aimed at the base of its tail with a magnifying glass. As soon the mouse feels the heat, it quickly jerks away its tail. Using a photocell shadowed by the base of its tail, we can quite accurately determine how soon after the heat stimulus (when we switched on the light bulb) the mice jerked away its tail.

Box 51 Why isn't the Earth covered by a continuous blanket of mice?

Really, it's a mystery. Females of all known animal species – except, perhaps, for humans in most modern, developed countries – have an average of two (though usually more) offspring in their lifetime. It follows that the population should continuously increase. So how come the Earth isn't covered by a single continuous blanket of mice (or platypuses, or even tapeworms, in which the female can produce several thousand eggs a day over a period of five years)? A species' population can temporarily increase or decrease, but in the long term it stays about the same. Maintaining the same population size in an environment of ceaseless, unpredictable change requires regulating either the growth or mortality rate in relation to population size. Nature applies both types of regulation, based on two kinds of negative feedback (see Box 52 *The feedback loop, and why scientists cherish it*). The first type, called **chemostatic regulation**, occurs in species whose population growth is restricted by the availability of a certain limited resource, such a food or shelter. If the population happens to increase, each individual will get less of the resource, which limits the speed of the population's increase. Meanwhile, the mortality rate remains fairly constant, so the population gradually decreases. The second type of regulation is **turbidostatic**. Turbidostatic regulation acts on species whose mortality rate depends on the activity of predators or parasites. If a chance fluctuation increases a species' population, then the predators and parasites of that species will also multiply, and once more decrease its population. When the species population is decreasing, its predators and parasites (who are also subject to chemostatic regulation) begin to die out, which lowers their effect on the size of the regulated population. The existence of two types of population regulation has a number of serious ecological and evolutionary implications. For example, it enables two species which require the same resources to live side by side over long periods of time (if one is regulated turbidostatically and the other chemostatically). The evolution of species that are regulated chemostatically aims towards more efficient use of resources (a so-called **K-strategy**; for example, scrounging more energy out of a molecule of sugar). In contrast, turbidostatically regulated species steer towards a faster use of resources (an **r-strategy**; the ability to utilize more molecules of sugar per minute)[40].

Aren't we natural scientists just like playful children? From a technical aspect, we conducted this experiment very well, but it turned out that there was no statistically significant difference between the Toxo positives and negatives in withdrawal reflex.

So why is there suddenly a box about the reproduction of mice, which has nothing to do with the previous discussion of reaction times? Is there a reference to it in the next experiment – was the box misplaced by a printer's error? Far from it. This box is unrelated to anything else – I just needed somewhere to brag about my very first evolutionary discovery, the theory of turbidostatic and chemostatic selection. I came upon the theory in my first year of college, when originally trying to illuminate the cause of aging in multicellular organisms. Unfortunately, I did not succeed – a shame, since pretty soon the information could come in handy.

Box 52 The feedback loop, and why scientists cherish it

When a nuclear physicist, a molecular biologist and a psychologist are discussing their work (and don't happen to be trash-talking crazy bosses, incompetent lab workers or stingy tax payers), they often hard-pressed to find a topic of common interest. The goal of any scientific field is to understand the workings of the world we live in – in other words, to create a model, the behavior of which corresponds with the behavior of the real world. Each scientific field has selected part of the world to study, and each field has a distinct, limited arsenal of elements for creating its models (see also Box 27 *Why to model in science, and what can and can't be modeled* and Box 65 *How are hypotheses tested in science?*). Scientists treat these elements like **black boxes**. They know how the elements behave; therefore they can deduce what set of output signals they will obtain from a set of input signals. But the reason behind the transfer, the mechanism which makes input into output signals (i.e. the contents of the black box) does not interest them. Indeed, this approach is key to the success of science: what one scientist sees as a black box, another pursues as the object of his research. The research topic of a psychologist is for example aggression; his black box is the human brain. The neurophysiologist's topic is the brain; his black box contains each type of nervous cell. These cells are studied by the cellular biologist; his black box is an arsenal of various molecules and macromolecules. These molecules are dissected by the chemist, whose black box includes atoms and atomic particles – which, in turn, are studied by the physicist. Scientists of every field can simultaneously research on different levels. Chemists don't have to wait for the questions of physics to be resolved; biologists don't rely on the discoveries of chemistry; and so on. If the physicists find that the atom works differently than they had thought, it most likely won't have too big of an impact on chemistry. The chemists may switch out some of the contents of their black boxes, but their actual theories and hypotheses generally remain unaffected. Scientists are used to occasionally changing some more or less important contents of their black box. Truth be told, they often don't even register the change, or it doesn't really impact them on the professional level. (Sometimes it does: changing the contents of a black box can change the transfer of input to output signals of a particular element, which may affect that element's behavior and role in a system.) Therefore, a scientist should, at least out of the corner of his eye, follow the progress of other scientific fields, and time to time look through the most important multidisciplinary journals, like *Science* or *Nature*.

Something which is prominent in all of science, and happily discussed among scientists of seemingly unrelated fields, is the feedback loop. Every scientist is familiar with it, and looks for it in his systems. A feedback loop is the direct or indirect effect of a certain element's output signals on its input. There are two types of feedback loops: negative and positive.

The negative feedback loop forms the basis of any kind of regulation. In a negative feedback loop, the signals from the output damp down the input. Let's say that the output signal happens to grow stronger. For example, when a steam engine speeds as it rolls down a hill, then the speed of its centrifugal governor increases. The axis of the centrifugal governor is aligned with the axle(s) of the wheels. As the centrifugal governor spins, momentum moves the attached havy flyballs out and up, a mechanism which opens the valve on the steam cylinder, lowering the pressure of the steam within. This slows the turning of the wheels, along with the speed of the locomotive and of the rotating balls. As the momentum of the flyballs decreases, the balls move back inwards and downwards, reducing or closing off the throttle valve from the steam cylinder. Now the pressure in cylinder begins to decrease, etc., etc. A negative feedback loop works in nature on myriad levels, and scientists of all fields encounter it.

A positive feedback loop involves a positive effect of the element's output on its input. While a negative feedback loop gives a system stability, a positive one causes instability, and triggering its self-increasing cycle often leads to the destruction of the system. For example, in one round of the experimental Public goods game (see chapter XII), several players randomly contribute little to the public pool. Many of the other players feel cheated, and in the next round they also contribute little to the public pool. Therefore, in the third round even more players will feel cheated, so these will also stop contributing. Over the course of several rounds, cooperation may completely fall apart, with nobody contributing anything to the common bank. A technical application of the positive feedback loop is the atomic bomb; in contrast with the negative feedback loop which operates in the nuclear reactor of a power station. Scientists like to look for negative and positive feedback loops, for the discovery of any kind of feedback loop can often explain the existence of interesting phenomena. In and of itself the feedback loop is so interesting that one is almost always able to publish its discovery in a high-ranking journal. Again, scientists of any field – as well as the reviewers of the respective manuscript – generally agree that discovering a new feedback loop is valuable and worthy of being published.

Another result of our mouse studies was our discovery that at least some behavioral changes of Toxo positive mice, such as a delayed reaction in jumping off a hot plate, decrease over time after the infection. Eventually, perhaps two months after infection, the changes disappear completely[41]. This brings us to a crucial general conclusion. The majority of hitherto published research on the effect of toxoplasmosis on the behavior of lab mice does not study the effects of long-term latent infection, but rather observes the passing behavioral changes which accompany acute toxoplasmosis, or the phase just after. This, of course, is an important distinction. When a mouse is sick, it's not surprising that it behaves differently than when healthy. About a dozen works published by British authors in the 80s may not actually describe the manifestations of *Toxoplasma*'s manipulatory activity, but rather the late symptoms of acute toxoplasmosis. When testing the manipulation hypothesis, one must wait until the manifestations of acute toxoplasmosis pass, and then take note primarily of those signals which grow stronger with time after infection, not weaker. The model of the lab mouse or practically any other rodent isn't particularly suitable for studying the manipulatory activity of *Toxoplasma*. A much better model for the study of latent toxoplasmosis is the brown, or Norwegian rat, which Joanne Webster and Manuel Berdoy began using for their studies in the 90s in Britain (Box 53 *How Oxford scientists study the effect of toxoplasmosis on the behavior of brown rats)*, and which have a much greater lifespan than mice.

Box 53 How Oxford scientists study the effect of toxoplasmosis on the behavior of brown rats

The same year that we published our first work describing the effect of *Toxoplasma* on human behavior, a British team also published the first article from their series of studies detailing the effect of *Toxoplasma* on the behavior of brown rats[42,43]. The subject of their study was a colony of brown, or Norwegian rats (*Rattus norvegicus*) raised in part-natural conditions, not the lab rats (white laboratory brown rats) that are used in most studies. Joanne P. Webster, the main author of recent publications from their interesting studies, revealed to me that their team began researching the manipulatory activity of *Toxoplasma* by accident, like we did. Originally she wanted to study a completely different parasite found in brown rats, the bacterium *Leptospira icterohaemorrhagiae*. It turned out, however, that only a minimal number of the animals were infected with this parasite. In contrast, a large number could be diagnosed with toxoplasmosis. In her first studies, Webster showed that the infected brown rats were more easily and sooner caught in traps than the uninfected rats, because they are not as afraid of unfamiliar objects and are more active. The most famous finding of the Oxford group is the phenomenon of "fatal attraction," in which infected brown rats seek out the scent of cats[19] (see Box 31 *What our British competitors discovered on animals, and how we will soon beat them*).

Another preferable model, which we use in our experiments, is the human. For brown rats and humans, acute toxoplasmosis is only a brief episode, considering their lifespan. If there are behavioral changes after this period, they will likely be manifestations of latent toxoplasmosis, not enduring manifestations of acute toxoplasmosis. In this sense, man is a particularly useful model organism.

While he is not the natural host of *Toxoplasma*, from which the parasite could get into the stomach of its final felid host – at least not today – the human has a long lifespan, and his period of acute toxoplasmosis lasts only about a month. Over the rest of his fairly long life, perhaps another 70 years, he should not exhibit the effects of his past mild illness. Any behavioral changes we observe about two years after infection will most likely be the manifestations of latent toxoplasmosis and the possible manipulatory activity of the parasite, rather than the side-effects of his past bout of acute toxoplasmosis.

Nevertheless, we must realize that it makes no difference for *Toxoplasma* that the behavioral changes it impacts on an infected mouse are transitory. The probability that the mouse would live more than two months in the wild is small anyways. So maybe it wasn't that great an error when, in the 80s, Hutchinson and his colleagues described the behavioral changes of mice infected with *Toxoplasma*, changes which, in the light of our current knowledge, seem to be the manifestations of acute rather than latent toxoplasmosis. Still, when testing the manipulation hypothesis or researching the possible effects of latent toxoplasmosis on humans, it is better to use a long-lived host as a model. Testing on an organism with a long lifespan means that there is less of a risk that we could confuse transitory behavioral manifestations of acute toxoplasmosis with the specific manifestations of the parasite's manipulatory activity in its latent phase.

A few more words on the course of toxoplasmosis in mice. Generally, it is presumed that acute toxoplasmosis has two phases.

The mouse begins to show signs of sickness about a week after infection. At this point the disease has its first peak: the mouse quickly loses weight, its fur puffs up, it grows listless, it stops eating, and, in the case of an infection which is stronger or of a more virulent strain, the creature dies.

Ten days after this phase, survivors begin to gain back weight, and seem to get well. However, about 30 days after infection comes the second peak of the disease, and once again some of the mice die. Deaths in the first peak are associated with the reproduction of tachyzoites in the tissues of infected mice, whereas the second peak is associated with the point of greatest rate of production of tissue cysts in the brain. Mice which are weaker or infected with more parasites die in the second peak of encephalitis.

Fig. 27 An approximately 20 month-old mouse infected with Toxoplasma. *The control mice did not show any signs of deteriorated health.*

It's interesting, and perhaps important for us long-lived *Toxoplasma* hosts, that later there appears a third phase of toxoplasmosis[18]. The following result was, again, obtained by accident. It all began when I was loath to kill the mice after finishing the ethological experiments. Even though it's against the rules for working with laboratory animals, I sometimes let them live out the rest of their lives in the mouse husbandry (Box 54 *How and why I don't always follow the rules for working with lab animals*). It wasn't entirely a matter of my softhearted nature – what if I could still use them at a later date, maybe to infect other experimental mice. At worst, my colleagues could take the control mice and feed them to their snakes or monitor lizards. So it happened that I kept some of the mice in the husbandry for a year or more. After this period, it turned out that the mice that had seemed to be completely healthy – which, two months after infection, had even regained the weight they had lost during the acute phase – in reality were far from healthy. The older ones had skin lesions, shed fur, and, in a number of cases, became paralyzed or blind. No such defects were observed in the control, uninfected mice (Fig. 27). In nature, a mouse doesn't usually get the chance to grow old, so only in lab husbandries could it become apparent that toxoplasmosis is far from harmless – as is often thought.

Box 54 How and why I don't always follow the rules for working with lab animals

Once an experiment is finished, lab animals are supposed to be killed in a humane way. They may not be used again, even when they were previously in the control group and nothing was really done to them. Clearly one cannot test on animals which have already been subjected to pharmaceutical or surgical procedures, given, perhaps, some unusual food. It might not affect the new experiment, and it is even possible that we could prove the existence of a certain phenomenon more effectively; but no one (including ourselves) would be able to easily replicate the results. If the animals in question are part of an ethological study, and only their behavior was observed, the rule that they cannot be used in another experiment becomes fairly absurd. So if the animals had not been subjected to anything, I often broke the rule on having to immediately sacrifice them, and always tried to find a way to use both the uninfected and infected animals. I don't believe that my toxoplasmosis – which causes lowered strength of the superego (willingness to comply with rules and social norms) – was responsible for this. Rather, if lab animals must die for my experiments, let it at least be for the greatest possible avail.

It would certainly be important to see if something similar happens in humans. Doctors presume that toxoplasmosis acquired as an adult poses no health problem, at least not *Toxoplasma* from Europe or North America. On the other hand, in South America, where several atypical strains of *Toxoplasma* circulate, toxoplasmosis is often accompanied by serious symptoms (Box 46 *There's no Toxoplasma like Toxoplasma*). But in the light of our chance observations on aged mice it seems that the negative effects of toxoplasmosis could manifest even in species in which this was hitherto unexpected, maybe even in man. Based on the symptoms of the aged mice, I'd guess that an autoimmune disease was to blame. I don't wish to foretell evil, but indirect proof of a negative effect of toxoplasmosis on the health of older organisms exists even for humans. When studying the prevalence of toxoplasmosis in different age groups, one often finds that the percentage of infected people at first rapidly increases, but later, in the older age groups, the growth slows.

In the Czech Republic, a large number of children become infected before the age of nine. It's almost certainly related to their playing in sandboxes or putting various unsanitary objects in their mouth, eating dirt and so on. After this sharp increase during early childhood, the prevalence of toxoplasmosis in the population grows more slowly. In women, there occurs one more sharp increase between the ages of 24 and 34. It's likely that this second peak is related to the fact that women are establishing families during this time, and begin cooking more – they may, for example, become infected through scratches in their skin when preparing raw meat, or perhaps by tasting a mixture for meatballs. After the age of thirty, the frequency of latent toxoplasmosis in the population grows more or less constantly until the age of 60. After this, growth slows or comes to a stop, and in the oldest age group the prevalence of toxoplasmosis is lower than in the younger age groups. Of course it is possible that older people are less likely to become infected. Older people are generally more conservative in their habits, so if they have not yet become infected, they are unlikely to do so now (unless in their old age they decide to return to playing in the sandbox). In some of the infected people, the level of *Toxoplasma* antibodies decreases, so they appear to us as Toxo negative. That is a more optimistic scenario. A more pessimistic scenario says that Toxo positive persons never reach this older age. I'm not sure which is more likely. I do know, however, which scenario would have more serious medical implications, and so I believe that greater attention (some, at least!) should be paid to the effect of latent toxoplasmosis on health. Our new studies confirmed this notion strongly[44].

Once more I'd like to return to the question of whether it's suitable to use man as a model. For *Toxoplasma*, man is basically a dead end – when the parasite infects a mouse, it has a good chance of getting into a cat, but when it infects a human, the parasite's path to its definitive host is likely forever blocked off. It is therefore relevant to ask (and the reviewers of our manuscripts, the vexing fault-finders that they are, often do like to demand) whether it isn't better to experiment on the natural hosts of *Toxoplasma*, on mice and brown rats (or other rodents). It may seem strange, but I think that even in this aspect man may be a better host model than a mouse or brown rat. The life cycle of today's *Toxoplasma gondii* works so reliably primarily because human settlements are surrounded by a large number of felines, from tame tabbies to feral cats. The populations of these domestic and "domestic" cats are so large, that the parasite easily finds its definitive host, and the prevalence of the parasite in the definitive and in the intermediate host stays at a high level.

But one must realize two things. Firstly, the domestic cat isn't *Toxoplasma*'s optimal definitive host. Usually the cat becomes infected as a kitten, then for some time it releases cysts, mostly for only a couple of days to weeks. After this time, it stops releasing them, and for the rest of its life it likely does not spread the parasite. Of course there are known cases, in which the cat releases cysts several times over its lifespan, but these are probably exceptions which may be related to a dysfunction of the immune system, induced, perhaps, by a different infection. For the spread of *Toxoplasma* it would be much more useful if the infected cat shed cysts for the entirety of its life, as does the definitive host of the tapeworm or fluke.

Secondly, one must realize that, until recently, the domestic cat was almost never found in our settlements. In Europe, this cohabitant became more widespread after the Middle Ages. I often tell students that before 1800 cats were but briefly kept by witches not yet burned at the stake. That may be something of an exaggeration, but cats, for example, show up in pictures only starting in the 19th century, so it is likely that before this time, cats in houses and around human settlements were not as numerous as they are today. I suspect that for our ancestors, cats were also welcomed as a source of animal protein, which effectively regulated their populations surrounding the human settlements, as well as the prevalence of toxoplasmosis. I'm not an expert in the delicacies of Chinese cuisine, but I have a similar explanation for the low prevalence of toxoplasmosis in China and Korea. I believe that toxoplasmosis long did not exist in Europe, and appeared only recently, with the spread of domestic cats. Later, in chapter XV, we'll return to this theory, but within a different context.

So who was the primary host of *Toxoplasma* before man domesticated the cat – or, as any cat owner knows, before cats domesticated us? If we restrict our hypotheses to the Felidae, and don't presume that the definitive host could be a member of, for example, the civet family (which thus far has not been proven, but then again, it's doubtful that anyone has really tested it), or perhaps of the hyena family (as the preliminary results of our scent experiments suggest[22]), we are left primarily with various small and large members of the Felidae. I don't know about the prevalence of toxoplasmosis in small cats, which are found more in Africa than in Europe, but in large cats, whether it be leopards or lions, toxoplasmosis is very widespread. For example, in 116 lions of four African reservations, the prevalence of toxoplasmosis was usually found to be 100% (only in Serengeti was it a "mere" 92%). And out of 8 studied leopards, 7 were found to be infected[45]. And it is clear than neither lions nor leopards catch mice very often – they do, however, frequently prey on monkeys, including apes.

Box 55 Are species evolutionarily adapted to current conditions?

Most biologists would say that unless the conditions have recently, radically changed, then generally species are. Today's biology textbooks write that species are constantly subject to natural selection, which weeds out the individuals not adapted to the environment they live in. If the environmental conditions change, then, due to natural selection, the species will adapt over several generations to the new conditions. As I explained in Box 35 *How I refuted Darwin*, this classic idea of all-powerful evolution may not apply to sexually reproducing organisms. According to the **theory of frozen plasticity**[11,26], a sexually reproducing species can change only just after its formation; for the rest of its existence it waits passively until environmental conditions have changed so much, that the species dies out. This would mean that species aren't adapted to the conditions in which they find themselves, but to the conditions which governed their environment as they were forming (or, more precisely, when they lost their evolutionary plasticity). Among other things, this explains why most of the species we find in nature are rare. The theoretical ecologist would expect that most species would have an average prevalence; there should be few abundant and rare species, and even fewer highly abundant and extremely rare species. In reality, every environment has but a couple of highly abundant species, but many rare species. This basic ecological axiom can be explained by the theory of frozen plasticity[27]. Young, still plastic species have the greatest populations, for they are now ideally adapted to their living conditions. Statistically, it is likely that (on average) the older the species, the more its current conditions differ from its original conditions. Older species are poorly adapted to current conditions, so their populations are not very large.

One can therefore imagine that, in the past, our evolutionary ancestors formed a natural part of *Toxoplasma*'s life cycle, and therefore that our experimental human-*Toxoplasma* model for studying the manipulation hypothesis is actually more natural than the often-used model of mouse-*Toxoplasma*. *Toxoplasma* definitely had more time to learn to manipulate the behavior of hominids for its own benefit than that of house mice (Box 55 *Are species evolutionarily adapted to current conditions?*). It is thus possible that today the *Toxoplasma* found in rodent hosts is merely trying to do what once paid off in the bodies of our evolutionary ancestors. By the way, the fatal attraction phenomenon has been recently observed also in chimpanzee[46].

XI. The tools which *Toxoplasma* uses to manipulate human behavior

Usually the natural scientist cares not just why something happens, but how it happens. He cares not only whether or not *Toxoplasma* manipulates human behavior, but about the tools which it employs to do so. So of course, from the very start, we pursued this question. Past studies conducted on animals indicate that the manipulation could occur using the neurotransmitter dopamine. Already in the mid-80s, a study showed that latent phase *Toxoplasma*-infected mice had a 15% higher concentration of dopamine in their brain than did uninfected mice[47]. Based on the results of this study, we expected that humans with latent toxoplasmosis might also have higher levels of dopamine. But for a long time, we didn't know how to prove such a thing using the arsenal of methods we had at our disposal. With a human, of course, one cannot simply look into his brain and biochemically measure the concentration of dopamine (our experimental subjects, for example, did not seem enthusiastic about this idea). Fortunately, there are also several possible indirect methods. Of these, we chose the most indirect, but also the cheapest method. It is based on the fact that higher levels of dopamine in some parts of the brain manifest in a lowering of the psychological factor "novelty seeking." This discovery originally comes from ethopharmacological studies on laboratory rodents. Later, American psychologist Claude R. Cloninger created a five- and then seven-factor questionnaire, called TCI, used to observe these factors in man (see Box 56 *What does Cloninger's TCI measure?*).

Box 56 What does Cloninger's TCI measure?

The Czech version of Cloninger's TCI (Temperament and Character Inventory) questionnaire uses 238 questions to measure four temperament dimensions (the tendency towards *"novelty seeking," "harm avoidance," "reward dependence", "persistence"*), as well as three character dimensions (*"self-directedness," "cooperativeness", "self-transcendence"*). Cattell attempted to identify primary, mutually independent psychological traits by statistically analyzing words that describe different personality characteristics (a technique known as factor analysis). Then, by trial and error, he formed the **Cattell's questionnaire** by creating questions that could be used to estimate these traits. **Cloninger's questionnaire** was created differently. The basic, mutually independent psychological factors weren't found using factor analysis of psychological terms, but derived from the results of neurophysiological and neuroethological studies. For example, laboratory mice were given various drugs which either mimicked or inhibited neurotransmitters (see Box 13 *Neurotransmitters*), and researchers followed how this influenced the behavior of the mice. Thanks to such experiments, we can also say which psychological factors correlate positively or negatively with which neurotransmitter (the tendency towards "novelty seeking" with a high concentration of dopamine, "harm avoidance" with serotonin, "reward dependence" perhaps with noradrenalin). It's interesting how little we humans have diverged from our animal ancestors – factors which were originally created based on experiments conducted on mice, are quite useful for describing the human psyche.

It is presumed that the levels of some psychological factors measured by this questionnaire reflect the levels of certain neurotransmitters in the human brain. One of these factors is the tendency towards "novelty seeking". It is expected to correlate negatively with the levels of dopamine in the brain not only in mice, but also in humans. So we gave each of our test subjects, first the soldiers and later the students and blood donors, Cloninger's TCI questionnaire, and then looked whether there was a difference in "novelty seeking" between Toxo positives and Toxo negatives.

To our surprise, there was a difference – and it exactly fit our hypothesis that there were heightened levels of dopamine in the brains of humans infected by *Toxoplasma* (Fig. 28). Toxo positive men and women had lower "novelty seeking" than did Toxo negatives. Up to 2007 we studied this phenomenon in five unrelated subject groups, and in three of them we managed to prove our hypothesis[36,48].

What is suspicious, however, is that differences in this factor were mostly apparent in test subjects from Prague; Toxo positive people from medium-sized towns (with a population of about 10-100 thousand), even exhibited a non-significant greater tendency towards "novelty seeking." In addition, we repeatedly found that Toxo positive people also have a higher Cloninger's factor of "self-transcendence." Unfortunately, this is a factor, the meaning of which probably differs between the Czech and American populations. The values measured in the Czech population reflect completely different psychical traits than those which Cloninger was trying to measure. It seems that in Czechs it reflects the tendency to be swayed by others, or even (negatively) the level of intelligence. Interpreting changes in this factor as being linked to latent toxoplasmosis is definitely still precocious.

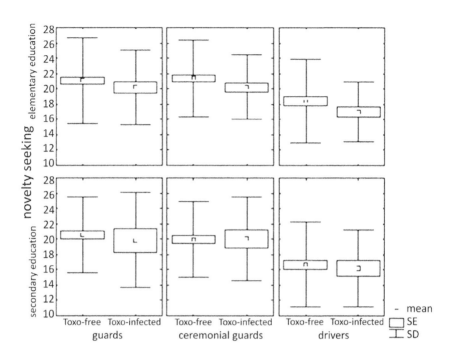

Fig. 28 Indirect proof of increased dopamine levels in Toxoplasma positive persons. The levels of this neurotransmitter correlate negatively with the psychological factor novelty seeking, the latter determined using Cloninger's questionnaire (Temperament and character inventory – TCI). Several of our studies, including this one, have demonstrated that infected individuals have a lower value of this psychological factor. In our study, conducted on soldiers of the mandatory military service, novelty seeking depended on the level of education and type of professions; therefore, we analyzed the relationship between Toxoplasma infection and novelty seeking separately for each subgroup.

It's interesting that, unlike a number of previously-studied Cattell's factors, Cloninger's factor of "novelty seeking" doesn't change with time after infection. Furthermore, it always deviates in the same direction for Toxo positive men and women. An explanation for this could be that, after infection by Toxoplasma, change in Cloninger's personality factors is faster than change in

Cattell's factors. In the case of Cloninger's personality factors, infection causes a change in neurotransmitters, which can result in an almost immediate shift in psychological traits, such as a lowered tendency towards "novelty seeking." In the case of Cattell's factors, the physiological change must first manifest as a behavioral change. The person must realize his changed behavior, and then adjust his list of personal values accordingly. This recognized shift in values is what shows up as a change in Cattell's factors, such as a lower tendency to follow social norms (Rule-Consciousness/Superego Strength). In a group of Toxo positives, changes in Cattell's factors grow gradually more defined, whereas changes in Cloninger's factors occur immediately after infection – so we cannot measure a correlation with time after infection.

What do we think is the specific mechanism that changes Cloninger's factors? A couple years ago I had a clear hypothesis, which agreed with the sources available on the subject, as well as with the results of our studies[49]. Small or large sites of inflammation form and persist in the brain of a *Toxoplasma*-infected human (or animal). At inflammation sites, active immunocytes release a variety of lymphokines, molecules which immune cells use to communicate. Some of these molecules, such as interleukin 2, stimulate the production of dopamine in surrounding tissue. According to my former hypothesis, higher levels of dopamine, and hence a lowered tendency towards "novelty seeking," is but one of the side-effects of local inflammation in brain tissue.

The reader may wonder whether it still counts as manipulation, when, according to our hypothesis, the phenomenon seems like just a side-effect of pathogenic processes in the brain. The problem is that there exists a similar dilemma for every useful trait we find in organisms. All such useful traits formed as side-products of random and useless processes. If *Toxoplasma* today can manipulate the behavior of its host for its own ends, then this is only just the product of a gradual improvement – an evolutionary upgrading of the original abilities which appeared with random mutations. The phenomenon of increased dopamine levels that accompany inflammation in the brain wasn't originally used by *Toxoplasma* to manipulate host behavior. Rather, this phenomenon evolved as a means of communication among different types of immune cells (some of which exhibit specific dopamine binding sites).

But when it turned out that aspects of the behavior induced by increased levels of dopamine help *Toxoplasma* spread to another host, then natural selection grasped this side-effect of infection. It took hold of *Toxoplasma*'s ability to increase the production of dopamine by causing inflammation, and, over the course of several generations, honed it (or at least substantially improved the ability). Strains of *Toxoplasma* which were able to induce chronic local inflammation in the brain of their host, and which were able to maintain heightened levels of dopamine, had an advantage over strains unable to do so. The strains with the useful ability spread more quickly than the others, so today we encounter only those strains which are able to raise dopamine levels. Today it is unimportant that *Toxoplasma*'s ability to manipulate the behavior of its host began as a side-effect of pathological processes. What matters is whether or not the ability to raise dopamine levels aids *Toxoplasma*'s chances of getting from an intermediate host to its definitive felid host. We could determine this using a very complicated experiment, by creating conditions under which manipulation would not be beneficial for *Toxoplasma*. For example, we could, over a long period of time, artificially transfer *Toxoplasma* from one host to another, and observe whether its ability to raise dopamine levels might change.

If this ability were indeed an active manipulatory activity, one would expect it to gradually weaken. Under such conditions, in which we provide *Toxoplasma* with a transfer mechanism, the ability to raise dopamine levels wouldn't benefit the parasite. To the contrary, maintaining the ability would only be a waste of resources which *Toxoplasma* could invest in something else, such as reproduction. But if raising dopamine levels were truly just a side-effect, then the ability should remain. Of course, such an experiment would be a difficult and long-term study. Moreover, we don't know how taxing it is, energy-wise, for *Toxoplasma* to raise dopamine levels, and therefore how quickly this ability would disappear if it were no longer useful for the parasite.

Our hypothesis was that changes in "novelty seeking" occur due to raised dopamine levels, caused by the (possibly evolutionary magnified) inflammatory processes which accompany the formation and maintenance of cysts of the brain. We attempted to prove our hypothesis at least indirectly, using a much simpler method. If a neurophysiologist wished to tackle the question using a classic method, he'd likely try to damp down the inflammatory processes in the body of an infected individual, to observe whether this would manifest in the behavior of that human (or, more likely, the scientist would use a mouse) – to see whether the individual's tendency towards "novelty seeking" would return to its original level. Such an experiment, however, would also be technically difficult, for damping down inflammatory processes means significantly altering an organism's immune system. This basically rules out humans as possible test subjects, and we'd have to develop an experimental system which would allow us to observe *Toxoplasma*-induced changes in the "novelty seeking" of mice. In addition, it would be very difficult to unambiguously interpret the results of such an experiment. For example, the administration of corticoid hormones, which can inhibit inflammatory processes, has drastic effects on the organism; so the lower dopamine levels induced by the decreased inflammation might not even be the cause of most, if any, behavioral changes observed during such an experiment. Interpreting the behavioral changes as a result of the decreased levels of dopamine, would be a ridiculous conclusion, akin to that of a scientist in a famous joke: The scientist concludes that a flea has gone deaf after he removes its last leg – because the flea stops obeying his command to "Jump!".

Our approach to the question was completely different, and, I'd even say, much better (although the methods were less sophisticated, and hence more difficult to publish). We tried to determine whether the same manifestations we saw in Toxo positive humans also occurred in humans infected with cytomegalovirus (CMV)[49].

The human CMV is a very widespread virus, belonging to the family *Herpesviridae*. In the Czech Republic, it has infected about 80% of the population. The virus spreads through close contact between an infected and an uninfected individual (such as kissing; the earlier popular method of transfer on gas masks used in civil defense training in the communist Czechoslovakia went out of fashion after we successfully lost the Cold War). This means that the life cycle of CMV is completely different from that of *Toxoplasma*, since *Toxoplasma* reaches its definitive host through a so-called alimentary way. In other words, the definitive host catches and devours the intermediate host. Nevertheless, everything else about *Toxoplasma* and CMV is fairly similar. If you were to take a review article on *Toxoplasma*, and everywhere replace the word *Toxoplasma* with CMV, you'd find that the review would still make more or less sense – except for, of course, the part about the parasite's transmission. Just like *Toxoplasma*, CMV has a long-term dormant phase in the brain of the infected human. CMV does almost nothing in the infected nervous cells; that is, until the infected host catches AIDS or is prescribed a strong immunosuppressant, for something like cancer treatment or because of a transplant.

Like *Toxoplasma*, CMV can become active under a weakened immune system, and the resulting encephalitis can be fatal. In addition, CMV also poses a serious risk during pregnancy. When a pregnant woman becomes infected by human CMV or *Toxoplasma gondii*, there is a chance that the infection could spread to the fetus; both species cause similar types of developmental defects (Box 57

How dangerous is Toxoplasma in pregnant women?). We were primarily interested in that CMV, like *Toxoplasma*, forms small sites of inflammation in the brain. If the increased "novelty seeking" we observed in Toxo positives were really a side-effect of these sites, then we'd expect that the factor would also appear in people infected by CMV. To test this hypothesis, we tested two large subject groups for the presence of antibodies against CMV[49]. One group consisted of soldiers of the mandatory military service, whereas the other was made up of blood donors; each had a couple hundred people. All of these people filled out a Cloninger's questionnaire so that we could see whether "novelty seeking" differed between those infected and uninfected by CMV. The results of both groups supported our hypothesis that an increase in dopamine levels is a side-effect of long-term local inflammation in brain tissue. Like Toxo positives, people infected by CMV exhibited a decrease in tendency towards "novelty seeking." Furthermore, with *Toxoplasma* we had found no correlation between "novelty seeking" and the concentration antibodies against the parasite – and the same was true for CMV. From this we concluded that the tendency towards "novelty seeking" decreased soon after infection by CMV, just as it did after infection by *Toxoplasma*. In addition, as was the case with *Toxoplasma*, we observed that the sharpest effect of CMV on "novelty seeking" was seen in people from big cities. I don't know why this is so. It's possible that the set-up of the questionnaire is responsible. Perhaps some of the questions which serve to determine "novelty seeking" may be answered affirmatively by someone from a small village, but negatively by the inhabitant of a larger city (or vice versa). Certain "novelties," like visiting the zoo, may be commonplace for a big city dweller, whereas others, like riding a goat, may be common for the small towner but not for the city dweller. (Just to be clear, Cloninger's questionnaire has no questions about visiting circuses or fooling around with domestic animals – that was just an example.)

Box 57 How dangerous is *Toxoplasma* in pregnant women?

Women today are usually aware that they face the greatest *Toxoplasma*-associated health risk during pregnancy. The magnitude and nature of this danger is less well known, and unfortunately even among doctors. Women with the latent form of toxoplasmosis are in no danger. If a woman knows that she has been infected for some time before her pregnancy (at least a year) and has no health problems related to acute toxoplasmosis (which is true for 99% of subjects with antibodies against *Toxoplasma*), she absolutly needn't worry about toxoplasmosis. But if she is Toxo negative before becoming pregnant, she should do her utmost to remain uninfected for the duration of the pregnancy. This means that she should avoid consuming raw meat, particularly not from livestock; she should avoid handling the litter box (though she certainly can pet the cat); and she must strictly follow the basic rules of hygiene when working with dirt, hay and unwashed root vegetables – in other words, with anything that could be contaminated with cat excrement. If a woman becomes infected during her first trimester (which doctors can easily determine based on the levels of IgM-class antibodies), there is about a 15% risk that the infection will spread to the developing fetus. In such a case, there is a danger of miscarriage, or that the child will be born with serious birth defects (hydrocephalus, microcephaly or other serious deformities). If she becomes infected during the third trimester, the chance of the child becoming infected is much greater, but the health implications are much less severe. Usually infection results in mild to more serious defects in sight and hearing. However, in several South American countries there are many highly pathogenic strains, and the health implications of infection (which are often apparent only several years after birth) are generally more serious and more common. In some countries, all pregnant women are screened for toxoplasmosis; and if a woman is found to be Toxo negative, she may have to be screened repeatedly. This practice, however, is often the target of criticism, since it is not entirely certain whether the treatment given to infected woman reduces the risk of infection spreading to the fetus to the extent that it outweighs the psychical stress each woman is subjected to when waiting for the results of her screening.

An interesting, unintended result of our CMV study had to do with another of Cloninger's factors, specifically the factor of "harm avoidance." This factor is supposed to correlate with levels of serotonin, another neurotransmitter. Something I did not mention: while screening our test subjects for CMV, we also tested them for *Toxoplasma*. In the case of "novelty seeking", we found that the effects of CMV and *Toxoplasma* were additive. The subjects infected with both parasites had (on average) lower "novelty seeking" than did subjects infected either by CMV or *Toxoplasma*. But for the factor of "harm avoidance," the relationship was more complicated. The thing is, Toxo positives and Toxo negatives reacted differently to infection by CMV. In Toxo negatives, CMV infection caused a lower "harm avoidance," whereas Toxo positives with CMV had a higher "harm avoidance". Until we confirm this result using other test groups, I'll refrain from speculating about its meaning.

In the year 2009 our hypothesis that raised dopamine levels are a side-effect (or an evolutionarily improved side-effect) of inflammatory processes in the brain suffered quite a blow from an unexpected direction. Molecular neurophysiologists at Leeds and Manchester discovered that *Toxoplasma* is the only protozoan known to possess genes for enzymes which catalyze dopamine synthesis in the brain[50]. It's not clear why it has these genes, but of course there is the simple explanation that *Toxoplasma* can use the enzymes to increase synthesis of dopamine, which has already been proven[51]. *Toxoplasma* may be increasing dopamine synthesis in order to manipulate the behavior of the intermediate host, to raise that host's chances of being eaten by a felid – this, however, remains to be definitively proven. Naturally, the discovery that *Toxoplasma* possesses genes for dopamine synthesis does not rule out our inflammation hypothesis. Inflammation in the brain, among other things, causes increased levels of interleukin, which in turn signal the brain to produce higher levels of dopamine. The cysts of *Toxoplasma*, by causing inflammation, could have at first increased dopamine as a side-effect; the parasite may have later improved on this ability by providing the brain with additional molecules of enzymes for dopamine synthesis. (Box 58 *How evolution forms useful traits*).

By the way, we have completely neglected the basic question of how *Toxoplasma* could benefit from lowering the "novelty seeking" of its intermediate host. But it's not difficult to formulate a hypothesis to explain it.

Box 58 How evolution forms useful traits

In his lifetime, Charles Darwin made a number of fundamental discoveries. Even if he hadn't discovered how biological evolution works, he most likely would still be famous today. His biggest discovery, which explained a great biological and philosophical mystery, is his explanation of how **useful traits** form during evolution without the intervention of a rational being. It's unessential that the mechanism he described applies only to asexually-reproducing organisms (see Box 35 *How I refuted Darwin*). Newer and more correct theories, whether it be the earlier **selfish gene theory** or the more recent **frozen plasticity theory**, only elaborate on Darwin's model and expand it to apply to all organisms. Darwin showed that every species produces individuals with traits which differ more or less from those of their parents. Many such deviations are hereditary, passed down from the parents to the offspring. An organism's traits determine its chances for surviving, reaching adulthood and also reproducing. The heritable variations (today called **mutations**) are stochastic in terms of their effect on fitness. The vast majority of mutations are neutral or worsen an individual's fitness – if we randomly change a part of a watch, its function most likely won't improve. Occasionally, there occurs a mutation which aids survival or reproductive ability. An individual with this kind of beneficial mutation successfully competes with the others members of its population, and thus leaves behind more offspring. His offspring will inherit this mutation, and also leave behind more offspring than other individuals. After several generations, the offspring of the mutated individual probably predominate in the population. Among these offspring, there will also appear beneficial and harmful mutations – the harmful ones disappear from the population, whereas the beneficial ones get passed down and slowly accumulate, a proces known as **natural selection**. Thanks to natural selection, a species accumulates more and more useful traits, and gradually improves on those which already exist. As I mentioned, mutations are random in terms of their effect on an individual's competitive ability. This means that a useful evolutionary novelty, an adaption, which depends on a single beneficial mutation, forms by chance – its value is revealed only subsequently, when it increases an individual's ability to compete. Most adaptations, however, depend on several or many accumulated mutations. In this case, one cannot say that the adaptation formed by chance, and that natural selection only subsequently revealed its value. Rather, chance only furnished the building material, the random mutations; the actual adaptation, such a camera-type eye, was formed gradually by the nonrandom process of natural selection (Fig. 29). Let's say that mutation A happens to cause a slightly beneficial (but imperfect) adaption – such as a primitive eye (eyespot apparatus). Individuals with this mutation can detect the presence of light, and take advantage of this ability. They leave behind more offspring, and after several generations, the ability will be held by every member of the population. In time, one of the individuals gains another beneficial mutation B (among a host of disadvantageous mutations), which gives the ability to recognize the direction that light is coming from.

The offspring of the individual with this new mutation will once more predominate in the population; and among them yet another a beneficial mutation C will eventually appear (there's a lot of offspring already bearing mutations A and B, so you'd hope that one of them would eventually get mutation C). This mutation might allow one to sense the shape of a light-emitting object. Individuals with this mutation (bearing the mutations A, B and C) will once more prevail, one will gain another useful mutation D, and so on; until finally the distant descendents of the first mutant develop a complete camera-type eye. It's clear that all the necessary mutations could not arise in one individual simultaneously; that is, they could, but it would take more

> time, than has passed since the origin of the universe. But with the help of natural selection, the necessary mutations will accumulate relatively quickly, therefore biological adaptations, as Darwin's mechanism describes, can also develop at a brisk rate.

For example, we might say that a mouse with a lower tendency towards "novelty seeking" won't become familiar with the area around its burrow; it won't know of the possible hiding places and dangers of the area, and will be more liable to become the prey of a cat. The problem is that we could just as easily formulate a hypothesis if our results were to show that *Toxoplasma* increases, rather than decreases, the tendency towards "novelty seeking". We'd probably reason that a "novelty seeking" mouse, instead of safely remaining in its burrow, chooses to venture out at every possible moment, to roam its surrounding and investigate every unfamiliar object – such a mouse would be more likely to wind up in the belly of a cat. Certainly, we could test both of these hypotheses. There undoubtedly exists a strain of lab mice with more and less curious individuals; in any case, we could probably find a way to lower or rise the "novelty seeking" of mice through pharmaceutical means. The difficulty of the experiment lies in that we cannot determine which species was *Toxoplasma*'s natural host, before the spread of humans caused enormous growth in the cat (and mouse) populations. As was discussed earlier, it's unclear whether the original, and thus more natural *Toxoplasma* host may have been a monkey (or an ape) rather than a mouse. Which host is *Toxoplasma* actually best adapted to – which host should we study?

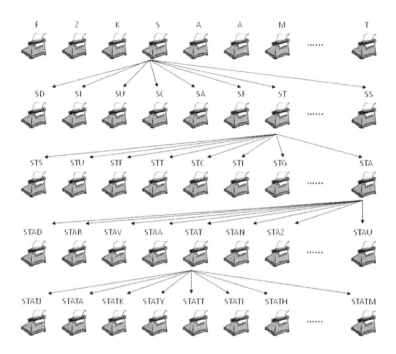

Fig. 29 How evolution works. Creationists often say that Darwin's natural selection cannot explain complicated adaptations. They say that the formation of beneficial structures like the human eye through chance mutations is just as improbable as a group of monkeys, randomly hitting on typewriters keyboard, creating the works of Shakespeare. In reality, even with the help of the monkeys and several dozen sturdy typewriters, we can create any text easily enough. However, we will have to simulate the mechanism proposed by Darwin, not the caricature presented to the public by our industrious (and undoubtedly well-intentioned) creationists. The procedure is simple. We give each monkey a typewriter, and have him type one letter (analogous to one mutation). Then we chase the monkeys out of the room and select the typewriter that has the first letter of our text (for example "H" for Hamlet). We take the paper from this typewriter, make several copies and put them in the other typewriters (analogous to natural selection). Then we invite the monkeys back for another round.

There is one more problem I should mention. Does dopamine always lower the tendency towards "novelty seeking?" Based on our experiences with Toxo's effects on human and rodent behavior, I doubt it[52,53]. Humans and mice certainly have one thing in common – they are irrepressibly curious creatures. If we give a mouse a new and old toy, then it will definitely play longer with the new toy. And when a mouse is infected with toxoplasmosis, its interest in "novelty seeking" decreases[54]. On the other hand, Norwegian rats (including both laboratory Norwegian rats and wild-laboratory hybrids, which Joanne P. Webster used in her experiments on the effect of toxoplasmosis on the behavior of its host) almost anxiously avoid new things[43]. After becoming infected by *Toxoplasma*, such rats have a greater tendency towards "novelty seeking." If I had to guess, I'd say that dopamine (and *Toxoplasma*) primarily lowers the individual's ability to recognize a novelty, to distinguish, for example, the novelty of a new toy. In species such as Norwegian rats, which normally avoid unfamiliar things, this leads to an increased factor of "novelty seeking;" whereas in species like mice and humans, which are naturally curious, it leads to a lowered tendency towards "novelty seeking." And so, my dear ethopharmocologists, I have a question for you to resolve: is the effect of dopamine on "novelty seeking" really the same in Norwegian rats as it is in mice?

XII. Why does *Toxoplasma* shift personality traits in opposite directions in men and women

From the very beginning of our Toxo human behavior studies, we were puzzled by the opposite shift in many psychological factors in men and women. Unfortunately, the reviewers of our manuscripts were very puzzled as well; and so this baffling observation often cost us a possible publication. Neither editors nor reviewers are fond of unexplained phenomena. It's fortunate that there are a great many scientific journals; so if an author is patient enough, he will eventually get his manuscript published (see Box 39 *How I outwitted unwelcoming editors and reviewers*).

One of our hypotheses to explain this phenomenon was based on the idea that *Toxoplasma* causes the same personality changes in men and women, but that one of the genders lies about these changes. They may be aware of their new, *Toxoplasma*-induced personality traits and be unhappy with them, or consider them to be inappropriate; so when filling out the questionnaire, they try to mask these changes. Unintentionally, they overdo their facade and the changes show up as the opposite of what they really are. For this reason, we were interested in monitoring these psychical changes in a more direct way; for example, by observing a person's behavior instead of determining it through a psychological questionnaire.

One experiment was practically begging to be enacted; it was also one of the first which we conducted on the students. We set a time to meet with the students (for testing or for taking a blood sample) and observed how promptly they arrived. We expected that people with a lower Superego strength (Cattell's factor G) would arrive later, whereas those with a higher Superego strength would arrive mostly on time, or even early. The results of the questionnaire survey had indicated that men had a weaker and women had a stronger superego. If one of the genders was lying, and *Toxoplasma* actually did have the same effect on the Superego strength of men and women, then infection should correlate with punctuality in the same way in both genders. In other words, both Toxo positive men and women should arrive more punctually or less punctually than Toxo negative men and women. The results of the behavioral experiment, however, corresponded with those of the questionnaire survey. *Toxoplasma* seemed to have an opposite effect on the Superego strength of men and women – men appeared to be less punctual, and women more.

Our other experiments[55] were more sophisticated and combined direct behavioral observation with questionnaire studies. When testing Superego strength, our questionnaire quizzed the students on their knowledge of various social norms. The logical assumption was that only people who know social norms can follow them. Students had to answer various questions, such as who should first enter a restaurant, a man or a woman; who should be first in going down the stairs; how you arrange the silverware for dessert; how you hold a spoon and fork when using both to eat; whether or not you should always remove your gloves when shaking hand, etc. In addition, we observed how long they were willing to spend on our questionnaire. We expected that people with a weaker superego would skip through a questionnaire that forced them to remember all sorts of details (see below), and end up finishing more quickly than people with a stronger superego, who are more conscientious. Furthermore, we observed how much care each person had given to their appearance. We wrote down the observations in a chart: how new and clean were the pants, skirt, sweater or shirt they were wearing; how well-kempt the person was; whether or not they wore accessories – rings, necklaces, brooches, etc. Without informing the test subjects ahead of time, we observed the expensiveness and cleanliness of their clothing, and finally the overall tidiness of a person's appearance (Box 59 *A blind and a double-blind experiment*).

Box 59 A blind and a double-blind experiment

It's clear that we couldn't inform the people we were observing for punctuality and appearance that we were doing so. Even knowing if they were Toxo positive or negative, could influence their behavior. Of course, under no circumstance could we let the students observing the test subjects knew which of the people was Toxo positive or negative. Judging the costliness and cleanliness of clothing already isn't a very objective matter, and if the observer knew which people were infected, he might also have a previous conception of their behavior. Therefore, the whole study had to be conducted as a double-blind experiment. We told the test subject whether they were Toxo positive or negative only after the study; and during the study, only one of the workers knew who was Toxo positive and negative – and this worker wasn't involved in observing the subjects. A **double-blind experiment**, in which neither the test subjects, nor those giving the test, know who is in the experiment and who in the control group, should be applied whenever possible. For example, when testing a new drug, it's clear than the test subject can't know who got the drug and who got the **placebo**, a pill which doesn't possess the active ingredients. Just the belief that one is being given medicine often has a positive effect on a person's health, even when the drug itself is ineffective. For this reason, people in the control group must get pills that look the same, but don't contain the tested drug. A number of studies also show that the doctor himself can influence the test subjects, if he knows which people are getting the drug versus the placebo. Hence an experiment must be set up so that nobody directly involved in the testing knows who is given what.

When testing sociability (warmth, extroversion, i.e., the analog of the Cattell's factor Affectothymia), which the questionnaire determined to be lower in infected men and higher in infected women, we asked questions like: how many parties you've been to lately; how many text messages you've sent over the past days; how much money you spend each week on phone calls. Then we tested whether they remember the names of various actors (we projected that actor's last name on the computer screen and had the test subject supply the first name). We ascertained whether they remembered the birthdays and name days of their close friends and family, and so on.

When measuring Suspiciousness (Vigilance), which the questionnaire had found to be higher in infected men and lower in infected women, we used a number of simple experiments, which were quite entertaining to come up with. For example, we asked the person to taste a liquid in a test tube, and observed whether or not the person would do so, or at least ask what was in the test tube or why he should drink it. Or we asked the test subject to sign a blank piece of paper, and then looked to see whether or not they complied; and if they did, whether they signed in an upper corner of the paper, so that nothing could be written above their signature, or if ingeniously wrote their name in the center. Just to evade possible prosecution, we showed the person that the paper was torn to pieces immediately after they signed it, so that they might not live out the rest of their lives worrying that we could somehow take advantage of their signature. Furthermore, we asked test subjects if we could photograph them, and noted how willing they were to agree. Similarly, we observed how willing they were to undergo anthropometric measurements. For the most complicated experiment, which we used to determine trustfulness, we had the test subject sit before a dusty ancient machine. We carefully set the dial to display 3000 volts, and asked the person to hold an enormous electrode in each hand, and, "when they were ready," to press the button on one of the electrodes. The electrodes, of course, weren't connected to a current. Even we were surprised at how many of our students followed our instructions without comment or complaint, and, hardly hesitating, pressed the red button.

From the above-mentioned questions and observations, we created factors analogous to those measured by Cattell's questionnaire. We measured a person's Conscientiousness, which should correspond to Superego strength (Rule consciousness, G); as well as an analog of Suspiciousness (Vigilance, L), and then an analog of Affectothymia (Warmth, A). These three were the Cattell's factors which most obviously shifted in opposite directions in men and women. Our results were unambiguous, and almost exactly matched the results of the earlier psychological questionnaire. Infected women were more open, sociable and warm-hearted in comparison with uninfected women, while infected men were more introverted and reserved than uninfected men. The results were similar in the case of the Rule consciousness (Superego strength). Here the differences were particularly obvious when observing how the test subject dressed. Toxo positive women came to the testing very tidied up, wearing newer and more expensive clothes, whereas Toxo positive men arrived in ripped up jeans and were less well-groomed – in comparison with both male and female uninfected peers (Fig. 30)[55]. In the case of Suspiciousness (Vigilance), the results were more complicated: the effect of toxoplasmosis on men and women depended on whether the person came from a village or a town.

Based on our results, we came to the conclusion that the differences we found between men and women, in regards to the effect of toxoplasmosis on the human psyche, are not due to one of the genders lying in the questionnaire. It appears that toxoplasmosis has a different effect on the actual behavior of men versus women.

Nevertheless, we weren't satisfied with these results, and tried to verify our surprising discovery that the two genders are often oppositely affected by latent toxoplasmosis, using the method of experimental games[56]. Experimental games are fairly recent, and used primarily in experimental economy, though can have other uses. Unfortunately, it later became apparent that they are but rarely used in psychology and ethology, so publishing our "a little bit" unusual results obtained through such an unusual method proved to be a near superhuman effort. At first, our study used two games – Dictator and Trust games.

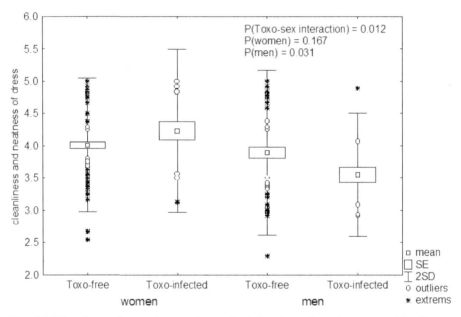

Fig. 30 The effect of toxoplasmosis on the behavior of students; specifically, on how much care they put into their appearance. The cleanliness and neatness of dress was estimated on a 7-point scale by female graduate student. She had no knowledge about the infection status of the test subjects; not even the test subjects knew this at the time. The graph demonstrates that infected female students were more neatly dressed than uninfected females. In contrast, infected male students took less care about their appearance than uninfected males. The difference in Toxoplasma's effect on each gender was statistically significant; the effect of toxoplasmosis was stronger in male than in female students.

For the Dictator game, we set 12 students in front of 12 computers so that the students couldn't see each other. We even had the first six students come fifteen minutes early, so we could have them sit at computer tables placed behind a screen which divided the room in half. The remaining six students sat on the other side of the screen, opposite the first six. A student on one side of the screen always played a student on the opposite side of the screen; in this way, each player couldn't see who his opponent was. Furthermore, people on the same side of the screen were given privacy by testing dividers, so that neighbors couldn't see each other's computer screens.

The students were told that the computer would divide them into pairs of "donor and recipient," that they'd participate in several rounds and be paired up with a different opponent each round. Each round, the proposer was given "an endowment" of 50 cents and was free to give how much he wished to give to the recipient. Nice donors would divide the sum equally with the recipients, but the mean ones often kept every cent. The roles of donors and recipients switched in every round, but the pairs were different. Of course, it was real money, and the students were allowed to keep it at the end of the game as a reward for their participation.

As often happens in this sort of game, it started out with the donors giving the recipients a fairly large amount of the money, but as the game progressed, they grew less and less generous. In the last round, most of the donors gave their recipients nothing, or the smallest sum possible, 5 cents (though this was probably more out of spite than any sort of sympathy). There were 12 rounds, so each player was a donor six times and a receiver six times. We expected that the Toxo positive woman donors would give their recipients more money, and that Toxo positive man-donors would give their recipients less money, than the Toxo negative men and women.

The second game, the Trust game, was a bit more complicated. The basic set-up was the same, but this time the computer formed pairs of proposer and responder. The game began with the proposer getting 50 cents, and he could choose how much of this money to give to his partner. The money given to the responder was tripled by the computer, and then the responder could choose how much of his money to give back to the proposer he was paired with. Let's say that the proposer gave the responder all 50 cents. The responder would then end up with $1.50, and could choose how much (if any) to give back to the proposer. There were also 12 rounds, and the players were paired up differently each time. In the Trust game, we observed how much the proposer invested, and with how much of the tripled money the responder would reward the proposer. Once again, we expected that Toxo positive men would give away less of the money and that Toxo positive women would give away more of the money than the Toxo negative controls.

At first, the results of both games were a bit surprising. It turned out that in the Dictator game, toxoplasmosis lowered the sum of money which both man- and woman-donors gave to their recipients. In contrast, in Trust game, infected woman-responders gave the proposers more money, whereas infected man-responders gave away less of their money. There was no difference between the amount of money that Toxo positive and negative proposers gave to the responders. In the end, we managed to formulate a reasonable explanation for these results – but little wonder, since we scientists are well-trained to find logical explanations for unexpected results. Our hypothesis is that latent toxoplasmosis introduces a mild, but constant stress factor[55]. It's known that stress causes men decrease their social interaction, whereas stressed woman seek support in their social surroundings, becoming more sociable. During the Dictator game, social interaction didn't play a great role in the relationship between donor and recipient. Players got to alternate between the part of donor and recipient, so there is no reason to think that highly sociable people would have given their recipients more money than unsociable people.

On the other hand, social interaction played a substantial role in how much money the responder gave back to the proposer in the Trust game. By investing his money, the proposer gives the responder his trust, and so one might expect that more sociable responders would be less liable to break this trust. So if our stress hypothesis is true, Toxo positive men and women playing the Trust game should have a tendency to give proposers less money. The stress hypothesis, proposed by Jitka Lindová, corresponds with our results. This of course, is unsurprising, since the hypothesis was suggested after the study, in an attempt to explain the unexpected results. In our defense, we have followed up with unrelated experiments to test the stress hypothesis, by measuring the levels of stress hormones and by using our favorite questionnaire method. That, however, is for another chapter.

Later we used experimental games to observe the effect of toxoplasmosis on the altruism of a student. Altruism is behavior which helps one's surroundings at the cost of the individual. Altruism has been observed not only in humans, but in a number of other species. The advantage of some forms of altruism was obvious, but other forms long resisted explanation. For example, reciprocal altruism is clearly in the interest of the individual. When North American vampire bats (of the genus *Desmodus*, which subsist from the blood of mammals or birds) return from a successful hunt, they regurgitate some of the blood for the less fortunate members of the bat colony. The next time these bats have an unlucky hunt and return hungry, the successful members of the colony will help them out in return. It's not true altruism, because bats can distinguish between each member of their colony, so a bat that didn't share what he acquired from successful hunts wouldn't get any help from other bats. Three consecutive unlucky hunts are enough for a bat to starve to death. It's also easy to explain altruism in regards to offspring, siblings or other relatives. When the genes for altruism cause the individual to help his relatives, which most likely also possess copies of these genes, it increases their chances of spreading to the next generation. So this also is not true altruism, because each gene has "calculated" (or rather natural selection has found) that it pays off when its individual sacrifices a little for the survival of other copies of the gene in that individual's relatives.

But in some cases an organism helps individuals that are not his relatives, and which can't be expected to someday return the favor. Evolutionary biologists have long known that the existence of this form of altruism is an evolutionary mystery. It's clear that a population with many such altruists is better off than one without them; the first type of population flourishes at the expense of those with few altruists. But it's also clear that selfish individuals have an advantage in the first type of population, for they are helped by the many altruists without having to compromise their own biological fitness in order to help others. In a population with altruists, the selfish individuals should reproduce the most and eventually push out the altruists. Over time, theoretical biologists have shown that there exist conditions under which natural selection for the benefit of the community prevails over selection for the welfare of the individual. Under such conditions, genes for altruism can prevail (Box 60 *When does altruism prevail over selfishness?*).

Box 60 When does altruism prevail over selfishness?

Altruists can triumph over selfish individuals primarily when the species consists of a large numbers of small populations, which constantly pass in and out of existence. The new populations must form from small groups of individuals which come from various populations. Ideally, the new populations form from individual migrants which left their original population. Populations with a lot of altruists prosper, and produce more migrants than populations which wither due to a lack of altruists. The populations dying out due to a lack of altruists produce fewer migrants that could start up their own population or join another population – in other words, highly selfish populations are less likely to produce migrants that could spread the selfish gene. When a selfish individual appears in a population of altruists, he begins to reproduce rapidly. But as his offspring start to spread throughout the population, the population will deteriorate. There is a less of chance of altruists existing in a species made up of just a few populations, with a new population forming only when an old populations splits about evenly in two.

For a long time, it was thought that conditions under which altruists could proliferate were rather rare. Recently, a relatively small but international, interdisciplinary scientific team (made up of myself and Tomáš Kulich of Comenius University in Bratislava, Slovakia), found that in sexually reproducing species the conditions are more advantageous for the spread of altruists than it seems at first glance[57]. Our model comes from the theory of frozen plasticity (see Box 35 *How I refuted Darwin*) and presumes that a particular trait – in this case, altruism – depends on multiple genes. Previous models were set up rather unrealistically, as though altruism depended on only one gene. Assuming that altruism depends on several genes, a family of altruists may give birth to a selfish individual, and vice versa. In this scenario, the survival of altruists isn't constantly penalized – if altruists gave birth to only altruists, their offspring would survive and reproduce less than the selfish individuals, and their genes would eventually die out. Altruists appear in a population seemingly randomly, at a frequency which maintains a constant number of altruists in that particular population. The populations of a species can compete amongst each other, as to which population has more altruistic genes; while the individuals within a population don't need to compete based on who is more selfish and thus more likely to reproduce, because neither altruism nor selfishness is particularly heritable.

Experimental games are useful for studying altruism – we, for example, used two such games, called *Public goods* and *Public goods with punishment*. Public goods is a simpler game. 12 students sit at separate computers so that they can't see each other. Each person is given a dollar, and is free to contribute how much he wishes to the public pool. The rest he keeps. The total sum of these "public goods" is doubled and equally distributed among the 12 players, regardless of how much each person contributed. It is most advantageous for the group when everyone contributes all their money to the public pool – if each person contributes their dollar, then everyone will get 2 dollars back. But for the individual player, it is most advantageous when everyone but him contributes all their money. The 11 dollars in the group pool will be doubled to make 22 dollars. At the end of the round each person will get a twelfth of the 22 dollars, a total of about $1.83, except for the person who didn't contribute. He'll get $1.83, plus the 1 dollar which he kept – a tidy sum of $2.83.

Our students behaved rather typically. In the first round they put a fairly large amount in the group pool, but very quickly they realized that altruism – and primarily, a belief in the altruism of others – isn't very advantageous in today's cruel world. So the average contribution to the group pool plummeted over the course of six rounds. The amount contributed in the Public goods game reflects each player's belief in the altruism of others, rather than the extent of their own altruism. On the other hand, Public goods game with punishment better reveals the altruism of the individual. This game begins the same as Public goods game. But after the players finish contributing to the group pool, each person's contribution is made public (of course their real name isn't made public; rather, they are identified by numbers, which change every round). And now things get interesting.

Players can buy the right to punish another player – which means that the person who takes it upon himself to punish someone sacrifices a substantial amount of money. So if one player skimps on his donation to the public pool, he may pay for it twice over; if he is punished then he loses all the money which he withheld in that round. Giving the punishment is altruistic act. The person doling out the punishment must pay for his right to punish, and the possible benefit that comes from disciplining the penny-pincher applies equally to the rest of the players (which didn't have to pay for it). Once again, our students behaved rather typically. They frequently, altruistically punished selfish players. As result, people contributed more money to the public pool than in the simpler game Public goods (without punishment), and their contribution remained consistent throughout.

So what did our experiments show? What is the effect of latent toxoplasmosis on the altruism of our students? Once more we saw differences between men and women. In the Public goods game, which threatened no punishment, toxoplasmosis had no effect on the amount of money put by men or women in the public pool. But in the game with punishment, Toxo positive men contributed significantly more in the 2nd through 4th rounds, and punished more in the 1st through 3rd rounds than did Toxo negative men. Toxo positive women, on the other hand, contributed less and punished more than did Toxo negative women in all the rounds – the differences, however, were not significant. As could be expected, contributions to the public pool decreased over the course of the

Public goods game (men went from 70 cents in the first round to 20 in the last, whereas women went from 60 cents to 15 on average). In contrast, contributions stayed fairly high in the game with punishment available (the contributions of men stayed around 70 cents, whereas those of women even increased from 55 to 65).

We used these two games over the course of about five years. For one, the students liked them. If you're going participate in a test, why not earn a couple of dollars? These games helped us attract more students to our experiments. But the main reason we continued using these tests, was that the results led us to a number of interesting phenomena, quite unrelated to toxoplasmosis. These included **Justine's effect** and the existence of perverse punishers[58]. **Perverse punishers** among our undergrad students? Great heavens! (Box 61 *How we discovered perverse punishers among our students*.)

Box 61 How we discovered perverse punishers among our students

During the experimental games, it was important that we always had 12 players. Several times it happened that one of the students didn't show up, and even that the alternate didn't come. When this happened, we had to use one of our people to act as the missing student; he had to follow a scenario which we had prepared ahead of time. The scenario told him how to behave in each round (how much money to give to his partner, or put in the public pool). One time our head statistician Aleš Kuběna acted as the missing student, and he noticed an interesting phenomenon: twice he was punished when had contributed the maximum amount of money, 1 dollar, to the public pool. After further examination, we verified that this wasn't a chance occurrence, but happened in almost every game. In a group of 12 students, there were almost always two or three "**perverse punishers**," who were stupid or vindictive enough, that they didn't hesitate to use their money to punish the most altruistic of the players. When we studied up on this phenomenon, we soon found that it is not specific to the students of the Prague Faculty of Science. It was noted, though not particularly elaborated on, by other researchers as well. If we consider the popularity of common saying, "no good deed goes unpunished," we can see that people have long understood this phenomenon's existence. Before we could finish, evaluate and publish our study, we found that other studies, which focused particularly on the existence of perverse punishers, had been published in the meantime. One of these studies showed that the prevalence of perverse punishers correlated negatively with the development of the civil society in a given country. It reported that the fewest perverse punishers occurred in Australia and Scandinavia, whereas the most were found in Oman and Post-Soviet Republics[59]. Thankfully, the Czech Republic was not represented in the study. Fortunately, most of these published studies used about four players in their experimental games, so it was difficult to determine who was the primary target of the perverse punisher. Our experiments involved 12 players, so we could organize the results of each round according to how much each player contributed to the public pool, and then look at who was most likely to be the target of punishment. We found, of course, that the people who contributed least to the public pool were most likely to be punished. The more that a player contributed to the pool, the smaller his chance of being punished. People least likely to be punished contributed about the fifth largest sum of money (out of 12 people). But players that contributed more than this started to have an increased probability of being punished – so the greatest altruists, that contributed the most to the bank, had a relatively high risk of being targeted. We named this phenomenon **Justine's effect**[58], after the altruistic heroine of Marquis de Sade's novel *Justine*, who is the victim of constant attacks of fate and her surroundings. The effect describes this: the further a person strays from the expected, or slightly above average, level of altruism – the closer they get towards maximum altruism, the more likely they are to summon the wrath of a perverse punisher. I think that the author of the above-mentioned saying about the punishment of good deeds, as well as the fictional Justine (had she not been struck down by lightning at the end of the book) would be touched by our findings.

XIII. How *Toxoplasma* changes the appearance of its human host

As I mentioned, one way we measured suspiciousness with behavioral tests was by asking the test subjects if we could take an anthropometric measurement. We then observed, how willing the person was to agree, and how cooperative they were during the measurement.

A side-product of this test was that we were left with detailed anthropometric data for about 500 students. With each student we measured about 30 body parameters, including earlobe height and width, wrist width and head circumference. With this data available, we decided to see if Toxo positives and negatives differed in any of these measurements. We were primarily interested the so-called **fluctuating asymmetry** of Toxo positive humans. It's commonly known that humans aren't perfectly symmetrical; they may have a wider left or right wrist, or a longer left or right palm. The direction of the asymmetry differs among individuals, and even from organ to organ – sometimes the left side is larger, sometimes the right. This is why the asymmetry is termed as fluctuating.

In addition, a number of organisms exhibit **directional asymmetry**, which means that most of the members of a given species have one side of the body more developed. It is thought that the level of fluctuating asymmetry reflects the quality of an individual's development – individuals that were exposed to more disruptive effects during their individual development, whether as the result of a mutation, an unfavorable gene combination from their parents or harmful environmental effects, turn out asymmetrical. Many scientists believe that females, including human females, choose the more symmetrical male during courtship, because his symmetry indicates a more likely favorable gene combination. Because many of our test subjects were infected as children, long before they finished development, we hypothesized that infected individuals would exhibit higher fluctuating asymmetry than those who were uninfected.

As always, our lovely *Toxoplasma* had a surprise in store. It turned out that Toxo positives and negatives exhibited minimal differences in fluctuating asymmetry, but significant differences in specific anthropometric measurements. If there was any asymmetry, then it was likely directional – in several anthropometric measurements, all the Toxo positives were asymmetrical to same side. Toxo positives had a wider forehead, a wider left ear, wider and longer palms, longer fingers on both hands and wider ankles. The most obvious difference that we noted in men had to do with body height – Toxo positive men were an average 3 cm taller than Toxo negatives[60].

Another difference that stood out was the length ratio of the pointer and ring fingers on the left hand. This was interesting, because scientists think that the ratio correlates negatively with the concentration of testosterone which the embryo is exposed to during intrauterine development. Men usually have a shorter pointer than ring finger, which means that the length ratio of the 2nd to 4th finger is less than one. In women, this difference isn't as distinct – they often even have a longer pointer than ring finger, so the ratio is greater than one (Fig. 31). For each gender, the ratio correlates with a number of characteristics – in men, with sexual orientation, and mathematical and musical talent; in women, with things like fertility (Box 73 *Do homosexuals have a longer pointer than ring finger?*).

Whenever I mention this anatomical characteristic during a lecture, I might as well excuse myself from the podium, because the majority of the audience begins examining their fingers. Maybe they're not sure about their gender identity or sexual orientation, and think that the ratio of finger length can serve as guidance. Another possibility is that they want to make sure that the speaker isn't spouting nonsense (as is often our tendency).

The length ratio of the 2nd and 4th fingers is also a matter of interest for evolutionary psychologists. Curiously enough, while a stronger correlation is generally observed between the above-mentioned characteristics and the length ratio of the fingers on the right hand; there is a stronger correlation between *Toxoplasma*-infection and the length ratio of the fingers on the left hand. In women, the effect of toxoplasmosis on this ratio was also evident, but not statistically significant.

Later, we verified that the concentration of testosterone in saliva correlates better with the ratio of the fingers on the left hand than the right. I'd say that the right hand seems to reflect the traits we were born with (the concentration of testosterone that were exposed to as a developing embryo), whereas the left reveals how we were affected in later life (by things such toxoplasmosis). But since something similar is already expressed by palm-readers, and we scientists put no stock in superstition, I wouldn't say (or even write!) this under duress.

In the conclusion of our published article, we simply stated that when studying the relation of psychological characteristics to the length ratio of the fingers on the left hand, it is important to statistically filter out the effects of *Toxoplasma* infection and testosterone concentration – these confounding factors could have a strong effect on the digit ratio for the left but not the right hand, and, if not controlled properly, might obscure any existing relationship of the digit ratio with the studied factors[60].

Everyone must admit that such a statement is substantially different from supporting fortune-telling superstition; at least, written this way, it sounds much more scientific. In any case, I suspect that most palm-readers don't read the *American Journal of Physical Anthropology* too often.

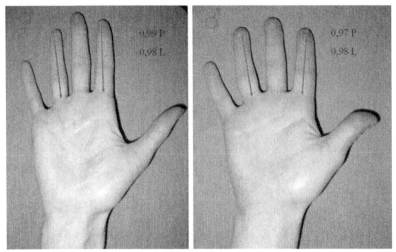

Fig. 31 The length ratio of the pointer and ring fingers. A typical woman hand (left) has a greater pointer to ring finger ratio than does the hand of a typical man (right). This means that her pointer finger is longer than a man's is in comparison to the ring finger. The length ratio on the right and left hand for our female students was 0.986 and 0.981, respectively, and 0.972 and 0.979 for the male students. The difference between the genders is more apparent on the right hand, which corresponds with other reports. Interestingly, a similar difference between Toxoplasma-*infected and uninfected people was more prominent on the left hand.*

Since we've already digressed to denying superstition: my colleague Lukáš Kratochvíl and I also refuted one interesting belief regarding the length ratio of the pointer and ring fingers. This belief was the central postulate of people studying this field; it was the belief that an individual's gender (as well as most of other characteristics) influences that length ratio. True, this ratio is lower in men than in women, but our results clearly showed that this is only because men usually have larger hands. As the size of the hand increases, the length of the ring finger increases at a greater rate than does that of the pointer. If we made pairs, each of a man and woman with hands of the same size, we'd see no difference in the length ratio of the 2nd and 4th fingers. So it is more correct to say that characteristics like musical talent, homosexuality and fertility, correlate with the length of the hand, rather than the length ratio of the 2nd and 4th fingers[61]. The difference, of course, is substantial.

It's rather difficult to imagine how the concentration of testosterone would specifically affect the length of the 2nd versus the length of the 4th finger. It's less surprising that the level of testosterone would affect general growth of the hand and fingers (Box 62 *Troubles with ratios*).

Testosterone affects anatomical growth in two ways, and its effect on body height and shape depends on the developmental phase in which the individual is exposed to greater levels of the hormone. On one hand, testosterone speeds up longitudinal bone growth; but on the other hand, it causes precocious puberty, and hence a premature closure of the epiphyseal plates.

Box 62 Troubles with ratios

The size of individual body parts is often measured in relative terms rather than absolute values – for example, as a ratio to body size. An average size nose in a small face appears large, whereas the same nose in a big face appears small; 180 lbs is overweight for 5 ft tall person, but underweight for nearly 7 ft beanpole. It is generally convenient and quite common to express body measurements relatively, as ratios. For example, the length of the 2nd finger as a length ratio of the 2nd to 4th finger; the width of the shoulders as a ratio to the width of the waist; weight looked at as body mass divided by the square of height, etc. The problem with this system is that individual parts of the body change at a different rate, and beginning from a different baseline, with overall body size and age. Scientifically, they grow

allometrically – each with a different slope and constant. The existence of allometry has substantial ramifications for the results of studies on relative values, and should be (though it often isn't) taken into account when selecting a method to evaluate such data. In 2009, Lukáš Kratochvíl and I published an article in the journal *Biology Letters*[61], showing that when, instead of using the thus far accepted method of comparing the finger length ratio in men and women, one takes a more correct approach (comparing the length of the 2nd while filtering out the length of the 4th finger using the GLM), the difference between genders disappears. So the differences that have been described between the genders in the ratios of finger length are due to the fact that women usually have smaller hands than men. Scientists that have spent years studying the length ratio of the 2nd and 4th fingers and published hundreds of papers in this field over the past ten years were certainly not happy to hear of our discovery. I'm interested to see the reaction our next article will elicit; it discusses a similar problem regarding relative values used for years in anthropological and evolutionary psychological research (BMI, WHI, etc.). Our data, for example, show that the male visitors of the Prague city library tend to be more obese than the female visitors – but this is only when we compare the genders using the accepted BMI index (body mass index), which is the ratio of body mass to the square of height. When we use a more correct method, which compares body mass after filtering out the effect of body height (using the GLM or ANCOVA method), we no longer see differences between men and women in obesity prevalence (Fig. 32).

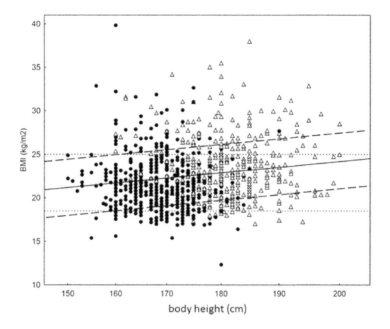

Fig. 32 Mismeasuring overweight vs. underweight. Usually nutritional status is determined by the body mass index (BMI). BMI is a ratio of weight (kg) to the square of height (cm) multiplied by 10,000. If we will plot BMI versus height, it is obvious that the two variables have a positive correlation. Therefore, some tall people can be incorrectly categorized by the BMI as overweight, and some short people as underweight, even when their nutritional status is within normal range. In our experimental group of a thousand visitors of the Municipal library (circles: women, triangles: men), 40 people were incorrectly identified as overweight and 68 as underweight (they were outside the area marked off by the horizontal dotted lines, but still within the range designated by the inclined dashed lines). This demonstrates that the BMI is not the best estimate of nutritional status.

Our data show that Toxo positive male students experience raised levels of testosterone (as shown in the next chapter). The effects of the hormone on body height, as well as the length the 2nd vs. the 4th digit of the hand, probably depend on when the man was infected. In the Czech population, men are often infected in their preschool years, long before the closure of the epiphyseal plates, so they experience increased body growth. It's likely that in countries where infection occurs even earlier, or significantly later, the effect of toxoplasmosis on the body height of men is different, maybe even opposite.

XIV. Cherchez la testostérone!

When we discovered that Toxo positive and negative men differ in the length ratio of their fingers, as well as body height, we immediately considered the possibility that the relative differences in psyche and morphology could be caused by a change in testosterone levels. Testosterone levels are known to have a significant effect on a number of human characteristics, ranging from behavior to anatomical proportions. One of these characteristics is the masculinity of an individual's appearance. Because we had many photographs of students as a by-product of our tests for Suspiciousness (Vigilance), we had material on which to test our hypothesis on that there were higher testosterone levels in Toxo positive men. We had the female students of another college, who didn't know our students, evaluate the level of masculinity and dominance of the men on the photographs, based on an eight-point scale. From these evaluations, we calculated an average value of visually-determined masculinity and dominance for each student. True to our hypothesis, it turned out that Toxo positive men appear significantly more masculine and dominant to female evaluators than do Toxo negative men. But after conducting the same (reciprocal) test with the photographs of the female students, we found that male evaluators didn't see any appreciable difference in femininity and dominance between Toxo positive and negative women[62].

We wanted to show the readers of our article the differences in appearance between toxoplasma positive and negative men, without making public the photographs of our students. To this end, we used composition photography, a technique invented by Darwin's cousin, Francis Galton. To see what the typical criminal looked like (something that would be near-impossible today, for reasons of political correctness), he exposed a number of individual photographs of criminals on photographic plate, creating a single composite portrait. Today the techniques for composite photography are a bit more sophisticated.

First each photograph is marked with dozens of reference points on the computer screen, and then a special program projects the individual portraits over each other, so that the reference projects the individual portraits over each other, so that the reference points match up as best as possible. The result is a single photograph of the "average person," in which individual features disappear, whereas facial characteristics representative of the group remain visible.

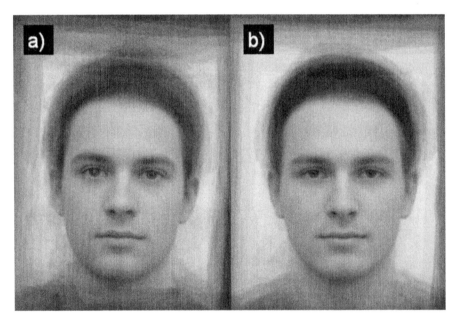

Fig. 33 Differences in the facial features of Toxo negative and positive students. Composite photographs from 22 pictures each of (a) Toxo negative students and (b) Toxo positive. Toxo positive men on individual pictures were evaluated by female students as more dominant and masculine than uninfected men; these characteristics are also apparent on the composite photographs.

So if we take 30 photographs of individual students, randomly divide them into two groups and make a composite photograph of each, we should end up with two very similar composite portraits. Considering the very racially homogenous population of the Czech Republic, 15 photographs would suffice for the individual facial features to cancel each other. To make composites of our students' photographs, we separated them according to gender and presence of *Toxoplasma* infection. Hence we created four composite photographs: the "average" Toxo positive man, Toxo positive woman, Toxo negative man and Toxo negative woman. To ensure that the possible differences in the composite photographs weren't coincidental, we used 22 instead of 15 student portraits (that was the maximum number we had available for Toxo positive male students). The resulting composite photographs of the men can be seen in Fig. 33. The composite photographs of the Toxo positive and negative women are almost identical (not shown). In contrast, the composite face of the Toxo positive male students look more dominant and masculine than that of the Toxo negative male students[62]. Just curious tidbit: the evaluators also agreed that the "average" Toxo positive man looks older. In reality, the Toxo positive male students who made up the composite photograph were, on average, almost a year younger than the Toxo negatives (Box 63 *How to compare photographs using a one-sample test – do we like self-similar faces?*)

Just as an aside, since we already had a program set up for evaluating characteristics from photographs, along with the data from the Cattell's questionnaire's, we decided to see if our evaluators would be able to guess some of the characteristics of the students, based only on the photographs of these students. We had already determined the students' characteristics using the psychological questionnaire. In her study, Anna Kotrčová-Rubešová discovered that women in particular are pretty spot-on in their guesses. Their guesses regarding the Cattell's factors of Warmth (A), Liveliness (F) and Social boldness (H) correlate strongly with the factors determined with Cattell's questionnaire. Men were not as talented in this discipline, but nevertheless managed to guess some characteristics of the photographed people surprisingly well. We must also realize that the evaluators had only a single photograph of that person's face (with the hair edited out) to work with; furthermore, the photographed people had been instructed to pose with a neutral expression. In normal, everyday life, a person gets much more information with which to evaluate others – and so it's likely that they are also more successful in this endeavor. As Věra Pivoňková proved later on, women were even more successful in guessing psychological traits when they were given composite photographs consisting of several people that achieved an extreme score for a given factor (a very high or low value).

Box 63 How to compare photographs using a one-sample test – do we like self-similar faces?

There are two ways to determine whether photographs of Toxo negative or photographs of Toxo positive people appear more attractive to evaluators. Either we can show the photographs individually one after another, and have the person evaluate each for a certain characteristic on a scale of 1 to 8. Or we can always project a pair of photographs, one Toxo positive and the other Toxo negative, and have the evaluator choose which he thinks is stronger in the given characteristic (such as more dominant or attractive), and maybe even decide by how much. For example, in one of our studies[63] Jitka Lindová looked at how attractive people found faces that were similar or dissimilar to their own. First we prepared a set of 15 **composite photographs**, each constructed from three photographs of various English students. Because each composite photograph averages the features of only three students, each composite face was fairly distinct. The photographs, however, were not of any particular students – so that our evaluators wouldn't recognize them. The thus created 15 composite photographs were then tailored to each evaluator we invited to take the test. Using a special program, we either added the features of the evaluator or subtracted them from the composite photograph. So when the evaluator (a student, whose photograph we had obtained from our earlier suspiciousness test) logged on to the website under his designated username, he was successively shown 15 pairs of photographs. Each pair of photographs was very similar, but one resembled the evaluator more, whereas the other did not (Fig. 34). The differences were very subtle; none of the evaluators noticed that half of the 30 total photographs somewhat resembled their own face. For each pair of photographs, the evaluator was to decide on a scale of 1 to 8, whether he found the face on the right or left more attractive. (1: left is very clearly more attractive, 2: left is clearly more attractive, 3: left is a little more attractive, 4: left is barely more attractive, 5: right is barely more attractive, 6: right is a little more attractive, 7: right is clearly more attractive face, 8: right is very clearly more attractive). To avoid introducing a systematic error, we alternated the placement of the similar and dissimilar face as projected on the left or right side. (We simultaneously alternated the polarity of the scale, so that strong preference of the self-similar face was always indicated by 8 points, regardless of its position on the screen). Furthermore, each evaluator saw his or her 15 pairs of composite photographs in a different order.

If the evaluators were not influenced by the similarity or dissimilarity of each face to their own, then their average evaluation should lie between a 4 and a 5. In reality, it wasn't so. Women, for example, preferred similar or dissimilar faces based on whether or not they were in the fertile phase of their menstrual cycle. It took us about ten years before we succeeded to publish the results of this study[63] – two times since it was finished, Jitka Lindová happened to be very attracted to her husband during the fertile phase of her menstrual cycle. The statistical test that we used to analyze the study is classified as a **one-sample test**. It compares the calculated value of a random sample, which is subject to random error, with the theoretical value (in this case, 4.5), which is not subject to random error. A one-sample test is considerably stronger (more sensitive) than a **two-sample test**, which compares two values computed from two random samples (whose values are subject to random error). Usually they are the average value of the dependent variable from the experimental group and the control group.

Of course, it's a question whether the physiognomy of the human gradually changes to match his personality, or whether the human learns to behave and think to match what his environment expects from him based on his appearance (Box 64 *Are brown-eyed men more dominant than the blue-eyed, and is it because of their eyes?*). When perusing the panopticon of our leading politicians, I sometimes wonder if a person who looks like a bastard at first glance, might be a bastard in real life. It's probably not politically correct, but what if there was something to it?

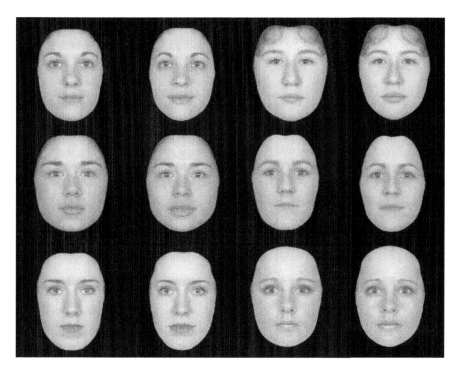

Fig. 34 Use of composite photography and a morphing technique to determine preferences for self-similar persons. Each pair of pictures was created through computer modification (morphing technique) from one original composite. In each pair of composite photographs, the picture on the right was made more similar to the features of the evaluator, and the picture on the left less similar – by adding or subtracting, respectively, the characteristics features of the evaluator from face on the composite photograph. The original composite pictures were formed from three (in each case different) photographs of students from England. The evaluator was to determine which of the two faces in his pair is more attractive. Among female evaluators, the preference for self-similar faces changed over their menstrual cycle.

Box 64 Are brown-eyed men more dominant than the blue-eyed, and is it because of their eyes?

The answer is yes and no. As I wrote earlier, Karl Kleisner and I studied the human eye as a possible organ for communication. The color of the iris is prominent in the human eye, especially in contrast with the very visible white sclera. In most mammals, eyes are not this prominent, so it is possible that in humans they developed the secondary function of communication – that through them, man conveys information to his surroundings. For example, the movement of the eye made visible by the white sclera can reveal precisely where a person is looking, so that a woman wearing a low-cut top on the subway can see, out of the corner of her eye, if the gaze of the man sitting across from her has finally wandered to where she, as well as the designer of the shirt, intended. But it is possible that eye-color could also reveal certain information. When we had evaluators (primarily female students) decide the dominance of brown- and blue-eyed students based on their photographs, we found that on a seven-point scale the brown-eyed students were seen as more dominant (Fig. 35). For the control, we used a computer program to switch the eye colors – that is, we gave the blue-eyed photographs brown eyes, and the brown-eyed photographs blue eyes. And then we repeated the experiment with a different group of evaluators. And you wouldn't believe what happened! Nothing whatsoever. The originally brown-eyed men were still evaluated as dominant, even though we changed their photographs to show blue eyes. This must mean that the women didn't evaluate dominance based on eye-color, but facial features; brown eyes happened to be set in a "more dominant face." The most likely explanation we have so far come up with, is something that we called the "**social feedback loop hypothesis**"[64]. (Remember, it's not important who first proposes the hypothesis, or who explains it the best, but rather who comes up with a name that sticks.) According to this hypothesis, all children are born blue-eyed but some of them later develop brown eyes (in the Czech Republic, about half of children). If a boy is blue-eyed, then he is treated as a child for a longer period of time. This leaves an impact not only on his behavior, but also on his usual facial expressions, which over time is inscribed into his facial features. Blue-eyed boys (at least in our current central-European population) start off with a greater probability of looking submissive, as opposed to brown-eyed boys, who start off more likely to seem dominant, all because their environment expects it of them.

We decided to test our hypothesis about higher testosterone levels in Toxo positives using direct biochemical methods as well. In another series of ethological experiments, we took samples of saliva from students and used radioimmunoassay to determine the concentration of the testosterone. It turned out that Toxo positive men really do have significantly higher testosterone levels. That was expected.

But what surprised us was that Toxo positive women had a significantly lower concentration of testosterone[65]. The fact that the same factor – in this case, infection by a parasitic protozoan – can raise testosterone levels in men while lowering them in women, is pretty strange. On the other hand, this fits with the results of our previous studies, which showed that toxoplasmosis causes an opposite shift in men versus women for a number of factors. Originally we tried to find a psychological explanation for this phenomenon, and nature unexpectedly presented us with not one but two – a psychological and an endocrinological explanation. It's clear that a number of psychological factors, including the Superego strength (factor G), could correlate with the level of testosterone. If toxoplasmosis raises testosterone levels in men but lowers them in women, it's logical that psychological factors related to testosterone concentration would also shift in opposite directions. The actual mechanism which *Toxoplasma* uses to influence testosterone levels is still unknown. Increased testosterone levels in Toxo positive men could be explained by the fact that dopamine production correlates with testosterone production. Humans and lab animals with high levels of dopamine in the brain are also known to have high testosterone levels. This phenomenon, however, does not explain why infected women, who also exhibit higher dopamine levels, have lower testosterone levels.

We repeated the same study with a different group, a fairly large group of patients from an immunological clinic who were primarily treated for allergies and immunodeficiencies. With this group, we were unable to prove a relationship between toxoplasmosis and the level of testosterone (or estradiol or cortisol). What was interesting, however, was that the level of testosterone in men increased with time after infection (this time was estimated based on the decrease of specific *Toxoplasma* antibodies). It's apparent that this group experienced the sieve effect, which could have impacted our results. In the Czech Republic, toxoplasmosis is about equally prevalent in men and women. But in our group of 312 women and 228 men, toxoplasmosis occurred in 24% of the women (which is close to the normal value) but only in 10.9% of the men (ridiculously below average)[66]. As I explain in a later chapter, *Toxoplasma* significantly influences the immune system of both men and women.

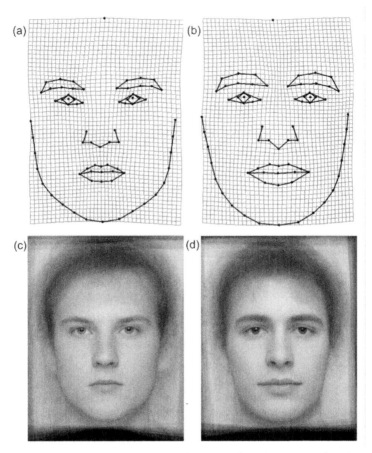

Fig. 35 Differences in the face shape of blue-eyed vs. brown-eyed male students. The bottom two pictures are composite photographs of the average blue-eyed (left) and average brown-eyed (right) student of the Faculty of Science. The top two pictures have the typical characteristics from the bottom composites (the differences between the left and right figure) enhanced by computer. Based on these morphological features, student evaluators ranked individual photographs of originally brown-eyed students as more dominant than those of originally blue eyed students, even after we used a computer program to change the eye-color from brown to blue or vice versa. Regardless of eye-color, female evaluators perceived originally brown-eyed students more dominant. These results are surprising since eye color depends more or less on one gene, so in each generation brown eyes should "move from" one face to another, and not be connected to a certain type of face.

Whereas Toxo positive women show signs of a more active immune system, Toxo positive men show certain signs of immunosuppression. It's possible that Toxo positive men are protected against allergy, so we find very few of them among the patients of an immunological clinic. It's even possible that the immunosuppression in Toxo positive men is caused by the increased testosterone levels. The 14 Toxo positive men that made it into our group may have had a deficiency in testosterone production, so even *Toxoplasma* couldn't save them from allergies. That would explain why we were unable to find higher testosterone levels in the infected men of this group, even though their testosterone levels increased with time after infection. Of course this is only a hypothesis, which needs to be verified in the future (Box 65 *How are hypotheses tested in science?*).

Box 65 How are hypotheses tested in science?

It's difficult, but maybe that's why we scientists enjoy it. In general, we have to comply with a rule explicitly described only in the first half of the 20th century by Sir **Karl Raimund Popper**: In science, hypotheses cannot be proven – only refuted. We consider a hypothesis to be (conditionally) true, when it has survived a sufficiently long onslaught of sufficiently intensive attempts to refute it. The word conditionally, included in parentheses, is immensely important. Scientists, and also the public, should accept that a scientific "fact," hypothesis or theory, even one which has rarely been doubted and is commonly thought to be "safely proven," can at any time be refuted. It doesn't matter how many times our experiments confirm a certain hypothesis; how many times the results of our empirical studies agree with the expectations that come from our hypothesis. The same results can agree with other hypotheses that we haven't yet thought of – and so hypotheses that we haven't tested. But if our empirical studies give us a result which disagrees with our hypothesis, we should rightfully be excited, because we succeeded in refuting the given hypothesis. Of course, if the refuted hypothesis is our own, the enthusiasm usually isn't completely sincere. But a scientist who is greatly averse to refuting his own hypotheses can choose to test exclusively the hypotheses of others, and then he's in the clear. However, the situation is a bit more complicated than depicted in basic textbooks of scientific methodology and on Wikipedia. For example, Popper's principle about hypotheses that cannot be proven but can be refuted applies only to those hypotheses which take the form of a statement with a generalized quantifier; those hypotheses which take the form: *For all x, y is true*. The hypothesis that "all birds have one pair of wings" is impossible to prove (we'd have to catch all the birds in the world and check that each has one pair of wings). If we find just one bird with two pairs of wings, our hypothesis is refuted. Popper's principle doesn't apply to the hypotheses that take the form of a statement including an existential quantifier; hypotheses that take the form: *There exists at least one x, for which y is true*. The hypothesis that "there exists a leprechaun who always hides my lab keys" would be difficult for anyone to disprove based on empirical data (just this morning the terrible creature hid them twice!), but it is possible to prove – I only need to catch him in the act (he had better be ready!). Popper would probably easily handle this objection. He would probably argue that for every hypothesis there exists a superior hypothesis stating that "all empirical consequences implied by our hypothesis are true." Since this superior hypothesis takes the form of a statement with a generalized quantifier, it cannot be proven, but with a little luck, it may be refuted. However, even this would not completely save Popper. In the second half of the 20th century, the historian and scientific theoretician **Thomas Samuel Kuhn** claimed that no theory can really be refuted by an empirical experiment, because the theory can always be modified to include the facts that didn't fit with its original version. (A theory is basically the same as a hypothesis, but is usually more complicated and explains a wider range of phenomena.) In general, scientists abandon an old theory only after inventing a new one to take its place. At first the new theory is less precise, and sometimes even worse at explaining the known facts; but it's also simpler and more elegant (if only because there hasn't been time to make it more complicated). Switching to a new theory is generally a very gradual process. The supporters of the old theory don't just wake up one day and say, "the new theory is better, let's forget about the old one." Usually proponents of the old theory have to die out (or at least go into retirement), and then proponents of the new theory take their place.

To get back to something more specific: naturally, we didn't cast aside our hypothesis at the first sign of conflicting results. We expected that *Toxoplasma* raises testosterone levels in men; and we discovered a group in which infected and uninfected patients had the same testosterone levels (the Toxo positives even had them a little lower). Instead we modified our hypothesis: "in the general population, *Toxoplasma*-infected men have higher testosterone levels; but in a population of patients with allergies and immunodeficiencies, they have the same and maybe even lower testosterone levels as a result of the sieve effect" (see the mechanism that includes the effect of immunosuppression, described in the main text). And so we salvaged our hypothesis. When it becomes too complicated, we'll abandon it, so you won't have to wait around for my retirement. I'm usually not too enamored with my hypotheses and theories – I prefer inventing new ones.

We used the model of lab mice to verify the observation that Toxo positives have altered testosterone levels[67]. Our experiments confirmed the results on humans, but are nevertheless difficult to interpret. We expected to see a phenomenon similar to the one observed in rats[68] and among our students; that Toxo positive males have higher testosterone levels and Toxo positive females have lower testosterone levels. Instead we found that both male and female lab mice had significantly lower testosterone levels after infection. We still have to confirm this result with other experiments. If we do confirm it, and discover other groups in which toxoplasmosis does not raise testosterone levels in men (we found this in two groups so far: the group of patients with allergies, and a group of 100 infected and 100 uninfected soldiers), then we'll have to consider the possibility that something about our students is weird. For example, we might suspect that toxoplasmosis does not increase the levels of testosterone in male students, but rather that male students from the country, where the prevalence of toxoplasmosis is higher, have higher levels of testosterone than do male students from the city.

Originally we didn't know what molecular mechanism *Toxoplasma* could be using to influence the behavior and psyche of its host. Currently, we sort have the opposite problem. We have several factors that could be responsible for the changes in behavior and psyche in infected people. First there is dopamine, which we think may affect the tendency towards "novelty seeking." In this case, the psychological shift occurs in the same direction in men and women. Then there is testosterone, which could be responsible for the changes in other psychological factors. Furthermore, increased levels of testosterone in men and decreased levels in women could explain why a number of psychological and behavioral characteristics shift in opposite directions in infected men and women. Another question is whether these factors – testosterone and dopamine – are really independent of each other, or whether changes in testosterone might be caused by raised levels of dopamine.

XV. Does *Toxoplasma* cause schizophrenia?

The fact that *Toxoplasma*'s manipulatory activity is most likely enabled by changes in dopamine levels in the brain of its host, is quite intriguing. It could also explain the long-known relationship between toxoplasmosis and the serious psychiatric illness of schizophrenia. Already in the mid-20th century, it was described that toxoplasmosis is usually much more prevalent among schizophrenics than among people without this disease. To date, there have been dozens of independent studies published on this topic. Furthermore, it has been found that patients with more serious cases of acute toxoplasmosis often show neurological and psychiatric, though usually transitory, signs which would otherwise be characteristic of schizophrenia. American scientists Edwin Fuller Torrey and Robert H. Yolken have long devoted themselves to studying the relationship between toxoplasmosis and schizophrenia. They first showed that toxoplasmosis and schizophrenia share at least one risk factor – contact with cats. Their very first questionnaire study showed that people who come into contact with a cat are more likely to develop schizophrenia that those who do not[69]. Similar results were obtained from a study based on telephone polls of a patient's family members[70]. Professor Torrey and his colleagues found that schizophrenia appeared in Europe around the time when cats started show up in paintings as living inside human dwellings. The frequency of schizophrenia rapidly increased in Europe and America from the middle of the 19th century, when cats, formerly only the companions of devils and witches, became beloved household pets. They moved from the stables and granaries into the center of human abodes (today, this probably means the couch in front of the TV). Based on their results, the American authors suggested that at least one form of schizophrenia may have infectious origins, and that cats could be the source of infection for humans. Seeing as *Toxoplasma* is a significant parasite of the domestic cat, and that toxoplasmosis has already been related to schizophrenia, they were gradually inclined towards the hypothesis that *Toxoplasma* could be the parasite which induces schizophrenia. Originally they also suspected the herpes viruses, because they found increased levels of the respective antibodies in patients with schizophrenia. But a number of studies later suggested that the antibodies come from activation of the latent form of the virus, enabled by a *Toxoplasma*-disrupted immune system. The possible effect of toxoplasmosis on the origin and course of schizophrenia is a key part of the studies conducted by the Stanley Medical Research Institute, along with number of scientists all over the world who are funded by this organization (Box 66 *Why it (sometimes) pays off to be unorthodox*).

The reason I mention the discovery that *Toxoplasma* increases dopamine levels, in relation to schizophrenia, is because of the widely-accepted 30-year-old dopamine hypothesis of schizophrenia. This theory states that schizophrenia, which currently afflicts about 1 in a 200 people[71], is caused by an imbalance in dopamine levels in the diencephalon and telencephalon. The role of toxoplasmosis in the development of schizophrenia is not yet proven, and other factors are certainly involved. Nevertheless, there are strong indications that toxoplasmosis could play a key role. At the very least, the statistical association between latent toxoplasmosis and schizophrenia is much stronger (hah!) than that between schizophrenia and any genetic factor described to influence the risk of the disease[72]. Recently, another hypothesis explaining the relationship between toxoplasmosis and schizophrenia was proposed. Again, it involves neurotransmitters – specifically kyneuric acid, a metabolite resulting from decomposition of the amino acid tryptophan, which is used to synthesize serotonin. Decreasing the levels of free form tryptophan is a significant defense mechanism used against parasitic protozoans, including *Toxoplasma*, because many parasitic organisms including protozoans need tryptophan to survive and reproduce in their host.

Box 66 Why it (sometimes) pays off to be unorthodox

Edwin Fuller Torrey is not only a psychiatrist, but a publicly known figure with highly unorthodox, and – in today's politically hyper-correct America – fairly controversial views. In his best-selling books he doesn't try to hide his opinion that the term "former patient with schizophrenia" is just a nonsensical euphemism; or that involuntary treatment with modern antipsychotics should be administered, even for treatment at home, to those patients whose health condition requires it. While advocates of patient rights may disagree, his arguments are apparently convincing; in several cases, he's managed to influence the legislation. He also claims that truly serious psychiatric diseases are but rarely induced by the patient's social environment. Usually they have biological origins. Biological causes include genetic predisposition, as well as infectious agents (such as *Toxoplasma* in the case of schizophrenia). Last but not least, Torrey's books are well written. After reading one of his books, multimillionaire Stanley, whose son fell prey to manic-depressive psychosis in the 80s, contacted Torrey and provided him with the resources to establish an independent research institute for the study of schizophrenia and manic-depressive psychosis (today it's more commonly known as bipolar disorder, so that the patient and his surroundings won't freak out at the term "psychosis"). Furthermore, Stanley funded the establishment of a grant agency that would support this research. In 2003, the Stanley Medical Research Institute already had an annual budget of 40 million dollars, and in 2004 it financed half the studies on bipolar disorder and a third of the studies on schizophrenia in the United States. And that was just in the US. At the time, Stanley's foundation financed a number of studies world-wide, including one of my smaller project in Prague. So it seems that sometimes it pays off to express one's unorthodox views. I'll have to think long and hard, about where I'm going wrong. Maybe the problem is not in that my ideas are too orthodox but rather in that our multimillionaires and potential sponsors are currently otherwise occupied, and, above all, reside in exotic places (like the Bahamas, the South African Republic, Switzerland...) where the poor guys never get a chance to read my books.

If the immune system recognizes the presence of an infectious agent, the body begins synthesize an enzyme which breaks down this amino acid. Products of the break-up, namely 3-hydroxykynurenine and kyneuric acid, bind to neurotransmitter receptors. It's thought that these raised levels of kyneuric acid, observed in schizophrenics, could play an important role in the origins or manifestation of the disease.

In the last decade, British and American authors found that certain psychopharmaca, used in the treatment of schizophrenia, inhibit the reproduction of *Toxoplasma in vitro* – and this inhibition proved to be very strong and highly specific[73,74]. These authors showed that some of the ethological and behavioral manifestations of toxoplasmosis in Norwegian rats can by blocked with psychopharmacological drugs normally used to treat schizophrenia or manic-depressive psychosis. The longitudinal study on American soldiers also brought interesting results. These soldiers regularly give blood samples, so it was possible to determine whether (and when) each of the 180 soldiers released from the army due to an out-break of schizophrenia had begun releasing *Toxoplasma* antibodies into the blood. The results showed that the released soldiers exhibited these antibodies suspiciously often, and that it occurred just before the outbreak of schizophrenia[75]. Of course we can't expect that schizophrenia has only one cause, and that being infection by *Toxoplasma*. It's obvious that schizophrenia is not malaria; clearly, a number of genetic and non-genetic factors are involved in its development. Nevertheless, several independent studies show that in at least some cases, toxoplasmosis plays an important – and maybe even crucial – role.

We began studying the relationship between toxoplasmosis and schizophrenia fairly recently. Collaborating with Jiří Horáček, David Holub and Lucie Bankovská-Motlová, we obtained slightly different results than previous authors. Above all, we didn't prove that there was a higher prevalence of toxoplasmosis among our schizophrenics than among the normal population[76]. It is possible, however, that this could have been caused by pre-selection – the sieve effect. We were only allowed to include schizophrenics who agreed to participate in the study. This likely eliminated the patients with more serious clinical signs, who would be less willing to participate; and these may have been the people whose schizophrenia was induced by toxoplasmosis. Past and certain recent studies[77] included all the schizophrenics in a health institution, or those who had at some point sought medical aid, or experienced an attack of schizophrenia. These experiments would not have suffered from the sieve effect; they included people with all forms of schizophrenia. From the perspective of protecting patient rights, the current approach of respecting a patient's wish not to be included in a study is justified; but from the perspective of research studies (which could bring improved treatment for schizophrenic patients), this approach, put mildly, is somewhat unfortunate.

Returning to our study, there weren't significantly more Toxo positives among our patients than among the normal population. At first, based on the already available clinical data, we couldn't even find significant differences between the Toxo positive and negative patients regarding the severity of their schizophrenia. Only that doctors were more likely to give the Toxo positives higher drug doses. But a psychiatric examination proved that infected patients exhibited more intensive, so-called positive symptoms of schizophrenia, such as delusions and hallucinations, which had been already described by Chinese and Turish psychiatrists recently[78,79].

Their intensity was generally higher in patients with low levels of *Toxoplasma* antibodies – that is, people who became infected long ago. In the end, we did find two prominent differences between the Toxo positive and negative patients, differences that had escaped the notice of other researchers. Schizophrenia occurred earlier in the Toxo positive men, and later in the Toxo positive women than in the Toxo negative people (Fig. 36). Overall, this corresponds with our findings on the risk of *Toxoplasma* infection in the Czech population[76]. Men are usually infected earlier than women. In women, there is an increased prevalence of toxoplasmosis around the age when women start setting up families, cooking more and dealing with raw meat. If we presume that schizophrenia can develop either in relation or not in relation to *Toxoplasma* infection, we can expect that schizophrenia will appear earlier in Toxo positive men and later in Toxo positive women than in Toxo negative people (for whom schizophrenia development is presumably age-independent). And our study confirmed precisely this hypothesis. In addition, Toxo positive schizophrenics (men and women) were, on average, hospitalized longer than the Toxo negatives. Our results therefore indicate that schizophrenia associated with (or maybe even induced by) toxoplasmosis represents an independent (a perhaps more serious) category of psychiatric disorders.

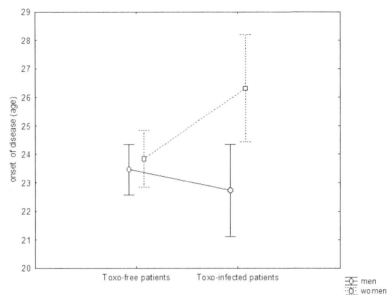

Fig. 36 Differences in the age at which Toxo positive vs. negative patients were hospitalized with schizophrenia (usually one year after the actual onset of disease). The graph demonstrates that both men and women uninfected by Toxoplasma, *on average, are diagnosed with schizophrenia between the age of 23 and 24.* Toxoplasma *infected women are diagnosed with schizophrenia later – around the age 26 to 27. In contrast, infected men are hospitalized sooner (before they are 23 years-old). This observation coincides with the fact that in Czech Republic, men are infected with this parasite sooner than women. These results suggest that a certain number of schizophrenia cases might be induced by* Toxoplasma *infection.*

Recently, we obtained more direct data to support this hypothesis[80]. Modern imaging techniques, particularly magnetic resonance imaging (MRI), have long since shown that the brain anatomy of patients with schizophrenia differs, on average, from the brain anatomy of healthy people. There are great differences among individual brains, so in order to compare schizophrenic with normal brains, we created composite images to cancel out most of these individual differences.

We projected 20 images of healthy brains over each other, and 20 images of schizophrenic brains over each other, and after comparing the two composite images, we could see that the internal anatomy of the schizophrenic brain is distinctly different from that of a healthy brain. Several parts of the brain, including the neocortex, hippocampus and some brain nuclei, show up on such composite MRI images as having a lower density of gray matter in schizophrenics, meaning that the neurons in that area got smaller or less numerous. Jiří Horáček of the Prague Psychiatric Center conducted individual MRI-analysis for schizophrenics with and without toxoplasmosis; and, as a control, for mentally healthy people with and without toxoplasmosis. He found that above-mentioned differences in brain anatomy occur only in schizophrenics with toxoplasmosis[80]. The brains of Toxo negative schizophrenics were not statistically significantly different from mentally healthy brains, and what's more, there are also no differences between the brain anatomy of Toxo positive and Toxo negative non-schizophrenics (Fig. 37)[80]. This indicates two things. Firstly, that the observed differences in brain anatomy are not a sign of toxoplasmosis, but of some form of schizophrenia. Theoretically, it could be the opposite way, and the differences between normal and schizophrenic brains, described in psychiatric literature, could be because there is a higher prevalence of Toxo positives among schizophrenics. But if this were true, then there would have to be differences between the Toxo positive and Toxo negative brain of people without the disease.

Secondly, Horáček's results indicate that the schizophrenia of Toxo positive people differs from that of Toxo negatives; only the schizophrenia of Toxo positives is associated with anatomical abnormalities in the brain. Basically, there exist two possibilities, both clinically significant, which could explain these findings. Either toxoplasmosis worsens the course of the disease; or it may even induce one of the more serious forms of schizophrenia, which requires longer hospitalization and is associated with anatomical abnormalities in the brain. In another study, working with David Holub and Lucie Bankovská-Motlová, we administered various cognitive and performance tests to schizophrenic patients of the Prague Psychiatric Center, to see if the Toxo positive and negative subjects performed differently. Furthermore, we were interested to see how the Toxo positive and negative patients would react to schizophrenic treatment, as well as to a training program aimed toward increasing their performance (Box 67 *What is the difference between the paired and unpaired t tests, and why is the paired one better?*). Definitive results for the second half of the study are not yet available; in any case, we were not able to prove a difference between the Toxo positive and Toxo negative patients in the first tests, before the treatment and training programs. This, however, could have also been due to the sieve effect. It's quite likely that mostly patients with less serious forms of schizophrenia, whether they be Toxo positive or negative, would have been willing to participate in our study or even in the training program.

Schizophrenia is most serious mental disease found to correlate with the occurrence of toxoplasmosis. But it is not the only one. Recently, a German study tested a large group of schizophrenics, and found a significantly higher prevalence of toxoplasmosis among those people who had also been diagnosed with personality disorder[81]. There are also studies which indicate that toxoplasmosis could play a role in the probability of development of Parkinson's disease[82,83] and Alzheimer's[84]. Finally, a significantly higher occurrence of toxoplasmosis was noted in patients with manic-depressive psychosis (bipolar disorder)[85]. Interestingly, some of the drugs used to treat the acute phase of this disorder, specifically haloperidol and valproic acid, are highly effective in inhibiting the reproduction of *Toxoplasma*[73,74].

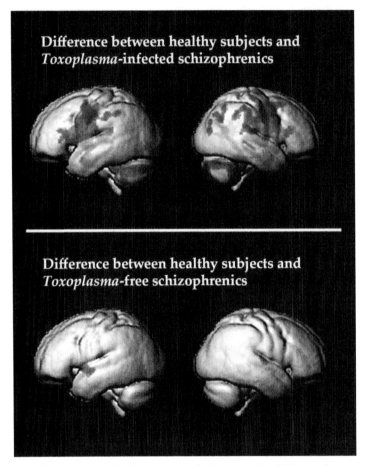

Fig. 37 Differences in the brain morphology and of Toxoplasma-*infected schizophrenia patients and healthy controls (top picture) and of* Toxoplasma-*free schizophrenia patients and heathy controls (bottom picture). The areas of smaller size or significantly lower gray matter density are indicated in dark color. The brains of uninfected and infected non-schizophrenics are almost the same (not shown), whereas the brains of uninfected and infected schizophrenic patients manifest a number of mostly degenerative changes. The most probable explanation is that two different diseases are behind schizophrenia diagnosis; the first is not associated with morphological changes of the brain, and the other, perhaps more serious disease is associated with these changes and is also associated (or even caused) by infection with* Toxoplasma. *The second possibility is that toxoplasmosis substantially worsens the course of schizophrenia. Images by Jiří Horáček.*

Box 67 What is the difference between the paired and unpaired t tests, and why is the paired one better?

If we're studying the effect of a certain factor on a dependent variable, such as the effect of a training program on the results of the schizophrenics' performance tests, we can theoretically use two types of analysis tests – a paired or an unpaired test. An **unpaired test** compares the average performance of a group of people exposed to the given factor, with the performance of the control group, which was not exposed to the given factor. A **paired test** compares performances using pairs of individuals; the two individuals somehow fit together, and within each pair, one individual was exposed to the factor, and the other was not. Each pair is formed by fitting together the two individuals who were originally the most similar (before one was exposed to the given factor). They might be the same age, the same gender, come from the same city or both be smokers or non-smokers. For each pair, we subtract the control individual's dependent variable value from the other individual's dependent variable value. If the studied factor had no effect on the individuals, then the average difference of all the pairs should equal zero – which one can easily test using the (very sensitive) **one-sample test** (see Box 63 *How to compare photographs using one-sample test, and do we like self-similar faces?*). In an ideal scenario, a pair is made up of the same person twice – before he was exposed to the factor, and after he was exposed to the factor. Here, the individual acts as his own control. This often occurs in experiments, but generally not in observational studies (with the important exception of longitudinal studies, see Box 41 *Longitudinal and cross-sectional studies*). In such an experiment, we obtain the data by first measuring the parameter we're interested in for each individual. Then we expose all the individuals to the studied factor, and once more measure the parameter. For each individual, we subtract the first value of the parameter (before exposure to the factor) from the second (after exposure to the factor). Using the one-sample test, we ascertain whether the average difference could be equal to zero (which would mean that the studied factor either had no effect on the given parameter, or that it influenced the parameter positively in some individuals and negatively in others). The arrangement where each person acts as his own control, is useful because it filters out the influence of unknown variables, which often confound results. The paired test is actually as special case of **the repeated measures tests.** The same object or individual is measured several times, and then, using the repeated measures ANOVA, three things are determined. The first is the statistical significance of the so-called **between subject effect** (for example, whether a toxoplasma positive versus negative person differ in the studied parameter, e.g. reaction times). The second is the **within subject effect** (for example, whether there is a difference in the studied parameter from measurements performed on the same individuals at different times after exposure to the studied factor, toxoplasmosis). Finally, the analysis test determines the interaction between the *between* and *within subject* effects (whether a Toxo positive versus Toxo negative person reacts differently to the factor over time; for example, whether performance worsens more quickly in Toxo positives than in Toxo negatives).

Maybe even more interesting is that the same antipsychotics, when given to mice and Norwegian rats that had lost their natural fear of the scent of cat urine after *Toxoplasma* infection, were able to inhibit this "defect"[86]. The possible effect of toxoplasmosis on the onset of depression could also help explain the greater risk of suicide among infected people[87]. The onset of depression could be influenced by decreased levels of serotonin in the brain, which, along with tryptophan, get broken down more quickly as part of defense against parasites. Toxoplasmosis may also play a role in migraines[88,89].

However, we must admit that there are results which call into question a direct role of toxoplasmosis in various mental illnesses. For example, a recent study by Turkish authors shows that the risk of schizophrenia significantly correlates with the presence of *Toxoplasma* antibodies (indicating latent toxoplasmosis)[90]. But after statistically filtering out whether or not the person had come into contact with a cat, this positive correlation disappeared – actually, a slightly negative correlation took its place. This suggests that schizophrenia is more likely induced by a different pathogen spread by cats; the occurrence of toxoplasmosis only signifies that the person came into contact with a cat and the other, still unknown parasites it transmits. Research by German scientists has similar results – it also shows that the correlation between toxoplasmosis and schizophrenia disappears after statistically filtering out contact with cats[81]. I must admit, that if not for our own studies on anatomical abnormalities in the brains of Toxo positive schizophrenics[80], I'd have serious doubts about a direct role of toxoplasmosis in the development of schizophrenia. As it is, I only have reasonable doubt (see Box 48 *One can never be too careful…*).

XVI. How we unintentionally discovered the function of the Rh factor and probably solved the 50-year-old mystery of Rh polymorphism

Good luck has always played an immensely important role in our studies. I don't think that it's true for only our studies – the general significance of luck in science is constantly underestimated. A well-planned study can bring valuable results, but the most crucial results, something entirely novel, are usually stumbled upon when least expected. This is what happened in the case of one of our discoveries – possibly the most important to date – which revealed the influence of the Rh factor on latent toxoplasmosis in humans.

Our good fortune lay in that we studied the effect of toxoplasmosis on the human psyche and performance using several large groups of blood donors. And blood donors, of course, are always tested for their ABO blood group and their Rh factor (Box 68 *Blood groups*).

Box 68 Blood groups

Humans (as well as other species) have several possible blood groups. This, of course, is crucial information for carrying out blood transfusions and transplants, because a blood transfusion between individuals of different blood groups can easily lead to the receiving patient's death. The most commonly known blood group system is the ABO system (in Czech written as AB0). People of the blood group A have different sugars (oligosaccharide chains) attached to the outer membrane of each red blood cell (RBC) than do people of the blood group B. People of the AB blood group have both types of sugars on their RBC membranes, and humans of blood group O have neither type. These two types of carbohydrates are also found on the cell walls of certain bacteria, so a human also has antibodies in his blood to act against sugars not present on his own RBCs (of course, a human tolerates his own sugars). When someone with an A or O blood group receives a B or AB blood group transfusion (which I certainly hope is not common nowadays), they experience an acute immune reaction carried out by their antibodies against the foreign blood cells – and most likely die. The same happens when someone with a B or O blood group receives a transfusion of A or AB blood, or when someone with O blood receives a transfusion of any other blood group. A person of the AB blood group is a universal receiver, and can accept any blood; whereas someone of blood group O is a universal donor, and their blood can be accepted by anyone. It's advantageous for the human species to have several blood groups, with different sugars on their RBC membranes, because this means that people of different blood groups produce different antibodies targeting various structures on the surfaces of parasites – so that they are resistant against different species of parasites. For this reason, parasites cannot easily adapt to the human population, which is useful for our species – always at least part of the population resists the attack of a parasite. Another important antigen (a substance which the organism can recognize as foreign and therefore produce antibodies against) that defines human blood groups is the Rh factor. The Rh factor is an antigen capable of inducing the strongest known immune reaction against red blood cells. Unlike antigens of the ABO system, an Rh factor is a protein (actually, just part of protein, called a D antigen), and is not found on bacteria, so unless an Rh negative person comes into contact with foreign Rh positive blood, he won't have antibodies against the Rh factor. Until recently, neither the influence of the Rh factor on physiological or other human characteristics, nor the biological reason for Rh polymorphism (the presence of Rh positive and negative humans in the population) was known.

At first we didn't think that the blood group data from these studies could be useful for something, but since we already had it available, naturally we examined it to see if blood groups correlated either with the presence of toxoplasmosis, or with its behavioral manifestations. Our initial findings weren't too promising: apparently neither the ABO nor Rh factor blood group played a significant role in the risk of *Toxoplasma* infection. But later we discovered that the ABO blood group does play a certain role in the probability of *Toxoplasma* infection. The smallest risk of infection was exhibited by people of the blood group O, and the largest risk by those of blood group AB. But we uncovered this much later, after testing on large subject groups, namely a couple batches of several thousand soldiers each[91].

But let's get back to our original study conducted on the blood donors tested for toxoplasmosis and blood groups. Like I said, the initial results weren't to encouraging. The performance of the blood donors did not in any way seem related to their blood group. In the 1999 undergraduate thesis based on this study, written successfully defended by Jan Havlíček, I believe it was concluded that blood group doesn't impact performance.

After some time, we returned to the original set of data and conducted a new, more meticulous analysis. It turned out that in the first analysis we made a novice error. In the time crunch (undergraduate theses are always completed at the last minute; it must be some natural law, or a perhaps the students were instructed to do so somewhere in the college handbook) we analyzed the effect of the Rh factor and toxoplasmosis on subject performance for each factor separately. But when we analyzed both factors together, we found that the effect of toxoplasmosis on performance is significantly different in Rh positive versus Rh negative people. Among Toxo negative people, the Rh negative subjects performed much better in the simple reaction time test, exhibiting much shorter reaction times than the Rh positives. Among the Toxo positive subjects, the results were drastically different: the Rh negative people performed much worse than did the Rh positives. While the Rh positives in the Toxo positive and negative groups performed about equally, the *Toxoplasma*-infected Rh positives and negatives were markedly different – indicating that after infection, the performance of an Rh negative person gets significantly worse[92,93].

We confirmed this surprising discovery on a number of subject groups, some of which numbered several thousand people, and saw that the joint effect of *Toxoplasma* and the Rh factor was usually very strong. These results were significant but unexpected, because to date none had uncovered the biological function of the Rh factor, nor how it could influence human behavior and physiological characteristics. It's known that the Rh factor is a protein found on RBC membranes. In a significant part of the population, the respective gene has a large deletion – a large chunk of it is missing. A human, whose two copies of the gene have this deletion, is called Rh negative; there are no Rh proteins on his RBC membranes. If at least one copy of the gene does not have the deletion, then the person is Rh positive. Rh positives can be separated into homozygotes and heterozygotes. An Rh positive homozygote has both complete copies, while an Rh positive heterozygote has only one. The function of the protein on the RBC membranes is unknown; it seems to be a membrane pump, but it's not clear whether it pumps ammonium ions or CO_2 from one side of the membrane to the other (currently, CO_2 seems to be the more likely option).

Until now there were no known biological manifestations of Rh negativity or Rh positivity. The only discovered manifestation of the two forms of the Rh gene was not related to the factor's biological function. Over fifty years ago, it was discovered that when the child of an Rh negative woman and an Rh positive man gets the Rh positive allele from his father, then the mother becomes immunized against the Rh factor during the pregnancy or delivery. Her white blood cells (WBC) begin producing antibodies against the proteins on RBCs of Rh positive people, and these antibodies can harm the fetus, especially when the mother is carrying her second or latter Rh positive child. Usually, during the first pregnancy with an Rh positive child, the mother is just immunized; but in subsequent pregnancies, her immune system attacks Rh positive children more and more. Today, of course, doctors routinely screen for the risk of this **hemolytic disease of the newborn**, and if a mother is Rh negative, then her child is treated immediately after birth. The Rh factor of the father does not influence the doctor's decision to administer treatment; the risk that the alleged father is not actually the biological father is too great. To prevent the actual immunization, Rh negative mothers are given antibodies against Rh positive blood – these antibodies latch onto the RBCs of the child that made it into the bloodstream of the mother, so that the mother's immune system never realizes their presence and doesn't start producing its own antibodies (Box 69 *Are women chimeras, and if so, what does it mean for them?*).

Box 69 Are women chimeras, and if so, what does it mean for them?

Chimeras are mythological creatures, composed of the parts of different creatures. Biologically, a **chimera** is an organism whose body consists of entire organs which are genetically distinct, while a **microchimera** contains only individual genetically separate cells. Strangler figs are found in the tropical rainforest; they use other trees as a climbing framework, and generally end up killing them (usually by completely blocking off their access to sunlight). At first and second glance, the strangler fig looks like a normal tropical species. But a genetic analysis of the tree shows that its body consists of genetically distinct segments. The strangler fig belongs to a group of species whose seeds make their way onto tree branches in bird droppings. In order to grow into a tall, stately tree, a seedling must first let its roots crawl several meters from the treetop to anchor themselves in the ground. Meanwhile, the seedling is racing against time, and maybe even the stranger figs that sprouted from the seeds found in another pile of bird droppings. The group of seedlings which first takes root wins, and eventually strangles not only the tree that it's climbing, but also its competitors – the other strangler figs. That is why it pays off for the seedlings in one pile of bird droppings to work together to form a single composite tree. Most humans are probably microchimeras, because occasionally during pregnancy some of the cells from the mother break into the embryo. Conversely, cells from the embryo also find their way into the mother. The embryonic cells carry genes from the father as well as the mother – and some of the gene variants from the father may not be found in the mother. This is of great value to the mother, because many of the escaped embryonic cells make their way into various tissues in the mother and begin to differentiate among each group of specialized cells. There have been cases in which a woman suffering from a genetic defect got significantly better after going through pregnancy, because cells from the embryo carrying copies of the functional gene from the father "fixed" parts of her body. It's possible that this colonization of the mother organism by cells from the embryo developed because it was evolutionarily advantageous. For the child, it is clearly beneficial to fix its mother in time, thereby its chances of getting better and longer care once it is born. It's even possible, that part of the reason women have a longer average lifespan than men, is because their bodies are rejuvenated during pregnancy by embryonic cells. Microchimerism, however, is not always beneficial for women. If a woman has had children with several different men, then her body contains various populations of genetically distinct cells, so her body must learn to tolerate multiple kinds of antigens. It has been suggested that this could be responsible for the deteriorated health of such women.

Please excuse a brief digression. Among Rh negative women we found an unusually high prevalence of latent toxoplasmosis. It's possible that when these women are preventatively given Rh positive antibodies, they also get *Toxoplasma* – or, they may only be getting antibodies against *Toxoplasma* along with the Rh antibodies. In the second case, the women would still show up as Toxo positive, because our diagnostic test is based on the presence of *Toxoplasma* antibodies. I sincerely hope that the second case is true; we should certainly determine that it isn't the first. Infecting thousands of Rh negative mothers with toxoplasmosis during the preventative administration of antibodies, isn't something that the doctors (and mothers) would be too happy about. The existence of two forms of the human Rh gene was a great evolutionary mystery. It's hard to imagine how this polymorphism could have developed, and primarily, how it can be sustained. Clearly, the carriers of the less common Rh gene type should be at a disadvantage in natural selection. Imagine that originally, everyone in a population was Rh negative, until there appeared one Rh positive mutant. The majority of the population was Rh negative, so an Rh positive male offspring of this mutant would usually reproduce with Rh negative women. Most of his children would die from the hemolytic disease of the newborn, so he'd leave behind fewer descendants. Natural selection would penalize carriers of the rare mutant gene, and according to evolutionary rules, it seems that sooner or later the Rh positive form should die out. The same applies vice versa. Let's imagine a population of only Rh positives, in which one individual were born an Rh negative mutant. Again, he and his offspring would be at a disadvantage to carriers of the original Rh positive gene form. In this case, the Rh negative women (with two copies of the mutant gene) would be disadvantaged, because they would usually reproduce with Rh positive men and some of their offspring would die of hemolytic anemia (Box 70 *Genetic polymorphism: what it is, where does it come from and how can it sustain itself in nature?*).

Box 70 Genetic polymorphism: what is it, where does it come from and how can it sustain itself in nature?

Genetic polymorphism is the presence of different variants of the same gene (called **alleles**) in a species population. It is a nearly universal phenomenon. It's nothing strange to find a population with one very frequent allele and several almost negligibly rare ones. New gene variants (alleles) are constantly created by mutations, and simultaneously eliminated by natural selection. Most new alleles are harmful, and carriers of a new gene variant are therefore disadvantaged and die out. Occasionally a beneficial mutation will form, which affords its carriers greater biological fitness, so they leave behind more offspring than do the carriers of the original gene variant. As a result, the new beneficial allele grows to predominate in the population, and the genetic polymorphism returns to a low. It's harder to explain why many genes have multiple variants which remain at comparable frequencies. Most often it's the result of cyclical selection, frequency-dependent selection or selection which favors heterozygotes. **Cyclical selection** occurs due to cyclical changes in the environment, due to things like seasonal variation, so in different phases of the cycle, the carriers of different alleles are at an advantage. In **frequency-dependent selection**, an allele is harmful or beneficial depending on its prevalence in the population. For example, when two gene variants differ in terms of preferred diet, the less common variant will always be at an advantage, since it will have less competition for food. If gene variant A is less frequent in the population, then the respective food source A will be more available to variant A carriers – so they will be at an advantage. They'll reproduce and have more offspring than variant B carriers, so their prevalence in the population will grow, and they'll lose their advantage. The third possibility is **selection for heterozygotes**. Strictly speaking, it's in principle a type of frequency-dependent selection. Heterozygotes, with two different alleles, exhibit the greatest biological fitness; whereas homozygotes, with two identical copies of any one allele, are disadvantaged. As soon the frequency of a certain gene variant A dramatically decreases in the population, then allele A will be found almost exclusively in the heterozygotes (the chance that two rare allele A carriers will find each other and produce an allele A homozygote becomes very low). Since the heterozygotes have more offspring, the frequency of the now rare allele will begin to increase. As result, none of these two gene variants can continually predominate – genetic polymorphism will always be maintained (see also Box 35 *How I refuted Darwin*).

A number of famous evolutionary biologists looked for a mechanism which would explain why two forms of the Rh gene occur throughout the human population, but without success[94,95]. Our data shows that the long-sought mechanism could be a greater resistance of Rh heterozygotes against the negative effects of toxoplasmosis. If there were no toxoplasmosis in the population, as might have been the case in Europe before the arrival of domestic cats, then Rh negative people would be advantaged, because they have shorter reaction times. But if toxoplasmosis were widespread in the population – as it likely was in Africa, where our species evolved – then the Rh positives would be advantaged, because their performance doesn't worsen with toxoplasmosis. This could explain why Rh negatives are significantly less prevalent in Africa (and Asia) than in Europe.

Key to understanding the survival of both Rh alleles is the observation that Rh positive heterozygotes are more resistant to the harmful effects of toxoplasmosis (Fig. 38)[92]. When we looked at the levels of *Toxoplasma* antibodies (which can be used to approximate when a person was infected) and reaction times of our test subjects, we found that the reaction times of Toxo positive Rh negatives worsened soon after infection. The performance of Rh positive heterozygotes does not worsen with time after infection – their reaction times do not correlate with the antibody levels[92]. Rh positive homozygotes, with two functional alleles, slowly worsen with time after infection. The reaction times of the individuals with low antibody levels (long after infection) are about as bad as those of Rh negatives just after infection.

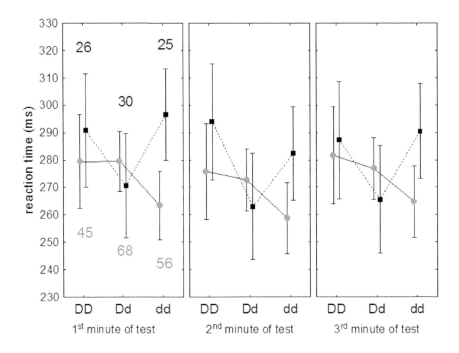

Fig. 38 The effect of the Rh factor and **Toxoplasma** *infection on the reaction time of blood donors in three minute tests. Rh negative homozygotes (dd) have the best (shortest) reaction times when Toxo negative (gray circles). but the worst reaction times when Toxo positive (black squares). As for Rh positive heterozygotes (Dd), their Toxo negatives have good reaction times, but the Toxo positive times are actually better. Finally, Rh positive homozygotes (DD) have below average times when uninfected, and worse times when infected (with the exception of the second minute of the test) – though not as bad as those of infected Rh negatives. The numbers in the first graph indicate the number of Toxo negative (gray) and Toxo positive persons (black) in each groups.*

The highest reaction time of the heterozygotes indicates that both forms of the Rh gene could remain in the population through the known mechanism of selection for heterozygotes (Box 70 *Genetic polymorphism: what it is, where does it come from and how can it sustain itself in nature?*). This is the same mechanism which maintains the gene codes for a special form of hemoglobin, called hemoglobin S, which becomes fatal for its carrier when that person has two copies (which makes him a hemoglobin S homozygote). Children who inherited this allele from both their parents are born with deformed sickle-shaped blood cells, and die of sickle-cell anemia. If the child is a heterozygote, and carries only one copy of the hemoglobin S gene (and the other copy is normal), then it suffers from a much milder form of the disease. Of course, even this milder form is disadvantageous for the individual. But in places with malaria, the presence of this deformed hemoglobin gives the heterozygote the ability to tolerate the disease. Malaria is a serious health factor – in some parts of Africa, many children die from it. So it's not surprising that the geographic distribution of malaria matches up with that of the gene for sickle-cell anemia. Our hypothesis is that a similar heterozygote advantage effect occurs in the case of Rh positivity; instead of malaria, the disease is latent toxoplasmosis and the associated worsened reaction time (possibly along with other, still unknown effects). As I mentioned, this mechanism could explain not only the old evolutionary mystery of the two Rh gene forms, but also the low frequency of Rh negativity in Africa, where, probably even today, toxoplasmosis occurred in about 90-100% of village inhabitants in some regions. Furthermore, it would explain the spread of the allele for Rh negativity throughout Europe, where, until "recently," there were no felids in close proximity to humans, and the prevalence of toxoplasmosis was likewise very low (Box 71 *Why are Rh heterozygotes better off, and what if they actually aren't?*).

Box 71 Why are Rh heterozygotes better off, and what if they actually aren't?

In the case of the Rh factor and the resistance against latent toxoplasmosis, it's not easy to explain why the heterozygotes should be better off. For other genes, the situation is simpler. Each variant of the gene has a different function or works optimally under different conditions. Heterozygotes take advantage of having both variants of the gene, and both functions available. The situation with the Rh factor is different because the Rh negative form isn't actually a variant of the gene – the deletion is so large that the protein isn't synthesized. Whereas Rh negatives have no Rh proteins on their RBCs, Rh positive heterozygotes just have less of them than do Rh positive homozygotes. But if having fewer Rh proteins were an evolutionary advantage, then natural selection would achieve it more easily changing regulatory elements of the respective gene (and then the advantage could be enjoyed by the whole population, not just heterozygotes). There are several possible explanations for the apparent heterozygote advantage regarding the Rh factor. It's known that the Rh protein occurs on the surfaces of RBCs in a complex with several other proteins. In Rh negative people, these protein complexes also exist, but the missing Rh protein is replaced by a similar protein coded by a different gene. It's possible that the two types of complexes (with and without the Rh protein) serve different functions, and so it benefits the heterozygote to have cells of both types. But there is also a completely different explanation. Rh positive heterozygotes and homozygotes aren't usually differentiated among blood donors. One would have to use expensive molecular biological methods instead of the commonly used serological techniques. We didn't definitively know the Rh positive homozygotes from the heterozygotes, but we were able to estimate it in another way, taking advantage of the existence of a so-called linkage disequilibrium. Genes found close to the Rh gene have several possible variants (alleles), and certain combinations of these alleles are almost always associated with the Rh+ allele, and others with the Rh- allele. So the advantage exhibited by the Rh positive heterozygotes could actually be due to the genes we used to estimate whether the person was a heterozygote or a homozygote. In the future, we'll have to repeat our study and distinguish between the homozygotes and heterozygotes using direct methods of molecular biology. It'd be funny to find that there was no Rh gene heterozygote advantage after all, and that it was our improvised, "incorrect" method that led to the interesting discovery. (But it might, with a little luck, lead to the discovery that other alleles of the neighboring genes are associated with the observed heterozygote advantage).

When we found that the effect of latent toxoplasmosis on the human organism depends on Rh factor, we re-evaluated our previous data. Whenever it was available, we added each person's Rh factor as another variable in the statistical models. We found that in many cases there was interaction between the Rh factor and toxoplasmosis, meaning that toxoplasmosis manifested differently in Rh positives than in Rh negatives[92,93]. An interesting result came from our long-term study of the effect of toxoplasmosis on the risk of accidents among military drivers[33]. Our coworkers tried to convince all the military drivers who were examined by the Psychology Department of the Central Military Hospital to agree to toxoplasmosis screening. When they finished their mandatory military service, about

12-18 months later, we examined the files and records of the military police to see which of drivers had a driving accident; and then looked to see if the risk differed between the Toxo positives and negatives. The set-up of this study was much better than the set-up we used for our first studies on the risk of car accidents among Prague inhabitants. The first studies had a basic set-up, and would be categorized as **case-control studies**. We looked at the prevalence of toxoplasmosis in two groups: in the drivers who had a driving accident, and in a control group of people without accident who lived in the same area. But this makes interpreting results difficult. We couldn't determine whether the differences in toxoplasmosis prevalence between these two groups were because the drivers who crashed were more likely to be Toxo positive, or because the control group was less likely to be Toxo positive, compared to general population. The control group was created when family physicians asked patients if they wanted to be included a serological survey – if their blood could be tested for the presence of antibodies against some pathogens. If Toxo positive people were less likely to consent, then our control group would have a falsely low prevalence of toxoplasmosis. As a result, we would incorrectly determine that *Toxoplasma* raises the risk of driving accidents, when it was really just lowering the chances that a Toxo positive would get into our control group. The set-up we used with the military drivers is called a **prospective cohort study**. It did not have the ambiguity of the case-control study, because it was carried out only on the drivers who were willing to participate in it. This ended up being practically all of the military drivers, because over 70% agreed to participate. We tested all of these soldiers for latent toxoplasmosis and their Rh factor; then we determined whether or not they'd crashed during their mandatory military service. The increased risk of driving accidents among Toxo positive drivers had to mean that toxoplasmosis affected the probability of an accident; rather just influencing an individual's willingness to participate in the study (Box 72 *You can't expect miracles, even from a prospective cohort study*).

Box 72 You can't expect miracles, even from a prospective cohort study

Using our **prospective cohort study** we were able to decide between the two hypotheses which could explain the results of our original **case-control study** – we found that *Toxoplasma* raises the risk of a driving accident, rather than lowers a person's chances of being in our control group. But even in the prospective cohort study, we didn't rule out the possibility that a third unknown factor could be responsible for the observed correlation between toxoplasmosis and driving accidents. For example, it's possible that careless individuals are more likely to get into driving accidents and get infected by a parasite. Or it's possible that drivers from villages don't have experience with city traffic and are more likely to get into accidents during mandatory military service. People who grew up in the country are also more likely to be infected by *Toxoplasma*. Of course, to explain the statistical correlation between toxoplasmosis and driving accidents using one of these hypotheses, we'd first also to explain why the correlation is true for only Rh negative people. Not that we couldn't do it – it would just be difficult. Such a hypothesis would have to be fairly complicated, and include additional assumptions: for example, that more Rh negative people come from villages than towns. A simpler and more reasonable explanation would be that toxoplasmosis increases the risk of driving accidents in Rh negative people – especially when we consider that in independent studies we already proved that toxoplasmosis worsens reaction time in Rh negatives. Statistics is a powerful tool, but we can't get far without common sense.

We started our study before knowing about the possible role of the Rh factor. The study ran around five years, and at first it seemed that it would bring negative results. Simple tests showed no statistically significant difference between Toxo positives and negatives in the risk of car accidents. But as soon as we included the variable of the Rh factor in our analysis, we got data which agreed with results from our previous performance testing of Rh positive Toxo positive people. In Rh positives, infection by *Toxoplasma* had practically no effect on the probability of driving accidents, whereas in Rh negative subjects it greatly increased this risk. In Rh negatives, the risk of a driving accident decreased with lower *Toxoplasma* antibody levels. Those with the highest antibody levels, who had been infected fairly recently, had a 17% probability of a driving accident – about six times greater than that of uninfected Rh negatives or Rh positives (both infected and uninfected) (Fig. 39). That corresponded with the results of the previous study, because even among Prague inhabitants the highest risk of driving accidents was among people with relatively high antibody levels. Once more we found that although reaction time worsens with time after infection, the infected drivers are gradually able to adapt to their worsened abilities.

Our study brought another result, which we probably could have expected. A suspiciously large number of the drivers who had a driving accident had not participated in our study. This indicates that the drivers with the greatest risk of driving accidents refused to participate in our testing. Unfortunately, we cannot publish this result in a scientific journal, because we don't have the informed consent of these "uncooperative" drivers. But it shows that a person's chances of a driving accident are influenced not only by his driving abilities, but also by his personality traits. Such as his willingness to cooperate.

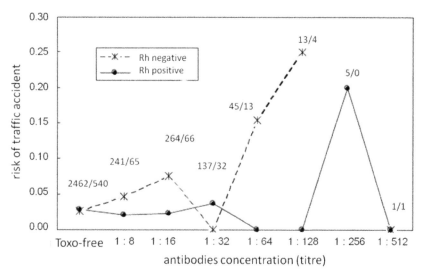

Fig. 39 The relationship of traffic accident risk and the titer of Toxo-specific antibodies in Rh positive (circles) and negative (crosses) military drivers. The uninfected drivers have a similar risk of a driving accident, regardless their Rh factor, but Toxo positive Rh negatives have a higher risk, which further increases with increasing levels of Toxoplasma *antibodies. (The antibodies were determined using complement-fixation test.) Rh negative drivers with a titer of 1:64 – individuals which were probably infected not long ago – have a six times higher (17%) probability of an accident during their military service than do uninfected drivers. The numbers indicate the ratio of Rh positive to Rh negative drivers with a given titer of antibodies.*

The case of the Rh factor and toxoplasmosis can be used as an example of an often-recounted mistake of scientists. The error probably comes from a time when sophisticated statistical methods weren't commonly available. In the 80s, when I was studying at the Prague Faculty of Science, my mentor Jiří Čerkasov tried to (fortunately unsuccessfully) drive home the rule: one factor, one experiment. In other words, a study should supposedly be set-up so that each experiment analyzes the effect of one factor. But if we had followed taken this approach, we never would have discovered the interaction between the Rh factor and toxoplasmosis. When we studied the effect of the Rh factor on reaction times for a mixed group of Toxo positive and negative people, as undoubtedly many scientists had done before us, we found no difference in reaction time between Rh positive and negative people. But when we included both the factors in our analysis (toxoplasmosis and the Rh factor), we suddenly discovered that uninfected Rh negative subjects have better reaction times than do uninfected Rh positives – but infected Rh negatives have much worse reaction times than Rh positives. The same problem would have happened in our first studies on *Toxoplasma*'s effect on the human psyche, if we had analyzed the men and women as one group. Since toxoplasmosis often shifted the same Cattell's factor in opposite directions for men versus women, we never would have discovered the effect of the parasite without taking gender into account.

In my experience, any study requires one to look for and then simultaneously analyze as many factors as possible. To this end, I always tried to track several variables and run the same people through the maximum number of tests. Then I could analyze a large number of relationships and interactions between the studied variables. Of course, this approach also has its bad parts. As we study more relationships, there is a greater risk of Type I errors – there is a greater probability that some of the relationships we observe between the variables will happenstance. As I like to stress, the p-value given by a statistical significance test (which helps us to estimate the probability that an observed phenomenon is the result of chance), can only be applied to a single statistical test. If we carry out 20 statistical tests, it's very likely that one of them will turn out as statistically significant just due to chance.

I believe that it's definitely worth it to run the risk. But you have to know how to deal with the results of such experiments. I teach my students to treat them like the results of an **exploratory study** (see Box 10 *Statistical evaluation of data*). You always have to meticulously explore the data from all possible angles and find as many potentially interesting phenomena as possible. It's not advisable to rely on correction for multiple tests, e.g. such as the Bonferroni correction; in other words, the kind of technique usually recommended by most of statisticians when carrying out several independent tests. It's much more useful to test an observed phenomenon on another, independent group. In a way, each of my studies is both confirmatory and exploratory. They're confirmatory because I try to confirm the existence of phenomena seen in previous studies or based on theories created by myself or other scientists. They are also exploratory because I always look for other possible phenomena in the new data, whether they relate to the original direction of our study, or are just relationships between variables that we happened to include.

Like I said, we usually test a large number of variables – both to statistically filter out their confounding effects on the target variable, and to discover any possible relationship between the confounding variables (see also Box 20 *Dependent, independent, and confounding variables; fixed and random factors*). When we first discover a new effect or an interaction between two variables, we don't put too much stock in it – until we find the same effect or interaction in a different group (or preferably, several groups). The smaller our data sample, the more false positive results we usually obtain. For this reason, we don't generally publish results obtained on one test group – even if the results were very interesting. But if we confirm them on other groups, we do try to publish the results, whether they relate to toxoplasmosis, or the relationship between sexual preference and the length ratio of fingers on the left hand (Box 73 *Do homosexuals have a longer pointer finger than ring finger?)* As a result, a person not familiar with our work might look at our published articles and be hard-pressed to determine our field of study.

Box 73 Do homosexuals have a longer pointer finger than ring finger?

It depends. All relationships between the length ratio of these fingers and psychical or biological traits are purely statistical. So the length ratio of the fingers cannot be used to determine whether someone is a homosexual or heterosexual, or even if they're a man or woman. Nevertheless, if we have a group of 30 men and 30 women, then according to the length ratio of the 2nd and 4th fingers, we'll easily tell the gender groups apart. In the case of sexual orientation, it's a bit more complicated. Among women, the difference between homosexuals and heterosexuals generally does not correlate with the finger length ratio. On the other hand, a difference in the length ratio for homosexual versus heterosexual men is usually observed in both Americans and Europeans[96-98]. The problem is, whereas among Europeans homosexual men have a lower length ratio than heterosexual men (and men identifying themselves as bisexual have an even lower length ratio), among Americans it is the other way around. We have not yet found an explanation. In one study conducted on visitors of the Municipal Library of Prague, we measured the length of each finger, and administered an anonymous survey to determine sexual preference and behavior. The group had about 1000 people, but only between 800 and 900 (roughly same amount of men as women) answered the questions regarding sexuality. Our results showed no difference in finger length ratio between homosexuals versus heterosexuals, neither among men, nor among women. Surprisingly, we found a significantly higher length ratio (a relatively longer pointer finger) among women who answered that they were sexually aroused by tying hands of one of the sexual partners

> (whether their partner tied their hands, or they did so to their partner), i.e. moderately sadomasochistic practices. On a 7-point scale, 56% of women and 46% of men put a 4 or higher for how much they were aroused by their partner tying their hands. As for tying their partner's hands, the same percentage of men and women (44 and 45, respectively) were very aroused, choosing 4 or higher on the 7-point scale.

After we started including the effect of the Rh factor in our models, we saw that the effect of *Toxoplasma*, or rather the interaction of *Toxoplasma* and Rh factor, showed up not just in the results of simple reaction time tests, but also in those of more complex performance tests[99]. Usually the interaction manifested similarly as it did in the simpler tests. Rh negatives performed better than did Rh positives, but only among Toxo negatives. When the people were infected by *Toxoplasma*, then the Rh negatives performed significantly worse. But in some cases this wasn't true. For example, we found that Rh negative Toxo positive men performed better in intelligence tests and have higher IQ values, than did uninfected Rh negatives. But among Rh positive men, we saw no such difference. We haven't figured out why the effect of the Rh factor and toxoplasmosis was different on intelligence than on reaction time. It's possible that Toxo positive Rh negative people have slower reaction times, but are more careful, so they are better at solving certain tasks. In this case, infection by *Toxoplasma* might have an effect opposite to what we observed for simple reaction times.

Our next results, obtained as a side-product of a primarily *Toxoplasma* study, indirectly supported this possibility. When we graphed reaction time versus intelligence for a group of soldiers, we found that the shorter the reaction time, the worse the result of the IQ test. But this was only true for tests which measure nonverbal intelligence. Tests which targeted verbal intelligences did not show such a relationship.

Since I already mentioned the results of the intelligence tests, I should probably admit that even after 20 years of research, we aren't sure if toxoplasmosis plays a role in intelligence. In our first studies, it seemed that the intelligence of infected men was lower than that of uninfected men. In some groups, the difference between the average intelligence of infected vs. uninfected men was statistically significant. For women, some groups showed an opposite relationship – that intelligence of infected women was higher than that of uninfected women. But in such tests it's always hard to differentiate between the direct and indirect effects of toxoplasmosis. For example, we can't determine whether Toxo positive women perform better in intelligence tests because they're really smarter, or because they try harder when completing the test. As I mentioned, infected women have a higher superego and are also more sociable (Cattell's factors G and A), which are certainly personality factors which can make someone try harder on the test. Furthermore, the intelligence of Toxo positive versus Toxo negative people can be different without toxoplasmosis having any effect – direct or indirect – on intelligence. First off, the cause-effect relationship may be the other way around. It's possible that more intelligent people are for some reason more likely to get infected than are less intelligent people. And secondly, there may exist an unknown, third factor which influences both intelligence and the risk of *Toxoplasma* infection.

Our results indicate that this third factor could be the person's resident population, or rather the difference between a city versus country life-style. A number of our subject groups, including the groups of soldiers, have data on the size of each person's city, town or village. When we looked at the size of a person's hometown versus his nonverbal intelligence (measured using the so-called VMT questionnaire), we found no statistically significant relationship. But when we examined the same thing for verbal intelligence (measured using the Otis questionnaire), we discovered that people from larger towns tested as more intelligent. Moreover, it's very clear that people living in villages have a much higher probability of catching *Toxoplasma* than do people from larger towns or cities. When we included the factor of residence (settlement population) in our models studying the relationship of toxoplasmosis and verbal intelligence – or when we looked at the relationship separately for people from villages, towns and cities – the correlation between Toxo-positivity and verbal intelligence was no longer statistically significant (Fig. 40). Currently, we are starting on a project in which we will meticulously study the relationship between latent toxoplasmosis and intelligence.

In this study, we will use a complex IQ test that measures a number of independent components of intelligence. I'm very curious to see the results – I find it hard to believe that *Toxoplasma* could influence several psychological factors but not tamper with intelligence.

Another study showed that the Rh factor significantly influences how an individual's personality type changes after infection[100]. For a group of blood donors, we measured reaction time and then asked the subjects to fill out Cloninger's and Cattell's psychological questionnaires at home. By mail, we received 302 questionnaires from 213 men and 89 women. About the same percent of men and women sent back the questionnaires – it's just that there are usually more male blood donors. Once again, we confirmed that Toxo positive people have significantly lower Cloninger's factors of NS (novelty seeking) and ST (self transcendence). Infected people also had a higher Cattell's factor of Superego strength (G) and a lower Cattell's factor of Vigilance (L) – this was true for both genders. We also found a higher factor N (Privateness) among the Toxo positives of both genders.

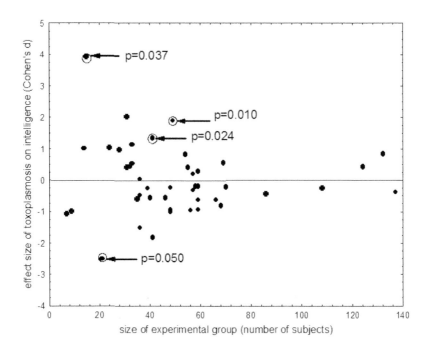

Fig. 40 A study of the relationship between Toxoplasma *infection and intelligence. Over the course of 5 years, we examined 42 groups (with 10 136 of soldiers in each group). Only in four groups were the differences between infected and uninfected soldiers in verbal intelligence, as determined by Otis test, statistically significant after filtering out the size of their settlement. The funnel plot, in which the size of observed effect is plotted against the number of individuals in the study, demonstrates that the effect of* Toxoplasma *was significant only in small or medium size studies, and that all individual points representing the effect are located symmetrically around the null line. Therefore,* Toxoplasma *infection doesn't influence the verbal component of intelligence. (In other words, if you believe my writing to be nonsensical or stupid, I regret to say that I can't blame it on* Toxoplasma*.) If this were a real meta-analysis (which funnel plots are commonly used for), and the individual points indicated the results of already published studies, then the symmetry of graph would testify that there is not any substantial publication bias in the specific research field. If there were publication bias, then values would be missing on part of the funnel plot's wide margin (on our graph, the values on the left) – the small controversial studies which results weren't in*

agreement with mainstream opinion about direction of observed effect would not be published. In small studies it is certainly possible to prove, for example, that Toxoplasma significantly increases or decreases intelligence. However, if most scientists believe that toxoplasmosis decreases intelligence, then reviewers or "auto-censorship" will not allow opposite results from small studies to be published. Also, in case of non-significant results, some researchers don't bother trying to publish them, even though it leads to bias. This "file drawer problem" may be addressed by shifting journal practices toward better chances of publishing null results. A funnel plot is usually hollow on the wide end (in this case, on the left, close to the null line) – studies demonstrating only a small effect are usually published only when conducted on a large subject group.

Because we included the Rh factor in the analysis, we could distinguish how changes in psychological traits depend on this factor. For example, we discovered that the Rh factor influences Cloninger's factors of HA (harm avoidance) and CO (cooperativeness), which are lower and higher, respectively, in Rh positives. It also influences Cattell's factors of C (Emotional stability) and L (Vigilance), which are higher and lower, respectively, in Rh positives. Moreover, we found that toxoplasmosis influences Rh positives differently than Rh negatives, for the following factors: Cloninger's RD (Reward dependence) and CO (Cooperativeness); and Cattell's C (Emotional stability), M (Abstractedness) and Q_4 (Tension). For example, infected Rh negatives have lower cooperativeness (CO) and lower Emotional stability (C) than uninfected Rh negatives, whereas it's the opposite way for Rh positives. We used the same data from the blood donors, and tried what would happen if we didn't consider the effect of toxoplasmosis in the analysis. It turned out that when we don't filter the effect of toxoplasmosis, the Rh factor has no statistically significant effect. Out of the seven Cloninger's and sixteen Cattell's factors, the only one that differed between the Rh positives and Rh negatives was Vigilance; after a Bonferroni correction for multiple tests, even this difference became statistically insignificant. Similarly, when we analyzed the same data for Toxo positivity without filtering out the effect of the Rh factor, we found statistically significant differences in only five psychological factors. Since nobody before us studying the effect of the Rh factor on personality included the effect of toxoplasmosis in their analyses (and why would they think to do so?), there were no publications indicating that the Rh factor could influence the human psyche. In the 70s, the great Raymond B. Cattell himself published a study describing the effect of the Rh factor on the human psyche[101], but even he wasn't taken seriously (I was tempted to write "he" with a capital H, but the editor would have probably changed it anyway). The problem was also that most authors focused on the possible effect of blood groups according to the ABO system, and neglected the Rh factor. It might be because the staunchest believers in the influence of blood groups on the psyche are the Japanese, who, like most Asians, are almost all Rh positives. Of course, after filtering out the effects of *Toxoplasma* and the Rh factor, I also examined our data to see if ABO groups had an effect on the human psyche. They don't. So the Japanese can keep trying, but they probably won't find any such effect. But that doesn't stop them from firmly believing in it (Box 74 *Why it's a shame that the Japanese and Australian aborigines are Rh positive*).

It's important to wonder how specific the protective effect of Rh positivity is. Does it protect only against the effects of latent toxoplasmosis, or does it impact other factors? Our results so far indicate that the second option could be correct[102,103]. For example, in our study on the effects of the Rh factor and toxoplasmosis on the human psyche, we noted that the effect of age on certain psychical factors differs depending on Rh positivity vs. Rh negativity[36].

Box 74 Why it's a shame that the Japanese and Australian aborigines are Rh positive

For the Japanese, the answer is simple – if almost all of them weren't Rh positive, then they could easily repeat our study, and we would become famous (at least in Japan). I spent over a year at the University of Tokyo, and can say that the talk at every good party eventually turns to blood groups and their effect on intelligence and the psyche in general. If you're bleeding to death in Japan and the doctor asks for your blood group, whatever you do, don't say that you don't know. The doctor might give you an understanding wink and immediately give you a transfusion of blood group B (I am just joking, of course, but only a little). The Japanese believe that people with the blood groups A or AB are more intelligent and generally more capable than those with blood group B, so when someone claims to not know their blood group, it's clearly because they belong to blood group B. And why is it a shame that the Australian aborigines are Rh positive? Because in Australia, before the arrival of Europeans, there were no felids, and hence no toxoplasmosis. If Rh negativity became widespread in Europe until the arrival of domestic cats, and presumably *Toxoplasma*, we might expect that this would apply even more to Australia. Oh well. Nature sometimes won't listen to the advice of the evolutionary parasitologist, and decides matters for herself. In any case, it is possible that a different gene variant in Australians carries out the function provided by the Rh- allele so widespread in Europe.

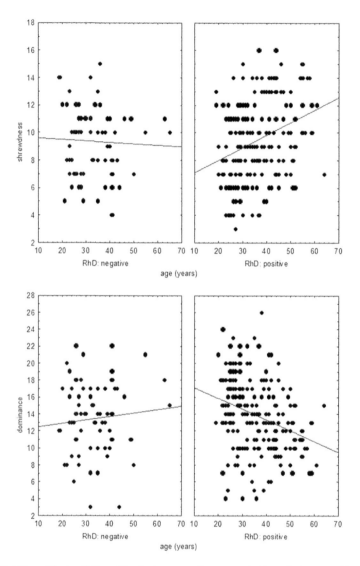

Fig. 41 The effect of the Rh factor on the correlation between the age of blood donors, and Cattell's factor E (Dominance, top graphs) and N (Shrewdness, bottom graphs). The graphs demonstrate that both psychological factors correlate with age only in Rh positive persons. In both cases, the correlation is statistically significant.

Our results showed that in blood donors, Dominance (factor E) significantly decreases with age, whereas Privateness (factor N) increases in infected people. A more detailed analysis showed that this relationship exists only in Rh positives (Fig. 41)[100]. It's an interesting and unexpected result, because in the case of reaction times and in the case of weight gain during pregnancy (see the next chapter), it is the other way around: the Rh positives are actually protected against the negative effects of *Toxoplasma*.

The most important results have been however, obtained just recently. Our large ecological study showed that the burden associated with many diseases correlated with the frequencies of particular Rhesus genotypes in a country and that the direction of the relation was nearly always the opposite for the frequency of Rhesus negative homozygotes (positive) and that of Rhesus positive heterozygotes (negative)[103]. We confirmed these astonishing results by a case-controls study performed on 3130 volunteers, members of the internet community "Pokusní králíci" (Guinea pigs)[102]. The results of this study showed that Rhesus negative and positive subjects differed in many indices of their health status, including incidences of many disorders. Generally, the Rhesus negative subjects reported to have more frequent allergic, digestive, heart, hematological, immunity, mental health, and neurological problems.

XVII. How I corrupted the youth, and why I intend to continue

When I still worked in the Department of Parasitology, I often had to defend my research methods and approach to molecular biologists and biochemists, who gradually grew to predominate there. Finally, I gave up my efforts and moved with my entire team to the Department of Philosophy and History of Natural Sciences, which has a branch of theoretical and evolutionary biology, where my approach didn't stick out. My colleagues in the Department of Parasitology often reproached my results for being inexact and ambiguous. They used to say that there was nothing or almost nothing to conclude from them – the performance of Toxo positives and Toxo negatives differs by only a couple percent, and only after running the data through a complicated statistical test, can we discover a relationship. When we conduct the exact same study on a different subject group, the relationship we originally discovered appears completely different – sometimes even opposite. When we use another, more sophisticated statistical test, we suddenly find a relationship we didn't see before. In short, they say that our data allows for too much casual interpretation, and sometimes complete subjectivity. In contrast, the sort of results that biochemists and molecular biologists get are clearly unambiguous and objective, which must mean that they are perfectly exact.

From my personal experience in the field of molecular biology and immunology, I well know that such results only seem unambiguous. It's because biochemists and molecular biologists use simplified systems are standardized to the extent that they will always give the same results. But in reality, just by using reagents from a different company, they will also get different results for the same experiment. And this is not even the biggest problem. Besides, in today's globalized world, the number of independent producers of research reagents is rapidly dwindling, so researchers are often forced to buy chemicals from the same sources anyway, so their results are more comparable. A much larger problem is the biological material. If we use a different strain of lab mice, then the results of the same experiment (especially in immunology) will often be opposite to those obtained with the other strain. To get rid of the nuisance of ambiguous results, immunologists always try to use a system standardized to the smallest detail, that corresponds with the system used by colleagues in other work places. But it's a question whether this effort for maximum standardization doesn't come at a high price, and sacrifice some of the quality of the research. It's of course great that molecular biologists, unlike for instance experimental psychologists, can repeat the same experiment a hundred times over and get the same results, if they picked any one of the 200 strains of laboratory mice. But it's less impressive that if they conducted their experiment only twice, but on different strains of mice, then they might find that their "highly reproducible" results looked quite different. The reproducibility of results in current molecular biology and biochemistry is often achieved at the cost of their validity (Box 75 *What is test validity, and what does the increase of interleukin 12 in Toxo positive mice indicate?*). Results obtained under highly standardized, and often highly artificial conditions are clear and reproducible. However, they may tell us little about the real biological significance of the observed phenomenon. Let me explain. Probably the most interesting molecules in organisms are enzymes – biological catalysts (Box 76 *Why are enzymes such lousy catalysts?*). When biochemists describe a newly isolated enzyme, they must first purify it from the rest of the cellular homogenate, and then find its physical and biochemical characteristics, including various enzymatic constants and the reaction kinetics. Few people realize that the standard conditions under which this purified enzyme is studied are drastically different from the conditions which exist in a live cell.

Box 75 What is test validity, and what does the increase of interleukin 12 in Toxo positive mice indicate?

The most important measure of the quality of any study is the **validity of its data**. Validity is how closely something represents reality. A test which gives us reproducible results, and is highly sensitive and specific, but actually measures a different variable than we'd like it to, is quite useless. If we want to know whether latent toxoplasmosis causes immunosuppression or immunostimulation in mice, it does us no good that we can measure precisely and reproducibly how much the production of interleukin 12 (a protein which certain white blood cells use to communicate with other parts of the immune system) has increased two months after infection in the BALB/c strain. It's very likely, that in one strain of mice the levels of interleukin 12 will increase to ten times their original amount, but not change at all in another strain. And that goes without mentioning other complications. Although a significant increase in interleukin 12 levels should indicate that toxoplasmosis stimulates the mouse's immune system, further experiments may reveal (as ours really did) that in this case the increased level of interleukin is the result of immunosupression rather than immunostimulation. In *Toxoplasma*-infected mice, the production of interleukin 12 is most likely increased because important populations of WBCs, which should react to the interleukin 12 and the presence of foreign antigens by proliferating and producing defense substances, are actually significantly suppressed and hence don't react to these stimuli. So the "frustrated" regulatory WBCs produce more and more interleukin 12, all in vain[104].

So while biochemists are able to measure the characteristics of an enzyme, these characteristics may be completely different in the cell. Under cellular conditions, an enzyme which, according to biochemical tests, catalyzes a reaction in one direction, may actually catalyze it in the opposite direction, or also be the catalyst for a different reaction.

Box 76 Why are enzymes such lousy catalysts?

Because the cell doesn't need better ones. But let's start from the beginning. From school, most of us get the impression that a catalyst speeds up chemical reactions. Like much of what we take from school science, this impression is false. In reality, a catalyst doesn't speed up a reaction (usually, it even slows the reaction), but only influences which of many possible reactions will actually happen. Without the catalyst, this reaction may have occurred so rarely, that we wouldn't take notice of its product. Enzymes are good catalysts in the sense that can very specifically support certain reactions while suppressing many others. Yet they are also lousy catalysts in the sense that the reactions which they supposedly "speed up," are usually unbelievably slow. Of course there are exceptions, such as the enzyme catalase which can enable the decay of a 10^5 molecules in one second, but a large number of enzymes enact one reaction per second. For example, the usual rate of an enzyme participating in energy metabolism is 100-1000 reactions per second, which is a snail's pace for a chemical reaction[105]. How come evolution didn't develop more efficient enzymes? Probably because they wouldn't help the organism. The speed of an enzymatic reaction is not limited by how quickly an enzyme "turns," but by how quickly it receives molecular substrates. The enzyme generally receives these substrates by diffusion (or enzymes of the same metabolic pathway pass them to each other when coming into physical contact – but in that case the enzymes themselves must diffuse, or at least each enzymes must change position to transfer the product of its reaction to the next enzyme). Diffusion, in comparison to a chemical reaction, is unbearably slow, so it's no wonder that evolution didn't bother developing enzymes that acted more quickly. It's more likely that evolution worked on speeding up or getting around the process of diffusion. In many cases, for transporting reactants, it probably replaced diffusion with electrophoresis or even isoelectric focusing[106] (see Box 37 *Does a cell conduct isoelectric focusing?*).

In other words, the exactness of current molecular biology and biochemistry is only skin-deep. Even these fields are prey to the arbitrary interpretation of the researcher. The difference is that the evolutionary psychologist can't buy a genetically identical group of human subjects from a specialized firm, a group of subjects who were exposed to the same conditions their entire life. If we're studying humans, we must accept that we're working with a genetically diverse species, whose individuals undergo unique and disparate experiences. That is why the same experimental or observational study conducted on the students of the Department of Natural Sciences in 1995, 2005 and 2010 can give us different results. The population changed over the years, and the different cohorts of students can react differently to the same factor – in this case, infection by *Toxoplasma gondii*.

The necessity to work with very diverse subject groups may complicate our research, but in my eyes, it also gives us a great advantage. Our results aren't as easily reproducible, but they're obtained in a natural system; so they can be more safely extrapolated to the general population than results obtained in more "exact" fields. If we used a company-produced, genetically identical (but obviously non-existent) group of humans, we could never be sure that the results obtained from these experiments were applicable to the general human population. And scientists are definitely more interested in how toxoplasmosis, or any other factor, influences the real, genetically and phenotypically diverse, human population, than in how it influences an individual with a specific (and possibly rare) genotype (combination of genes) and a unique life experience. With a group of genetically identical humans, we could easily prove (or disprove) the effect of toxoplasmosis much more easily than with a representative group of people, and our results would be simple to reproduce. But a large part of these results would apply only to that strain of humans, and we couldn't extrapolate them to the general population (Box 77 *Pseudoreplications, and why statisticians fear them like the plague*).

Another peculiarity of working with people, which causes many methodological complications, is that our test subjects participate in our studies of their own will.

Box 77 Pseudoreplications, and why statisticians fear them like the plague

If you measured the height of one Toxo positive and one Toxo negative man, and found that the Toxo positive were 3 inches taller, then you wouldn't conclude that *Toxoplasma* has a positive effect on body height (at least I hope you wouldn't; if I'm wrong, then I'm afraid that my previous chapters probably fell short). But if you measured a hundred Toxo negative and a hundred Toxo positive men (Where'd you find them! Could you give them some questionnaires? And do you happen to know their Rh factor? Sorry, I got a bit carried away...), then even if the average height of the two groups were different by only a third of an inch, then you could almost be certain that toxoplasmosis and height are related. It should be obvious that measuring 50 men cannot be replaced by measuring one man 50 times. But it's less obvious that a group of identical octuplets in our subject group would cause a similar error. (True, it's not a common problem among humans, but if we were studying armadillos, then it wouldn't be unusual.) Eight identical siblings are genetically the same, so they do not represent eight independent observations – eight unrelated individuals randomly selected from the population. Including them in the test group would be almost like measuring the same person eight times. When planning any study, one must consider the risk of **pseudoreplication**. Let's say that we wish to the compare the surface area of leaves from oaks found on the southern and northern sides of a hill. We cannot measure 100 leaves from an oak on the southern side, and 100 leaves from an oak on the northern sides; then using Student's t test, compare the average area of a leafs for each tree. We wouldn't actually be comparing 200 objects, as the computer would assume, but only 2 – we'd be comparing just two trees, so any differences between them could be attributed to chance. To correctly compare the tree leaves on each side of the hill, we would walk between 100 trees on the southern side, and 100 trees on the northern side – and measure one leaf at each tree. Using the Student's t test, we'd compare the average area of a hundred leaves taken from each side of the hill – each leaf taken from an individual tree. We would take a similar approach to determine whether Toxo positives or negatives contributed more to the common pool during the experimental Public goods game (see 208). We wouldn't use all the sums which each Toxo positive student contributed to pool over 6 rounds of the game and compare it to those of Toxo negative students. First we'd calculate the average contribution of each student to the bank, and then compare the average contribution of all the Toxo positives to that of all the Toxo negatives using Student's t test (there's actually a better and more sensitive method, called Generalized Linear Mixed Models (GLMM), but this would do). If we didn't worry about pseudoreplication and took the first, wrong approach, we might unwittingly choose an unusually generous or penny-pinching student for one of the groups, and his six aberrant contributions would skew the comparison with other group.

If people don't wish to participate in the study, there's no way to force them. This means we are never certain about how representative our subject group is – and to what extent their results are applicable to the population they came from.

The third peculiarity (and difficulty) of working with people, is that we often can't study a problem using experiments. Instead, we must turn to observational studies – even when the problem better fits an experimental study. Let's say we want to determine whether infection by *Toxoplasma* would cause lower tendency novelty-seeking in mice. To this end, we take two identical groups of mice, infect one of them with *Toxoplasma*, then wait and observe if the groups begin to exhibit differences in novelty seeking. If so, it'll be obvious that the infection caused the change; as opposed to the possibility that differences in novelty seeking influenced which mouse was infected. But as I've mentioned several times (with thinly veiled regret) humans cannot be experimentally infected with *Toxoplasma*. We must use appropriate (and not always completely reliable) diagnostic techniques to separate individuals into those who were already naturally infected, and those not yet infected.

Then we test their tendency towards novelty seeking and hope that individuals with an extremely high or extremely low tendency aren't trying to hide their unusual characteristic, consciously or subconsciously – or at least, that they won't succeed. And even if we find a difference between the Toxo positives and negatives, we can't necessarily conclude that infection by *Toxoplasma* causes lower novelty-seeking. Lower novelty-seeking might increase the risk of catching *Toxoplasma*, or a third factor, such as the size of a person's hometown, might influence both these factors.

Working with such a complicated population of test subjects, it's understandable that we can't rely on simple methods to evaluate our data. In molecular biology, researchers usually make do without statistics. They look at the results of an electrophoresis and determine, for example, that after the addition of soluble iron salt, the band which marks the location of a certain protein has been enhanced, grown fainter or disappeared entirely. A visible change in the levels of a certain protein on the electrophoretic gel is an unambiguous sign that needs no statistical evaluation. In molecular biology, we often need just natural intelligence to draw conclusions from our experiments. Fields like evolutionary psychology usually call for an additional, complicated step of statistical evaluation. We may be working with humans or animals caught in the wild, individuals who differ in age, gender and a number of other traits. Because this creates a very heterogeneous subject group, we must control for the effect of factors that may influence the trait we are studying (for example, reaction time) more than the factor that we study (e.g. toxoplasmosis), but are not the topic of our research. These confounding factors (e.g. age, health) must be filtered out, so that we can see the relationship between the studied factor (toxoplasmosis) and the dependent factor (subject reaction time). To minimize the effect of confounding variables, we must often employ complicated statistical techniques (see Box 78 *How to deal with confounding variables*). Such techniques are readily available today. Often, we even have a relatively easy-to-use computer programs that take on the complicated and time-consuming work. Of course, without knowledge of the statistical techniques, the operations we carry out with our original data may seem like New Age shamanism. In reality, our complex world leaves us with little choice. Sophisticated methods are often the only way to understand complex phenomena and systems. This means that data analysis takes up a significant chunk of time. In many cases, collecting the data is much less difficult and time-consuming than it is to analyze them.

Box 78 How to deal with confounding variables

Confounding variables, among other things, increase the variability of our results, and so lowers our chances of discovering an existing effect in our data. To stop this from happening, we cannot ignore them, but rather must deal with them appropriately. The most effective technique is **elimination**. We include only individuals who have the same values for all confounding variables (for example, 24 year-old men, from Prague, non-smokers). That gets rid of much of the variability that would have existed in our data, and increases our chances of discovering the effect of the studied factor. But we also risk that this specific group of people will not be affected by the studied factor. The factor might affect only older people, or smokers, or young women. And even if we find that the studied factor has an effect on the specific group, we won't know that the effect applies to the general population – perhaps the effect is only true for our 24 year-old, male, Prague non-smokers.

Another tactic is to **block variables**. If we need to block a confounding variable, we estimate the effect of the studied factor or factors on the studied (dependent) variable using a paired test – for each pair, the two individuals have the same value for the confounding variable (see Box 67 *What is the difference between the paired and unpaired t tests, and why is the paired one better?*). If we have several confounding variables, the situation is much more difficult. In this case, we should at least try to ensure that the groups which we're comparing don't differ in the representation of values for each confounding variable. Let's say we're interested in the effect of toxoplasmosis on reaction time. We try to include the same percentage of: male smokers and non-smokers aged 21-25, 26-30...years; female smokers and non-smokers aged 21-25, 26-30...years etc., in the Toxo positive and the Toxo negative group. Blocking variables is an efficient approach in experimental studies, but less so in observational studies. Moreover, it's clear that blocking a large number of confounding variables is sometimes not only difficult, but rather impossible. Facing such a scenario, we should **randomize the data** in terms of the confounding variables. This means that individuals with any combination of confounding variables should be equally likely to be in the group exposed to the studied factor as in the control group. For example, it's obvious that we shouldn't expose women to the studied factor and use the men as the control group. The same principle means that we can't give the people who came to the morning appointment the active substance, and give the placebo to those who came in the afternoon (see also Box 15 *Popular mistakes when making a control group*). The health of the individual might influence the time of day he arrives. Furthermore, we must ensure that both the test subjects and those administering the experiment do not influence what group each test subject is placed in. For example, it's useful to flip a coin for each test subject to determine whether he goes in the experimental or control group. In observational studies, we are generally forced to **subsequently filter out** the effect of the confounding variables. For every individual, we carefully take down the value of confounding variables, and then include them as other independent variables in our analysis. It does not harm to do this even if we've already blocked or randomize these variables.

That brings me to another objection voiced against our research by colleagues who study so-called white biology (see pp. 12) – the molecular biologists and biochemists. Often they complain that our laboratory does too little manual work. According to them, a student of biology should start pipetting solutions before (or preferably instead of) breakfast, then switch to running from one complicated instrument to the other, harvesting cells and collecting them with a centrifuge, homogenizing tissue, sequencing or loading samples on chromatography columns – so in the evening, completely worn out, his other pair (their third this month) of scuffed-out lab sandals on his feet, he falls asleep on the living room couch, for his sore feet won't carry him all the way to bed. In our lab, we spend most of the time sitting at the computer, entering in data from paper forms, checking that we entered it correctly; at best we might be conducting an analysis, but of course we're never sure whether we understand it in detail, and whether it's an analysis which really fits our data (fortunately, a random passerby can't tell). Furthermore, the methods we use to collect data are not similar to the usual methods carried out in biological laboratories. We test many hypotheses using a questionnaire. A lot more of our behavioral studies are observational than experimental. I usually heard remonstrances against my work in connection to the complaint that my lab students did too little hands-on work and learned few methods. Apparently, it wouldn't have been that bad if only I worked in this manner – but students of the Faculty of Science should learn modern methods they will use in future research. So the main objection against my research style was that I am in fact corrupting the youth. In the end, I preferred to go to another department. My less fortunate colleague Socrates, may he rest in peace, had it much worse. Even in this case, I think that the complaint isn't justified (which probably doesn't surprise you). Today, modern science develops at such a rate that the instruments students used in their undergraduate or graduate work, will undoubtedly be different from the ones they'll be working with when they graduate and begin their own research. And this applies not only to instruments, but to all experimental techniques. I remember, back in the day, when we'd walk reverently by the door of the laboratory where they knew how to sequence DNA. Today we can fly our samples to be sequenced in Korea and get it cheaper than if we did it ourselves with our expensive machine. And the kind and clever Koreans (I hope it's clear that I'm talking about South Korea here) will thank the person who sends them the most samples to be sequenced in a year, by mailing them a digital camera for Christmas. Today we possibly pass reverently by the laboratories which can sequence an entire genome or proteome. I'm sure that in a couple of years none will bother with something so laughably routine, and will send genomes or protein mixtures they want sequenced straight to a specialized company in Korea or maybe China. And the amiable and skilled Chinese will give whoever sent them the most genomes a digital ping-pong table with a chocolate fountain for Christmas.

In my opinion, our undergraduate and graduate students should leave our laboratories with the ability to set up a scientific study (be it observational or experimental) in order to answer a question; as the ability to analyze data, and particularly to interpret their results. This last thing is perhaps the most important – a student must learn to look at his results realistically, whether they agree with his hypothesis or not. In short, during his undergraduate or at least graduate work, he should learn to think scientifically and deal honestly with the data he obtains. I believe that the work carried out in workplaces like mine is better suited for teaching this than the kind of work carried out in many labs focused on experimental science. In laboratories using the most sophisticated techniques of the day, students usually master one or two (OK, three) complicated techniques, learn to manipulate a certain machine or several ones. Often the measured data needs little evaluation; the student only has to believe his mentor and the machine that measurements given really mean what the manual says they mean. In our laboratory, most students soon realize that data are very treacherous, and that their analysis must be handled with kid gloves. They discover (sometimes through bitter experience) all the problems that must be tackled when collecting data – all the things that can skew or invalidate results. From the perspective of training future scientists, the experience that students gain, for example, in our laboratory of evolutionary psychology is more valuable than that gained in a typical modern molecular biology lab. Frankly, the most valuable thing students can learn from a good laboratory (and such labs fortunately began popping up in the past 10 years in the Faculty of Science) – whether he spends his undergraduate years working with a single dilapidated machine, handling ten cutting-edge instruments, or studying in our lab, where the most complicated machine he'll meet is a computer or a scanner to transfer questionnaires from paper onto the computer – the basic principle he should learn, is that anything he does in science, should be done honestly and thoroughly.

XVIII. Is *Toxoplasma* related to memory and sadomasochism? (Discreet promotion of my next book…)

Memory does not seem to be affected by *Toxoplasma* – or at least not medium-term memory, which is the kind of memory we've mainly tested. We gave each student or soldier a piece of paper with 30 simple drawings, including pictures of a flower, water pump, chain, elephant, giraffe. The subjects had one minute to study the pictures, before they put the paper away. Then they had ninety seconds to recall the objects they had seen. (The 30 objects are shown in Fig. 42, so you can try this for yourself. But you have to do it **before you continue reading**, otherwise the test won't be valid. So go on, try the test, write down the pictures you remember, and then come back to this page and continue reading.)

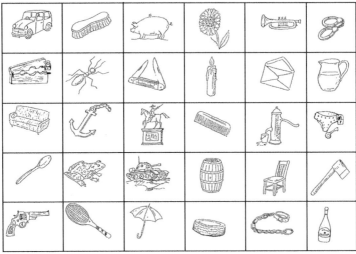

Fig. 42 You have one minute to remember as many objects from the picture as possible. Then close the book, please (don't worry, only for a short time, after which you may return to your interesting and valuable literature), and in the next 90 seconds write down all the objects you can remember. You can evaluate your results just after Box 79 Do men have worse memory than women?

The number of objects remembered by the Toxo positives versus Toxo negatives did not differ among the students nor among the soldiers. There was a certain difference in the number of incorrect answers. We still need to verify the results, but so far it seems that Toxo positives write down fewer objects that weren't actually on the paper. However, there was a marked difference between men and women – on average, men remembered significantly fewer objects (Box 79 *Do men have a worse memory than women?*). Interestingly, the Rh factor also had some effect on performance: Rh negative people made more mistakes, i.e. that made up more non-existent objects.

Box 79 Do men have worse memory than women?

According to our results, yes, but that may be due to the particular test and subject group. For example, if the subjects had to memorize a path through a maze, men would probably perform better. In any case, it's known that women perform significantly better in one type of memory test: the test of **unconscious memory**. We sit people in a waiting room, or have them walk through the room, and afterwards tell them to write down all the objects they remember from it. When the people know beforehand that they'll be taking the memory test, the performance of men and women is very similar. But when they aren't told ahead of time, the women always do much better than the men. Evolutionary psychologists think that this may be related with the division of labor in our evolutionary history. If it's true that women primarily worked at gathering, and men at hunting, then the ability to recall the location of a potentially useful plant could have been very beneficial to the women.

Our memory test is actually a bit more complicated than it pretends to be. We took **Meili's test of selective memory**[107], and made some minor modifications, so that we could use it to measure not just memory and aggressiveness (like in the original test), but also sadomasochistic sexual preferences. At that time, I got a student who wanted to do her graduate thesis on this topic, and no other. Of course my other colleagues were reluctant to explore such sensitive ground, but I was happy to become her advisor. Maybe because I suspected that, in comparison to this topic, the other problems researched in my laboratory would finally seem completely conventional to my colleagues.

Among the thirty pictures were a couple related to aggressiveness (the revolver, knife, tank and ax), some with a sadomasochistic theme (the handcuffs, collar, chastity belt and pillory). (Well? How many of these did you remember? According to Meili, you should count only the percent of these that are found among the first ten objects on your list.) I won't discuss what we expected in the case of sadomasochism – I'm saved this intriguing topic[108] for the next book (and believe me, dear reader, you have a lot to look forward to). But in the case of aggressiveness, we expected that the Toxo positive men would be more aggressive, meaning that they'd remember more aggressive-related objects, because they have more testosterone (Box 80 *What is the relationship between testosterone and aggressiveness?*).

But again nature refused to follow our expectations. We found no difference in the number of aggressive-themed objects remembered by Toxo positive or Toxo negative men or women. But it turned out that Toxo positive men remember fewer sadomasochistic objects and Toxo positive women recalled more of them. It doesn't seem likely that *Toxoplasma* would directly affect sadomasochistic sexual preference (but see[108]). Rather, it's possible that testosterone levels (which are greater in Toxo positive male students and lower in Toxo positive female students) influence sexual activity or at least sexual drive, and that sadomasochistic preference is more widespread in the population than commonly believed. Research by the famous American sexologist Alfred C. Kinsey shows that 12% of women and 22% of men are sexually aroused by a sadomasochistic story, and that 55% of women and 50% of men are aroused by a spanking from their partner. Our own results[109], obtained using an "internet trap", were quite similar – 42% of women and 51% of men who fell into our trap chose the "gates" with a sadomasochistic theme (Box 81 *How we caught sadists and masochists using an internet trap*).

Box 80 What is the relationship between testosterone and aggressiveness?

The relationship between level of testosterone and aggressiveness is probably just indirect. Intraspecies aggressiveness in males is normally connected with fighting for mates. In many species, it has been observed that the victorious male experiences an increase in testosterone level, while the loser experiences a decrease. Evolutionary psychologists think that this effect exists to encourage successful males to engage in further fighting for females, while inducing unsuccessful males to avoid such fighting, and instead try to win over females in a non-violent manner. Aggressiveness, or one's readiness and willingness to solve conflict with violence, truly correlates in males with the levels of testosterone, but the hormone itself does not induce it – testosterone only raises the male's sexual activity. According to recent theories, a better sign of increased aggressiveness is the ratio of testosterone to cortisol. In humans, changes in testosterone – an increase for victors, a decrease for the defeated – was observed in sports games, not only among the players, but also among the fans of each team. In our students, we observed[37] increased testosterone when they finished a written examination successfully (see Box 44 *Does a student's subconscious understand the material he's learning better than his conscious mind?*).

Of course, we could think of a completely different explanation, but better to wait until we confirm the results on other subject groups. Currently, we are attempting to verify the effect of toxoplasmosis on various types of medium-term memory, using variations on **Meili's test of selective memory**. We are trying to determine whether Toxo positivity will have an effect when the test subjects don't have to come up with the objects themselves. They will be a given a list of objects, and have to decide whether or not each object was among the pictures on the sheet. In another test, they will be instructed to click on the place where the given object was found on the previous screen.

Box 81 How we caught sadists and masochists using an internet trap

Imagine that you're on your favorite web browser, which you use to get to your email. A colorful banner ad pops up, saying "Gentlemen, come look at GROFOO!" (Fig. 43a). Or, if you registered as a woman on your email, it might say, "Ladies, look – it's GROFOO!" instead.

What do you do? Probably nothing, because one doesn't usually click on ads without good reason. But if the ad is seen by 400,000 women and 200,000 men, then about 1,000 of these women and 800 of the men will click on it. They'll find themselves on a homepage with three sadomasochistic pictures, and an area to indicate whether they are male or female (Fig. 43b). After selecting gender (the icon they click is shaded in blue), they continue to another page with six gates (Fig. 43c).

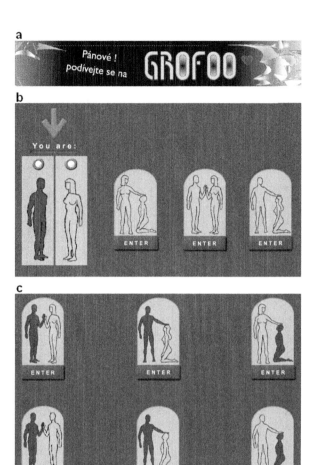

Fig. 43 An internet trap to "catch" sadists and masochists. On a certain unnamed search engine, very popular in the Czech Republic, this banner ad popped up (a). When the visitors clicked on it, they were brought to the introductory page (b), which asked them to indicate their gender. When they made their selection, the respective figure was colored in blue, and six gates appeared on the screen (c). Visitors usually persistently tried clicking on these gates, but all in vain. After clicking on any gate, they would see an hour glass appear on the screen with the message "The system is busy, please try again." The computer counted the order, number of clicks and time between the attempts to open each gate.

Now the trap awaits them: which gate will they choose? If a man chooses the gate where a blue male figure is kneeling before a not colored-in woman, the system records him as a heterosexual man with submissive (masochistic) sexual preferences. An hourglass appears on the screen, and after 5 seconds is replaced by the message "The system is busy, try a different gate." The system notes not only which gate is chosen, but also how long the person was willing to wait – how many gates, and in what order, they attempted before leaving the trap, probably quite disgruntled. Our victims were willing to spend an average 55 seconds in the trap, and about 20% of them tried 5 or more gates (some of them repeatedly). For example, the results showed the 46% of the men preferred a woman on their level, 34% preferred a submissive woman, 13% a dominant woman, 3% an equal man, 1.7% a submissive man and 2.5% a dominant man. For women, the results were similar: 52% preferred an equal man, 17.4% preferred a submissive man, 18% preferred a dominant man, 6% an equal woman, 3% a submissive woman and 3.2% preferred a dominant woman[109].

The effect of latent toxoplasmosis on long-term memory was tested using two methods. First we tried to use the results of the questionnaire that we had administered earlier, when we were studying whether the psychological differences we'd determined using Cattell's questionnaire also manifested in everyday behavior[55]. Among other things, we asked the students to answer seven questions regarding rules of social etiquette, to fill out the first name of famous Czech actors and actresses, to recall how much money and how many objects they have in their wallet, and to tell us whether they remember the birthdays and name days of their friends and relatives. Toxo positive and Toxo negative people gave different answers for a number of questions. But usually a qualitative difference was seen in the results of Toxo positive men and women (for example, infected men remembered fewer rules of etiquette, whereas infected women remembered more in comparison to uninfected people). This shows that the differences are almost certainly due to *Toxoplasma*-induced psychological shifts – in this case, Superego strength (Factor G) was lower in infected men and greater in infected women – rather than Toxo-induced changes in memory.

To further test long-term memory, we used our version of Meili's selective memory test. Two years later, we sent the 300 students who had taken the test an email, and asked them which of the objects used in the test they could still remember. Unfortunately, two years turned out to be too long, because we got very few usable answers: the students usually apologized, that they could not remember anything. We obtained usable data from only 115 students, including 10 Toxo positive women and 9 Toxo positive men. So it's not surprising that the results weren't statistically significant. But the Toxo positive students who replied remembered half as many pictures and made up less than a quarter as many objects as the Toxo negatives did. Based on these results, I'd say that if *Toxoplasma* influences memory, then the changes are more likely related to long-term than to medium-term or short-term memory.

XIX. Why infected women have longer pregnancies – the effect of toxoplasmosis on fetal development

I'm repeating myself already, but I must start by saying that chance often played a large role in our studies. On one such occasion, chance was responsible for our discovering that latent toxoplasmosis affects the course of pregnancy. As I already mentioned, one of our subjects' groups on which we were studying the effect of toxoplasmosis on the human psyche, included data regarding pregnant women who were screened for toxoplasmosis around their 16th week of pregnancy. Each woman had been determined to be 16 weeks pregnant according to two methods: the results of the ultrasound from her first visit to the obstetrician, and according to the starting date of her last menstrual cycle. Therefore, we had four pieces of data for each woman: the result of toxoplasmosis testing, the length of pregnancy determined by that ultrasound examination, the length of pregnancy according to the date of her last menstruation, and her weight at the time of the toxoplasmosis screening. Unfortunately, we had no data on her body weight at the beginning of pregnancy. For curiosity's sake, when entering these four pieces of data into the computer, we tested to see if Toxo positivity correlated with any of the other data. Statistical testing quickly revealed that Toxo positive women had a greater body weight at the time of the toxoplasmosis screening. Also, when using the menstrual cycle (but not the ultrasound) method to estimate the duration of pregnancy, Toxo positive women appeared to have been pregnant longer than Toxo negative women. First we'll look at pregnancy weight, because it's a simpler relationship, but still very interesting in terms of both the research methodology and health implications. Toxo positive women in their 16th week of pregnancy had a greater body weight than did Toxo negative women. But when we plotted a graph of *Toxoplasma* antibody levels versus body weight, we observed something strange – there was a positive rather than negative correlation between the antibody levels and body weight. The lower the antibody levels of a woman – the longer she'd been infected with toxoplasmosis – the less she weighed in her 16th week of pregnancy. For a long time, we couldn't to reconcile these two contradicting results. Finally, it occurred to us that it could be because of the women who were infected for the longest time – the women who had such low antibody levels that we falsely diagnosed them as Toxo negative. Because of this false classification of the longest-infected – and therefore also the lightest women – among Toxo negatives, we may have gotten the average weight of infected women seemingly lower than that of uninfected women.

This hypothesis, which supposes a false diagnosis in a significant portion of toxoplasma positive women, was, "surprisingly" enough, not appreciated by our colleagues who were carrying out the toxoplasmosis screening. It was also clear that it would be difficult to test this hypothesis, if only because we no longer had the original samples available, and so we couldn't repeat the serological tests. Finally, we tackled the problem using a test specially developed for this issue. It was not a statistical test, but a permutation test. Permutation tests belong among randomization tests, which can be used for a similar purpose as statistical test. In comparison to statistical tests, randomization tests have a number of advantages, and among other things, they can be much more easily adapted to a specific case. A permutation test is conducted by first electing a parameter that would reach a higher (or lower) value if a particular factor had an effect (such as the effect of toxoplasmosis), than if this factor had no effect on the data. For example, if we're interested in knowing whether *Toxoplasma* affects the weight of mice, we select as our parameter the difference between the average weight of infected and uninfected mice groups, and estimate the value of this parameter from our experimental data. Then we permute the experimental data – we randomly change the order of the weight values of all the mice in our file, regardless of whether the mice were infected or uninfected. And again we calculate our parameter for the re-ordered (permuted) data. After permuting the data many times, such as 999 times (of course, the computer does it for us), we finally have available 1000 values of the parameter, one of which was calculated for the real data and 999 calculated for permutated data. We order these values from smallest to largest and see where our not jumbled up data value winds up. If it's among the 2.5% lowest or 2.5% highest of the values, we can conclude that the given factor (toxoplasmosis), probably affects the weight of mice (Box 82 *One- and two-sided tests*).

We developed a permutation test which allowed us to filter out the effect of the incorrectly diagnosed Toxo positive people – that is, the women who had such low antibody levels, that they were falsely classified among the Toxo negatives[110]. We conducted the test by taking our data from about 760 pregnant women, which included their body weight throughout pregnancy. A previously selected percent of the Toxo negative women with the lowest weight was moved by our computer into the group of Toxo positive women – in four independent tests we tried reclassifying 5, 10, 15 and 20% of these Toxo negative women. After moving the lightest Toxo negatives into the Toxo positive group, the computer program calculated the average body weight of each group, and then found and stored in its memory the difference of the two averages. Then it randomly jumbled up our data (permuted it). Without regards to Toxo positivity, it separated the women into two groups which corresponded in size to the original Toxo positive and Toxo negative groups. Then the computer again moved the given percent of the lightest women from the subgroup that corresponded size-wise to the original Toxo positive group, into the second group that corresponded to the original Toxo negative group. For both permuted subgroups, the program calculated the averages, and finally calculated and memorized the difference between them.

Box 82 One- and two-sided tests

If we test the hypothesis, that a certain factor (maybe toxoplasmosis or Rh) somehow affects (we don't know how beforehand) a certain trait of an organism (such as intelligence of the test subjects), we must use a so-called **two-sided test**. Using this test, we estimate the probability that the given factor does not affect the studied trait – we compare this probability with the probability the factor does increase or decrease this trait. In some cases, we expect ahead of time that the given factor affects the studied trait in a specific manner, perhaps by lowering it. In the first study we may find that toxoplasmosis increases the intelligence of infected women, and in another experiment we try to verify this finding on independent data. Or we discover that toxoplasmosis increases body weight of infected people, and then subject this data to two independent tests to determine whether the given effect occurs in both men and women. In such a case we use a **one-sided test**, which allows us to estimate the probability that the given factor doesn't influence or lowers the studied trait – we compare this probability with the likelihood that the factor increases the studied trait. Some statistical programs automatically give you the results of both the two-sided and one-sided test; other times we must calculate on our own the results of the one-sided test from the results of the two-sided test, usually (but not always) it's very simple – we divide the value P from the two-sided test by two. Before the age of computers, the significance of a test was determined using statistical tables. In these tables, one found whether the calculated value of the test, in our case the t value, represented a statistical significance at the 5% (or 1% or 10%) level for a given degree of freedom, i.e. whether the probability of obtaining our data or more extreme data due to chance is lower than 5% (or 1% or 10%). When calculating a one-sided test, a researcher used the same tables as for a two-sided test, but considered results of the test to have 5% statistical significance when he found 10% significance in the tables. Of course, we must have a good reason to use a one-sided test (and a good reason most certainly isn't that we failed to find statistical significance using the two-sided test), and we have to decide to use it before starting data analysis.

The entire procedure of forming permuted groups was subsequently repeated many times, in our case 2999 times, so finally we were left with 3000 values, the difference in average body weight of the groups of women. And one of these 3000 values was the difference calculated from the original data, and the other 2999 values were the differences calculated from randomly jumbled up data. The last step was to look in what percent of the highest or lowest values the real-data value was found.

The results of the permutation test were unambiguous. We only have to move 5% of the lightest Toxo negative women into the Toxo positive group for our permutation test to show that Toxo positive women have significantly lower weight (as opposed to significantly greater, as we saw using the original data set). The value which expressed the difference between the average body weight of Toxo positive and Toxo negative women was found among the 2.1% lowest values. From this one can conclude that the observed difference in body weight between Toxo positive and Toxo negative pregnant women probably wasn't due to chance. The paradoxical finding that Toxo positive women have a greater body weight than Toxo negative women, even though women infected longer weigh less than those infected more recently, was most likely caused by incorrect identification of certain Toxo positives. The women who were longest infected with *Toxoplasma*, and had the lowest weight, were placed as Toxo negatives due to the insufficient sensitivity of the serological test[110]. And I was pleased that my cherished randomization tests once more triumphed over statistical tests (Box 83 *Randomization tests*).

Another curiosity we observed in our data was that the duration of pregnancy estimated according to the last menstruation, but not the duration of pregnancy estimated by ultrasound, was longer in Toxo positive than in Toxo negative women. That seemed to us both very interesting and very difficult to explain. From the start, we came up with several working hypotheses. One assumed that Toxo positive women conceived in a later phase of the fertile period of their menstrual cycle than did Toxo negatives.

Box 83 Randomization tests

The probability of the hypothesis, that a certain phenomenon (for example, an average longer reaction time observed in Toxo positive people) is the result of chance (i.e. the probability of a so-called null hypothesis), can be estimated using three possible methods. Most often we use a statistical test, in this case most likely Student's t test. **Statistical tests** give us only an approximate result, because regardless of the true distribution of the data in the subject group, the tests assume some standard shape of this distribution (mostly a normal distribution). However, statistical tests can also be nonparametric, in which case they require less assumptions about the parameters, e.g. the distribution of the data set. Nonparametric tests are usually weaker than the parametric tests, i.e. they have higher probability of providing false negative results. This difference, however, is not very large and I usually prefer to use nonparametric type of the test whenever available.

The precise probability of obtaining our or more extreme data under conditions of validity of the null hypothesis can be obtained using an **exact test**. Such a test uses combinatorial formulas to calculate how many different combinations can be made based on our data, and in what fraction of these combinations the studied effect is just as (or more) extreme as observed in our original data. For example, our program first calculates (or a stupidly written program uses the brute-force method of generating and checking all combinations) how many different ways the 760 pregnant women can be divided into two groups of sizes that correspond to the size of the Toxo positive and negative groups. Then it calculates what percent of these combinations has an equally larger or larger difference in average body weight between the two groups, as was found in the original data.

The third way to determine the probability of obtaining our or more extreme data under condition of validity of a null hypothesis and therefore to estimate the validity of null hypothesis is to use a randomization test. **Randomization tests** are similar to exact tests, but instead of finding the fraction of all possible combinations with equal or (more) extreme values than seen in the real data, we only find this fraction out of a randomly created sample (for example, out of 1000 random combinations). The accuracy of the test's result depends on the size of the sample we use; from a practical standpoint, it depends above all on our patience and also on the speed of our computer. Randomization tests can be further divided

> into permutation tests and Monte Carlo tests.
> **Permutation tests** compare real data with many samples
> of data created by permutations (random mixing up) of
> this real data. **Monte Carlo tests** compared real data with
> many samples of data generated using our model of the
> observed phenomenon. Let's say that we want to use
> a Monte Carlo test to estimate the probability that playing
> dice are false. When we throw ten dice and find that nine
> of them land showing a 6, we let the computer "throw ten
> dice" ten thousand times, and calculated what percent of
> these "throws" gave nine or even ten 6s.

But the reason why this would occur wasn't apparent. We considered both physiological and ethological mechanisms – for example, a change in the frequency of sexual intercourse. If Toxo positive women had less frequent sexual intercourse, one might expect that on average they become pregnant later than Toxo negative women. But why would Toxo positive women, who test as more welcoming, sociable and frivolous, have less frequent sex? Let's think along the lines of good ol' gender stereotypes. Maybe the Turkish researchers who revealed that toxoplasma infected women suffer more often from migraines are right[88].

Another working hypothesis, probably more serious in its implications, was finally shown to be true. It states that *Toxoplasma* slows the development of the human fetus. If the duration of pregnancy is determined from an ultrasound taken at the time of the woman's first visit to the obstetrician, then a fetus which develops more slowly will appear smaller and therefore younger, so the doctor will falsely estimate a shorter duration of pregnancy. Since a doctor usually screens women for toxoplasmosis in their 16th week of pregnancy based on the results of an ultrasound, rather than accordingly to less reliable data – such as the day the women remembers that she had her last period – he probably gives Toxo positive women a later appointment than to Toxo negative women. Therefore, the total duration of pregnancy if estimated from the date of the last menstrual cycle appears to be longer at the time of *Toxoplasma* screening.

We tried to test this hypothesis on other, unrelated subject groups[111]. Collaborating with three gynecological laboratories from two private clinics, we gathered a wide range of data regarding the pregnancy duration of Toxo positive and negative mothers. Using this population sample, we confirmed that at the time of the regular screening conducted around the 16th week of pregnancy, the pregnancy duration of Toxo positive women was longer than that of Toxo negative women, when estimated using the date of the last menstruation, but not when estimated using the ultrasound examination. In this case, we also had available data about the total length of pregnancy, as well as the birth weight and length of the newborn. Thanks to this, we were able to prove that pregnancy in Toxo positive women on average lasts 1.5 days longer than in Toxo negative women (Fig. 44).

That shows that *Toxoplasma* does slow the development of the fetus, probably in early pregnancy. Seeing as the newborns did not differ in birth weight or length, it's apparent that the pregnancy lasts until the fetus reaches a sufficient size. Only then does the woman give birth. Originally, you see, we also had the hypothesis that infected and uninfected may have pregnancies of equal duration, but that the newborns of infected women were on average smaller. It may seem that the 1.5 day difference in pregnancy duration due to toxoplasmosis is inconsequential when considering the general variability in pregnancy duration. In reality, the existence of even such a small difference could be important (Box 84 *The size of an effect in basic research*).

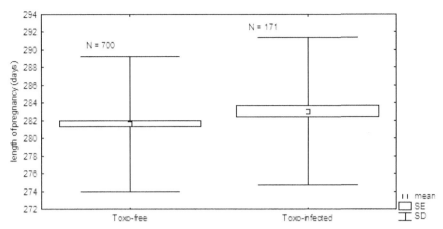

Fig. 44 The difference in the average pregnancy duration of women with latent toxoplasmosis and that of uninfected mothers. The difference is less than two days, but due to the low variability in pregnancy duration and the high number of test subjects, is statistically significant. You can very roughly estimate that the difference is statistically significant if the standard error rectangles don't overlap.

The indication that that fetal development in Toxo positive mothers is slower than normal, and primarily in the earlier part of pregnancy, means that this effect of the infection might be accompanied by other defects. For this reason, in the next phase of our study, we observed the postnatal development of children born to Toxo positive versus Toxo negative mothers. Even here we found several interesting differences.

It seems that children born to Toxo positive mothers also undergo slower postnatal development[112]. When the children were about 2-year-old, we sent the women we had screened for toxoplasmosis a questionnaire, which, among other things, determined the physical and mental development of the child. The women were asked when their child began lifting its head, when it started rolling over on its stomach, when it learned to sit on its own, when it began to crawl, when it began to walk on its own. In total, we got back completed questionnaires from 278 uninfected and 58 infected women. What was interesting, was that infected women who gave birth to a boy, were less likely to send us back a completed questionnaire than were the other women. After statistically filtering out the effect of the child's birth weight (which we found did not correlate with the Toxo positivity of the mother), we saw that children of Toxo-infected mothers had statistically significant slowed development in all the areas we asked about, except for when they started walking.

Box 84 The size of an effect in primary research

If, using a statistical test, we determine that a particular fertilizer raises the yield of a crop by 0.001%, it doesn't make much sense to further study the possible applications of this finding. But unlike in applied research, in basic research the **strength of the effect** plays a much smaller role (see also Box 49 *How to determine the effect size in statistics*). In basic research, we're interested in finding how the world around us works. We form individual hypotheses and progressively try to refute them using data obtained from simulations of the studied phenomena, or collected from experiments or observational studies. If our hypothesis states that a particular phenomenon does or does not occur under certain circumstances (for example, that the reaction time of infected persons worsens with time after infection), it is first important to determine whether this phenomenon exists – and not necessary to find how strong it is (for example, what percent of variability in people's reaction times is due to time after infection). It doesn't matter whether the length of infection explains 0.5 or 50% of variability in reaction time; either way, the results support our hypothesis that *Toxoplasma* worsens reaction time, and undermine the hypothesis that people with longer reaction times are more likely to get infected by the parasite. Of course, even scientists prefer strong effects to weak ones. Strong effects are less likely to be the indirect result of the influence of a different factor, a factor which we failed to include in our model. For example, a very weak correlation between time after infection and reaction time could be caused by the fact that some recently infected persons suspect that they had an infection (they recall suspicious symptoms), so they're more interested in the study and try more in the reaction time tests. But there's a similar (though somewhat smaller) risk also in the case of a strong effect. In science we must always approach results, our own and those of others, as provisionary, and we must also be prepared that they may mean something else than we originally believed (see Box 65 *How hypotheses are tested in science?*).

Since latent toxoplasmosis is not transmitted from the mother to the child, the children of Toxo positive women were not infected – nevertheless, their development was delayed. Of course, we can't rule out the possibility that our results don't show differences in the development of these children, but differences in how Toxo positive versus Toxo negative mothers perceive them. Or the results may be due to chance, and we may fail to replicate them on another test groups (Box 85 *When and when not to use a Bonferroni correction*).

Box 85 When and when not to use a Bonferroni correction

It is still a matter of contention, even among scientists, when it is and isn't appropriate/necessary to conduct a Bonferroni correction for multiple tests in basic research. To me it seems most reasonable to always apply a Bonferroni correction to multiple tests; but we cannot overestimate the results of the correction, whether it determines the tests to be statistically significant or insignificant. By applying sophisticated stepwise corrections, we can finally estimate the probability that the observed result is due to chance. (We will be not able to determine it solely using a standard Bonferroni correction, i.e. by multiplying the obtained P values by the number of subtests; it would be necessary adjust not only the P values, but also number of tests in which the effect was statistically significant – using, for example, the my favorite **Bejamini-Hochberg procedure**[113], or certain variant of the **stepwise Bonferroni correction.** But we usually need to determine, in which of the subtests the observed differences in the parameter are probably real and in which of the subtests they are probably due to chance. In such a case, any method of correction for multiple tests probably won't help us – the only thing that's left for us to do, is to repeat the study (preferably several times), to convince ourselves that the observed effect occurs in other, independent data.

We later found another very significant difference between Toxo positive and Toxo negative women. In one case, the observed effect was so strong that infected women reached on average a two times larger value in the studied parameter than did uninfected women. But these differences will be described in the next chapter.

XX. *Toxoplasma* prefers guys! How and why infected women give birth to more sons

When studying the effect of toxoplasmosis on the course of pregnancy we discovered another phenomenon, which we had not previously expected and whose existence shocked us. Šárka Kaňková, my undergraduate student at the time, noticed that latent toxoplasmosis also influences the sex ratio at birth (SRB); that is, the ratio of sons to daughters[114]. Specifically, we found that Toxo positive mothers gave birth to more boys than girls (Fig. 45). But this relationship is only true for women with high or medium levels of antibodies, i.e. for women who were infected for a relatively short amount of time – an estimated 1-4 years.

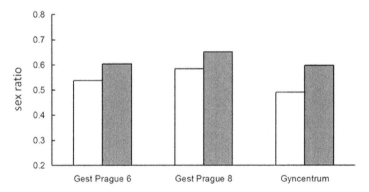

Fig. 45 The prevalence of sons in mothers infected by Toxoplasma. *In all three obstetric and gynecological clinics, Toxo-infected mothers (gray bars) gave birth to significantly more sons than daughters. With the exception of the Gyncentrum, uninfected women (empty bars) also gave birth to slightly more sons. We hypothesize that this is because Gest clinics are private clinics where mothers pay for obstetrical care; most likely these women have a higher economic status. In such a case, we would expect a shift to a higher proportion of sons due to the Trivers-Willard effect. The statistical significance of the effect toxoplasmosis on the gender index at birth was 0.001.*

In contrast, women with very low antibody levels, i.e., those who were infected long ago, had predominantly daughters. The observed differences were highly significant; for example, in 111 women with the highest antibody levels (women who were probably infected 1-2 years before pregnancy), the ratio of sons to daughters was 260 to 100 (Fig. 46).

Šárka Kaňková later confirmed this effect in two independent tests using mice as models[115]. The first experiment had 60 total mice, and the second had 80; in each experiment, half the mice were infected and the other half uninfected. About six weeks after infection, we put the males and females together, and then looked at the sex ratio of each litter – that is, the ratio of male to female offspring of each infected or uninfected mouse. Again we found that 2-3 months after infection, the mice gave birth to significantly more sons than daughters. With time after infection the ratio of male to female offspring evened out and began to reverse, so that towards the end of the experiment, mice which had been infected 4-6 months gave birth to more daughters than sons – that it, even more daughters than the control mice. The results obtained on mice, therefore, precisely correspond with the trends observed in pregnant women. In the earlier phases of latent toxoplasmosis we noted a predominance of sons, and in the later phases a prevalence of daughters.

The decrease of the sex ratio in later phases of infection – i.e., the birth of more daughters than sons – might be due to cumulative negative effects of latent toxoplasmosis on the host's state of health. The symptoms of such health impairment are discussed in chapter 10; and the Trivers-Willard effect (a decreased sex ratio in females with poor health) will be discussed at the end of this chapter.

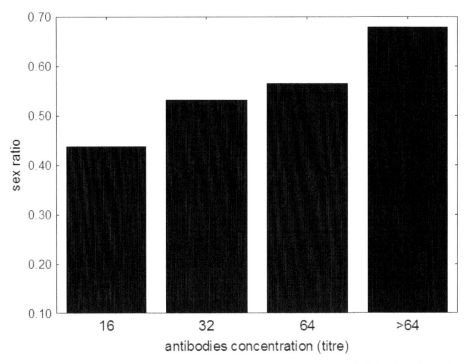

Fig. 46 The relationship between the gender index at birth (the fraction of sons in the offspring, or also the probability of having a son) and the concentration of antibodies against Toxoplasma – the latter correlates with the time elapsed after infection. The level of antibodies was determined using indirect immunofluorescence. Sixteen women with the lower concentration of antibodies – women infected longest ago – had more daughters than sons (a gender index lower than 0.5). In contrast, 132 women with the highest concentrations of antibodies (titer 64 and higher), women infected relatively recently, gave birth to more sons than daughters (gender index 0.68). This group of 132 includes 111 women with a titer of 128 and higher, who had a gender index of 0.72, a ratio of 2.6 daughters per son. Relationship of gender index on concentration of antibodies against Toxoplasma was highly statistically significant (P = 0.002).

The increased sex ratio in the earlier phases of toxoplasmosis is much more interesting. It may stem from one of three things: a side-effect of *Toxoplasma* infection; a side-effect of Toxo's manipulation of the immune system; or even a direct manipulation by the parasite of the sex ratio, in an effort to increase its chances of transmission to another host. It certainly isn't easy to recognize, whether we're observing a manipulation advantageous to *Toxoplasma*, or whether it's only a side effect of infection by this parasite.

In species in which a mother with latent toxoplasmosis cannot transmit the parasite to the fetus, it might be beneficial for *Toxoplasma* for mothers with acute toxoplasmosis (which can be transmitted to offspring) to give birth to sons. In most mammals, the males are the ones who migrate the greatest distances, and who therefore can act as a better vector for spreading *Toxoplasma* to new, not yet infected population. But in some species of mice, congenital transmission of toxoplasmosis from the mother to offspring can occur, and in this case it would be more advantageous for the parasite if the infected mother gave birth to more daughters, who could then pass down the parasite to their children. Since it isn't clear what host species *Toxoplasma* is originally adapted to (see chapter 10), it's difficult to judge what is and isn't beneficial for the parasite.

It's not too clear how *Toxoplasma* affects the sex of newborns. What seems most likely to us is that *Toxoplasma* induces immunosuppression, i.e., it lowers the immunity of its host, and thereby actually saves part of the mother's embryos, which would have been aborted. It's known that when eggs are fertilized by sperm, the sex ratio in humans is about 1:1. But when the fertilized egg nests in the uterus, this ratio significantly changes in the favor of sons; specifically about 2.5 to 3 times more male than female embryos begin to develop. But in the other phases of pregnancy, male embryos are much more susceptible to being aborted (Box 86 *Males as mutation gargage-cans and cheap testing material*).

Box 86 Males as mutation garbage-cans and cheap testing material

Nature honored males with these two functions, among others: the function of a trash can for mutations, and the function of serving as guinea pig, on which evolution can test its usually not too successful experiments. Above all, in males there occur significantly more mutations than in females. This is partially because, during the development of sperms there is greater cellular division than during the development of eggs, so that there is a greater chance of mistakes happening when the DNA is being copied. But this might not be the only reason: it's likely that at least in some species, females have a more efficient system for correcting mutations. In this sense, males serve as cheap material, which evolution uses to test new mutations. The vast majority of mutations are harmful, and their carriers are much less likely to survive to maturity and successfully reproduce. If males carry these bad mutations, then it doesn't jeopardize the population and species, because in most species just one adult male in the population is enough to fertilize all the females. A population with a certain number of females grows just as quickly, regardless of how many males are present, or how many died, for example, as a result of harmful mutations. Of course, in species in which both parents take care of the offspring, this isn't completely true; but even among humans there exists the expectation that during catastrophes women will be saved first. (Today I wouldn't count on it; I hate to think what would happen if on the deck of a sinking Titanic, I ran into a militant feminist, or heaven forbid the head of the department of gender studies.) Some of the mutations in the males can turn out to be beneficial, and these get into female genomes through the daughters of these males. But males also serve as a trash can, where the species tosses new mildly harmful mutations. The embryonic development of female fetuses in a number of studied species, including our own species, is substantially more resilient to negative effects than is the embryonic development of males. This resilience pertains to both the negative effect of the environment on the mothers, as well as to the influence of harmful mutations found in the genome of the fetus. Whereas the development of a male fetus may be strongly altered due to a certain mutations, and the biological fitness of the newborn male individual is significantly decreased, the development of a female fetus is affected much less by the same mutation, and the biological fitness of the child is often normal. Furthermore, it seems that male fetuses are exposed to a stricter "quality check" than are the female fetuses. A birth defect that would have led to an abortion in the case of a male embryo, often does not do so in the case of a female embryo. By aborting male embryos which carry combinations of harmful mutations, mothers rid the population's gene pool of these mutations, which is favorable in regards to the population and the entire species.

For this reason, when it comes to the birth, the ratio of males to females isn't 2.5 or 3 to 1, in favor of the males, but only 1.06 to 1 in favor of the males. And in getting rid of male embryos, the immune system of the mother plays a significant role. This is because male embryos are more immunogenic (meaning that they set off a strong response of the mother's immune system) than are female embryos. Besides the antigens found in both sons and daughters, there also exist H-Y antigens, which come from proteins typical to male tissue.

If *Toxoplasma* can induce immunosuppression, then it lowers the effectiveness of aborting male fetuses, and many more males will complete their development.

The same mechanism may also occur in the case of another interesting phenomenon, described by Czech parasitologists in the 60s. Otto Jírovec, the founder of modern Czech parasitology, with his coworkers showed that children with Down's syndrome often, in about 84% of cases, have Toxo positive mothers[116]. In a control group, which gave birth to children without Down's syndrome, the prevalence of toxoplasmosis was about 30%. In the fathers of children without Down's syndrome the occurrence of toxoplasmosis was also only 30%. The dramatically greater prevalence of toxoplasmosis in mothers of children with Down's syndrome could again be explained by the fact that most fetuses with chromosomal defects, in this case, fetuses which have an extra copy of the 21st chromosome, are aborted in healthy women, specifically aborted in early pregnancy. It's known that in the first weeks of pregnancy there occurs some sort of checking of the embryo's quality. Seeing as *Toxoplasma* suppresses immune activity, it may be able to lower the strictness of this control. As a result, a much greater percent of damaged fetuses survives, and that is why Toxo positive women give birth to more children with defects. From an ethical standpoint, it's an interesting question whether the parents of children with Down's syndrome should curse or thank *Toxoplasma* – the parasite doesn't actually cause Down's syndrome in the children, but only saves their lives.

We originally deduced this idea, that latent toxoplasmosis could be associated with immunosuppression, from the results of our studies regarding changes in the sex ratio at birth, as well as results described by Otto Jírovec. And recently we got the direct data to prove it. Working with Ilja Stříž of the Prague Institute for Clinical and Experimental Medicine (IKEM), we discovered that both men and women with latent toxoplasmosis have fewer B cells (white blood cells that produce antibodies) than do uninfected persons. In addition, we found that infected men have fewer white blood cells in general – and specifically fewer natural killer (NK) cells and monocytes. Interestingly, infected women have a higher number of white blood cells, including NK cells and monocytes[66]. It's possible that the differences between men and women are related to the fact that each gender has an opposite shift in testosterone concentration associated with toxoplasmosis.

Testosterone lowers immunity, and as we discovered, infected men experience an increase in the hormone, whereas infected women see a decrease[35]. The fact that infected women have a higher number of certain cells involved in immune reaction does not necessarily mean that aren't experiencing immunosuppression. Šárka Kaňková conducted experiments on the matter, collaborating with Vladimír Holáň and Alena Zajícová from the Institute of Molecular Genetics. These experiments showed that female mice infected with *Toxoplasma* have higher levels of certain regulatory molecules which stimulate immune reaction, such as interleukin 12. However, their macrophages (white blood cells, the purpose of which is to devour large foreign objects or dead parts of the body's own tissue), and lymphocytes (white blood cells which produce antibodies (B cells), or which kill foreign cells (T cells)) do not react appropriately to these stimuli. In contrast with the macrophages of uninfected mice, these macrophages produced less nitric oxide (a substance which the macrophage needs to kill the intruder). In addition, the spleen cells (which include a variety of white blood cells) produced less interleukin 2 (a substance that activates lymphocytes, namely T cells) and divide less than in uninfected mice when exposed to foreign cells from another strain of mice.

The results were unambiguous – while the immune system of mice infected with *Toxoplasma* could recognize foreign antigens, it was not able to react to them[104]. It's particularly clear that the cellular mediated immunity is damaged, and this is precisely what part of immune system we suspect could be responsible in uninfected mice and women for aborting defective male embryos. Now I will dare to paraphrase the famous last sentence of the article in which Watson and Crick explained the structure of DNA: "It did not escape our attention that the existence of immunosuppression in a significant part of the population" (in people with latent toxoplasmosis) "could also have serious consequences for public health." (Didn't I warn you in the introductory chapter that I'm modesty itself?)

Now that we understand the probable mechanism behind the effect, we can return to the question of whether the shift in the offspring's sex ratio at birth is due to *Toxoplasma*'s manipulatory activity, or merely a side effect of the disease. The second possibility is starting to seem more likely. Immunosuppression, particularly the suppression of the cell immunity that targets intracellular parasites, certainly helps *Toxoplasma* survive in the host, and the effect of lowering cell immunity on the sex ratio at birth could just be a side-effect of immunosuppression. But nature doesn't always abide by reason nor the popular principle of Occam's razor, so who knows if this is really true (Box 87 *Occam's razor*).

Box 87 Occam's razor

Medieval scholar **William Occam** may have been to first to establish the principle of parsimony or maximum simplicity, a principle which we know today as **Occam's razor**. According to Occam, "entities must not be multiplied beyond necessity." Today, this is interpreted to mean that where a simple explanation is sufficient, we shouldn't pointlessly impose a more complicated one. For example, we know that immunosuppression is beneficial for *Toxoplasma*'s survival, and that many species of parasites use it to combat the host organism's immune system. We also know that suppression of immune cells should automatically be associated with changes in the sex ratio at birth in favor of male offspring. In this case, it is not necessary to assume that *Toxoplasma* might be intentionally manipulating the number of male offspring. We employ the principle of Occam's razor, not because of a naïve assumption that nature adheres to it, and a belief that the simplest model is always correct. Rather, we know that the simplest model is the easiest to test, so we're more likely to discover if it's incorrect. In our case, we should definitely not abandon the distinct possibility that *Toxoplasma* intentionally manipulates the sex ratio at birth of its host – but the simpler possibility, that *Toxoplasma* doesn't do so, should be the one we first try to test.

When evaluating the data of our studies focused on the change in the SRB of Toxo positive mothers, we stumbled upon another interesting phenomenon, though it has nothing to do with *Toxoplasma* (yes, such effects do exist). It's known that in many animals the gender of the newborn depends on the health and social status of the mother. Females who are healthy and dominant in the social hierarchy have more sons, whether females with a low social standing and worse state of healthy have more daughters. The so-called Trivers–Willard hypothesis explains that there is much greater competition to reproduce among males than among females. In many species, only the top males reproduce, leaving behind an enormous number of offspring. The weak males don't mate at all. In females, this relationship between fitness and number of offspring isn't as crucial, since even weaker females usually reproduce. But if a female is healthy and in high social standing, she can invest enough resources in her offspring, so they will be more fit. In sons, fitness is important, for it can decisively influence their reproductive potential – again, only the top males will reproduce. So it pays off for females in high social standing to give birth to mostly sons, and for less fit females to invest in mostly daughters.

The Trivers-Willard hypothesis was tested several times on humans. It was discovered that even this atypical species likely fits the hypothesis, but unlike the studies on other animals, the results aren't entirely convincing. There are only a couple of studies which show that women with higher social standing really give birth to more sons than daughters. One such study was conducted on European nobility, which has detailed family trees. It was discovered that, unlike in the normal population, sons predominate.

Similarly, it was discovered that American presidents, as well as high-ranking generals and multimillionaires, have a greater ratio of sons. Just because only a few studies have been conducted on humans we were pleased to find that even our results indirectly confirm the applicability of this hypothesis to humans[114]. It turned out that in our sample of women, the highest percentage of sons was among women who went to the most expensive local obstetrics and gynecology clinic, followed by women of the cheaper local clinic, and then those of the cheapest. But even the women who went to the cheapest local clinic gave birth to more sons than did women anywhere in Prague. Most of the Prague women were under the care of institutes originally run by the state, where they don't have to pay for basic health care. This correlation between the expensiveness of obstetrical care and the sex ratio at birth was also statistically significant, and in our opinion represents another independent confirmation of the applicability of the Trivers-Willard hypothesis to humans. One may expect that women who go to a pricier local clinic generally come from circles that are socially and economically better-off than those frequented by women who attend a free clinic.

In chapter XVI, we saw that some effects of latent toxoplasmosis occur only in Rh negative people, and that humans of the Rh+ blood group are temporarily (Rh positive homozygotes) or even permanently (Rh positive heterozygotes) protected against them. Of course we were interested to know whether the protective effect in Rh positives also applies in the case of Toxo's effect on pregnancy. When we studied the effect of toxoplasmosis on the sex ratio at birth, we found no differences between Rh positives and negatives. On the other hand, we saw substantial differences in Toxo's effect on weight gain during pregnancy (Fig. 47).

Put simply, out of four possible combinations – Rh negative Toxo negatives, Rh negative Toxo positives, Rh positive Toxo negatives, and Rh positive Toxo positives – only one is significantly different from the others. It is the group of Rh negative women with latent toxoplasmosis[117]. In the first trimester, these women have almost twice the weight gain as do the other group of women. Around the 16th week of pregnancy, they have about a 1.6 kilograms greater weight gain, which is a statistically significant difference that remains constant until the end of pregnancy. Yet the length and weight of their newborns are not significantly different, which shows that the greater weight gain of the Rh negative Toxo positives is due to the greater weight gain of the mother – likely in her uterus, amniotic sac or amniotic fluid – not a higher weight of the embryo itself.

It's known that greater weight gain in early pregnancy usually signifies a defect in fetal development. We see it, for example, in mothers who smoke.

Therefore, our results again indicate that Rh positivity (though the mechanism is still unknown) protects the mothers against negative effects of latent toxoplasmosis, this time against the bad effects on pregnancy. In Rh negative women, the effect of toxoplasmosis on pregnancy is unusually strong. The weight gain of Rh negative Toxo positive women in the 16th week is about twice that in other women – the strongest effect of toxoplasmosis we have seen in all our years of study. It will certainly be essential to determine whether Rh positivity protects only against the negative effects of toxoplasmosis, or whether its influence extends to other factors, such as smoking, diabetes, or obesity.

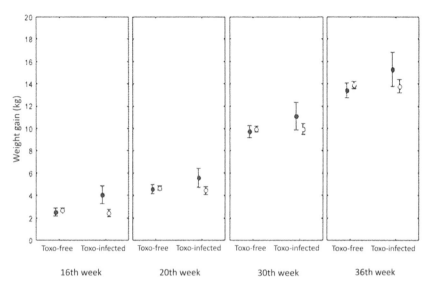

Fig. 47 The abnormal weight gain of Rh negative Toxoplasma *positive women during pregnancy. At the 16th week of pregnancy, the weight gain in this group was almost twice as big as that in other women. This is the strongest effect of latent toxoplasmosis on the human organism that we've observed in our 20 years of study. Rh negative women are indicated by black circles, and Rh positive women by unshaded ones. The study examined 646 Rh positive Toxo negatives, 138 Rh negative Toxo negatives, 167 Rh positive Toxo positives and 27 Rh negative Toxo positives. With the exception of the 36th week, the effect was always highly statistically significant.*

XXI. Getting Toxo, quick and easy – risk factors for toxoplasmosis

Another topic we studied long-term in our laboratory, but none too systematically, regards the effect of various risk factors on the likelihood of catching *Toxoplasma*. When we had our test subjects complete questionnaires, we almost always included questions related to possible risk factors that the person might have come into contact with *Toxoplasma*. Among other things, we discovered that in Czech population, the main risk of infection comes not from having a cat, but a rabbit. And we were surprised at how many Toxo positives kept rabbits themselves, or at least their family did. For example, in our group of 3255 soldiers of the mandatory military service, 33% of the respondents said they raised rabbits for meat[91].

There are two reasons why raising rabbits is a significant risk factor for *Toxoplasma* infection. First off, it's possible that the rabbit is entirely blameless, and that it merely indicates a country rather than city lifestyle – and the country lifestyle is associated with characteristics like closer contact with soil, which increase the risk of infection. Of course we tried to verify this possibility, and so, in our analysis, we included information about whether the subject lives in a village. It turned out the effect of the rabbit was apparent even after we filtered out the size of the settlement, in which that person spent their childhood or was currently living in. Still, this isn't definite proof that the rabbit is a direct source of infection. Even when a subject answers that he grew up in a small village of less than two thousand people, it's possible that his family lived a typical city lifestyle on the third floor of an apartment complex. On the other hand, a person who wrote that he lives in Prague, the capital, may actually-live in a small village which has been administratively joined to Prague, but actually reflects a country lifestyle. So it's possible that we can determine a country lifestyle more reliably based on the raising of rabbits, than according to the size of a person's settlement.

Of course, raising rabbits could be a direct risk factor, rather than merely an indication of certain lifestyle. Raising rabbits is associated with killing, skinning and cooking the rabbit, and during this process, infection can easily occur. Blood from the infected animal can get into scratches or abrasions on the skin, and this is an easy route of infection. A large percentage of rabbits in the country are infected by *Toxoplasma*. It's undoubtedly because they're fed with hay that was generally stored in silos or on dirt. Cats often loiter in these places, and probably leave behind droppings with *Toxoplasma* cysts. Contaminated hay can not only infect the rabbits, but also their owners.

Just having a cat isn't a very significant risk factor, though it is a source of infection to a certain extent. If the cat is kept indoors and given cooked food, it's hard to see how it could get infected. Even a cat free to go outside the house, that occasionally catches a mouse in the garden or neighboring field for a midday snack, actually isn't a likely source of infection for its human. An infected cat releases *Toxoplasma* cysts only during a brief period of days to weeks after the initial infection, before developing resistance to subsequent infections. Furthermore, when one follows basic hygiene and regularly cleans the litter box, it's hard to catch *Toxoplasma* from an infected cat. The cysts which the cat releases are not yet infectious; it takes several days for them to mature. Perhaps this is a safety mechanism for *Toxoplasma*, so that the parasite does not infect the cat which just released the cysts (Box 88 *Why parasites fear their own children, and how they defend against them*). If a person keeps the litter box clean, the risk of infection should be low. Of course, pregnant women should certainly leave cleaning the litter box to someone else; though they're unlikely to be infected, the consequences of toxoplasmosis reaching the fetus can be tragic (see Box *57 How dangerous is Toxoplasma in pregnant women?).*

Our studies show that aside from rabbits and cats, there exist other sources of infection, some of which are quite important.

Box 88 Why parasites fear their own children, and how they defend against them

Parasites are in danger from their own children. A parasite that reaches a host has found an island of plenty, surrounded by the wasteland that is the rest of the world. Many parasites produce an immense number of eggs in their life time, but most of the offspring never find a host, and die. If a parasite reaches the correct host, then it's like winning the lottery – he's often the only winner out of a million losers that has the chance to pass down his genes to the next generation. Evolution programmed the parasite to take full advantage of his opportunity. For example, the parasite must reproduce at the right rate, so that it can produce the maximum number of offspring within the host's lifespan. But that means that it cannot reproduce too slowly (which would produce too few offspring), nor too quickly (this would soon kill the host and also stop the parasite from reproducing). However, problems can occur in three cases. Firstly, when a host already infected by one parasite is infected by another strain, leading to **superinfection**; secondly if **mutants** appear among its offspring; and lastly, if the parasite in question **reproduces sexually**. In all three scenarios population residing in the host would become genetically variable. This creates a situation in which these different parasites compete to reproduce. But this race is destructive: the fastest reproducing, i.e. the most virulent, strain wins in that it creates the most offspring per day, but it also ends up prematurely quickly killing the host. This brings an end to the reproduction of both this strain, and of all the others, so that the parasites churn out fewer offspring overall. In parts of the host population where a parasite is highly prevalent, superinfection and the resulting destructive race (for the highest virulence) is more likely to occur. This explains why viruses whose genetic information is encoded in RNA, are often nastier to their hosts than are DNA viruses. RNA replication involves incomparably more mutations than DNA replication, so the many mutated strains of RNA viruses have a much more intensive battle for speedy reproduction. The fact that most parasites reproduce asexually, or even not all, inside their host may be a preventative measure against this destructive race. They reproduce sexually only to create offspring which are to leave the body to seek another host. Asexual reproduction is a safer method to employ inside the host, because it produces genetically identical individuals which cannot compete amongst each other and kill off their single host. Offspring from sexual reproduction swiftly leave the host – natural selection has proven that sexual reproduction resulting in variable offspring is necessary for success (or rather a draw) in the coevolutionary battle with a host – and therefore cannot initiate this destructive competition. This may also explain why *Toxoplasma* cysts must mature for several days before becoming infectious. An infected cat which releases *Toxoplasma* cysts in its feces, can wash its rear with no danger of being re-infected. And the *Toxoplasma* found inside the cat needn't fear competition with its genetically distinct offspring that would lead to premature destruction of the host.

Gardening is a very strong risk factor. If a person tends his own garden, then it's very likely that his or the neighbors' cats will dig a latrine in the garden bed, or rather several small latrines. The cysts in the dirt can remain infectious for several years, so when our gardener eventually munches on a carelessly washed carrot, he may easily be infected.

Another significant source of infection is the consumption of raw or undercooked meat. Based on our results, it seems that this infection source is quite prevalent in the Czech Republic. It's not that raw meat is a common dish, but rather that it is often sampled during preparation. For example, regularly tasting the dough for liver dumplings is a surefire way of getting infected. It's also possible for a cook who has abrasions on her skin to get infected by merely handling the raw meat. It's remarkable that men are usually infected by *Toxoplasma* in their childhood (when they're playing with dirt or in the sandbox), whereas women have an increased risk of infection when they're starting a family and begin cooking very often. The consumption of raw meat as part of a dish isn't a serious source of infection in the Czech Republic, because the most common raw meat dish is steak tartar, made from minced beef. Toxoplasmosis isn't prevalent in factory farmed cattle, and furthermore, cysts found in beef are usually small and probably not very infectious. The situation is probably different in countries that eat undercooked or even raw mutton or pork. In Czech Republic, of course, the greatest source of infection could be raw rabbit meat. And then custom of giving children raw liver as a source of iron is therefore a reliable way of infecting them with Toxo, particularly when it's raw pig liver and the animal comes from a homestead, or a modern bio-farm.

Aside from these known risk factors, we discovered three more. One of them is the already mentioned blood group. People with AB blood are significantly more likely to be infected than people with type A, B, or even O blood, which carries the lowest risk of infection[91]. Soviet researchers already noticed this, but their article was published only in Russian, so this risk factor is virtually unknown.

The other risk factor, which we found quite shocking, is the number of blood donations. In several groups of blood donors, we tested possible risk factors and repeatedly found that toxoplasmosis is much more prevalent among blood donors – a sector of the population that should be very healthy – than among control groups obtained from state serological surveys. A more detailed analysis revealed that the probability of infection increases with the number of blood donations, not with how long an individual has been donating blood. Our hypothesis is that frequent blood donations somehow weaken the immune system, and that at least the blood donors who don't maintain the advised intervals between donations suffer from some degree of immunosuppression, and therefore are more susceptible to *Toxoplasma* infection. This probably extends to infection by pathogens in general. This means that blood donors – and particularly paid blood donors – should be more closely monitored, to ensure that people don't donate too frequently. It might even be worthwhile limit the absolute number of blood donations (Box 89 *Asking too many (bad) questions will bring you lots of (nonsense) answers*).

Box 89 Asking too many (bad) questions will bring you a lot of (nonsense) answers

When studying risk factors, we discovered yet another interesting phenomenon[118]. It turned out that the usual epidemiological practice of verbally questioning the subject regarding his contact with each risk factor is very unreliable. When we conducted the same epidemiological study on the same population using both verbal questioning and a written form, we got significantly different results. We employed verbal questioning when screening our students for toxoplasmosis. The person conducting the intradermal test asked each student whether they often come into contact with cats and whether they eat or sample raw meat. The results showed that among people who didn't have toxoplasmosis, there existed a strong correlation between replying "yes" to both questions. Those who said that they eat or taste raw meat almost always replied that they often come into contact with cats. But when we mailed the same people a questionnaire which included these two questions, the correlation between cats and raw meat completely disappeared. The simplest explanation is that people are very suggestible, and when a doctor or researcher asks them about these two questions, they reply in the affirmative. Maybe some hypochondriac subjects already believe that they're Toxo positive, or perhaps our students think that their affirmative reply will please the questioner. In contrast, when we ask about the same two risk factors in an impersonal questionnaire, it rules out much of this psychological effect, and there's no correlation between the answers. Therefore, our results indicate that one should be cautious when considering verbally acquired answers, and whenever possible, rather employ a written questionnaire.

The third new risk factor was the number of sexual partners – toxoplasmosis could be sexually transmitted disease[119].

Another interesting finding from studying *Toxoplasma* risk factors regarded the psychological traits of cat owners and raw meat consumers[118]. Since we discovered in the mid-90s that Toxo positive and negative people differ in a number of psychological factors, we decidedly needed to ascertain whether the same factors correlated with keeping cats or eating raw meat. That would mean that the association between Toxo and particular psychological traits is because people with a certain personality profile are more likely to be cat and meat lovers, which increases their chances of being infected. So we calculated the statistical relationship between Cattell's psychological factors, and cats and raw meat. We found that keeping cats, as well as eating raw meat, does correlate with certain psychological traits – but different traits than those in which toxoplasma-free subjects differ from those with latent toxoplasmosis. Specifically, we noticed that people who kept cats had lower emotional maturity (factor C, Emotional stability) than did humans who didn't, and people who answered that they ate raw meat expressed a more phlegmatic personality (factor Q_4, Tension).

Therefore, our fear that the relationship between Toxo and the psyche could be due to a psychological effect on the risk of infection – as opposed to the possibility that infection alters the psyche – wasn't validated. At least our current results don't support it. But I must admit that we've conducted this study on only one, fairly small subject group, so we need to verify the results on others. We have the data for it, but time seems a bit harder to get hold of.

XXII. Tying things up – what else is in store?

A lot. Many results that we were unable to finalize and publish relate to the health of the test subjects. In a number of studies, we asked the people how often they get the common cold, whether they suffer from allergies or headaches, whether they feel physically and mentally well. I wrote in this place of Czech version in 2011: "So far it seems that there's no statistical significance to be found between these characteristics and toxoplasmosis." This is not true anymore. In 2014 we showed that prevalence of toxoplasmosis in 88 countries correlated with incidence of many diseases in these countries[44]. In a large cross-sectional cohort study we showed that 333 *Toxoplasma*-positive subjects scored worse than 1153 *Toxoplasma*-negative subjects in 28 of 29 health-related variables and reported higher incidence of 77 of 134 disorders[120].

In several subject groups, we observed a correlation between Toxo and smoking. For example, Toxo positive soldiers of mandatory military service smoked less than did uninfected soldiers. A possible explanation is that Toxo positive people have a lower tendency towards novelty seeking (a decreased Cloninger's factor NS). And it's known that people with a lower NS factor have a significantly lower tendency to seek out various kinds of risky behavior. There are fewer alcoholics, drug users and apparently fewer smokers among them.

Using a very detailed questionnaire, we determined how satisfied the people were with various aspects of their lives. It turns out that infected men were significantly less satisfied with almost all aspects of their lives than were uninfected men; but the biggest difference was between the answers regarding health. On the other hand, infected women are generally more satisfied with their lives than are uninfected women. The effect of *Toxoplasma*-gender on **satisfaction** with one's health had a statistical significance of up to

0.003; the effect on overall satisfaction had a statistical significance of 0.040. But it's not clear whether Toxo positive men are always negative whiners, and Toxo positive women happy-go-lucky, or whether men with latent toxoplasmosis really have worse health.

It'll also be important to experimentally verify whether Toxo infected individuals really **startle** less than Toxo negative people. So far we're relying only on what they told us in the Toxo questionnaire, but such subjective statements don't necessarily represent reality. We'll have to create a "startling" computer program (we're already excited), and test whether infected persons are really startled more easily. Similarly, we need to verify that infected persons are less fearful. So far we're planning to show horror films to small groups of students in the dark basement of the natural sciences building, and use an ECG (electrocardiograph) machine to monitor how afraid they are.

Speaking of scaring, we must also try to study in details how the **prepulse inhibition (PPI) of the startle response** works in Toxo positive people[121]. What does this mean? When we run background noise interspersed with irregular intervals of loud sound around 120 dB through the headphones of test subjects, the people are startled each time and blink. This movement can easily be recorded with an electrode placed in the vicinity of the eye. But if a softer acoustic impulse – in other words, a prepulse – precedes the loud sound, the people will not be as startled. From our perspective, the ability to measure PPI allows us to more meticulously observe the difference in the startling reaction of Toxo-infected people. Furthermore, it's known that people with schizophrenia have significantly different results from PPI tests. Schizophrenia patients (probably not all, and to various extents) don't have PPI of startling reaction, and react more to sound pulses with a prepulse than to those without.

But recently we discovered that morphological differences in the brains of schizophrenics are actually present only in Toxo positive patients[80]. You already know that these morphological differences don't occur in Toxo positive non-schizophrenics (Chapter XV). Therefore, we should determine whether the differences in PPI of schizophrenics and non-schizophrenics could also be caused by toxoplasmosis, which we know to be more prevalent in the schizophrenic than in the normal population.

Another issue we'd like to revisit regards the effect of toxoplasmosis on the levels of **steroid hormones**. So far, it's a mystery why Toxo affects testosterone levels in students – increasing them in males and decreasing them in females – but does not affect them in the patients of the immunology clinic. First off, we must try to confirm the results observed in the students on other groups (at the time you're reading this, we'll have tested the soldiers) as well as on lab animals. In mice it seems that toxoplasmosis lowers testosterone levels in both males and females[67]. Furthermore, we must look at the levels of other steroid hormones, such as the female hormone estradiol and the stress hormone cortisol. The fact that infected women give birth to more sons indicates that they might have increased levels of estrogen. So far, our results haven't confirmed this hypothesis (the observed difference in estrogen levels was in the predicted direction, but not statistically significant). But I must remind you that we studied hormone levels on a group of patients attending an immunology clinic, who might differ from in hormone levels from the general population. Once again, the truth is that we have data from other groups to test the hypothesis, but haven't grasped the time to analyze them. And so that I have an alibi beforehand, the hypothesis explaining the increased sex ratio in Toxo positive mothers by a higher concentration of estrogen isn't actually ours, but one which William H. James suggested to explain our sex ratio data – at least we won't be so disappointed, if we don't manage to prove it[122].

We're very excited for the results of scent testing on humans[22]. It'll be interested to verify whether some of the differences in the **olfactory preferences** observed in infected mice will also apply to people. So far, our results are quite promising, but I'd hate to jinx it (Fig. 48). It's a shame that currently the department of natural sciences is not supportive of keeping infected animals. In the past we conducted a number of interesting experiments on mice, and found that, under certain circumstances, infected females prefer the scent of infected males above that uninfected males. The differences in the attractiveness of male scent seem to relate to an effect discovered and meticulously studied by Denisa Hladovcová during her undergrad work in the department of zoology.

Her results show that in infected males, the production of proteins known as major urinary proteins (MUPs) decreases over the long-term. Mice use these proteins to release pheromones, molecules used for scent communication. Interestingly, the effect of toxoplasmosis on MUP production is incredibly strong – for the studied strains of mouse and *Toxoplasma*, it was comparable to the effect of castrating the male mouse. Males seem perfectly healthy eight weeks after infection, but they're no longer too keen on rolling in the hay.

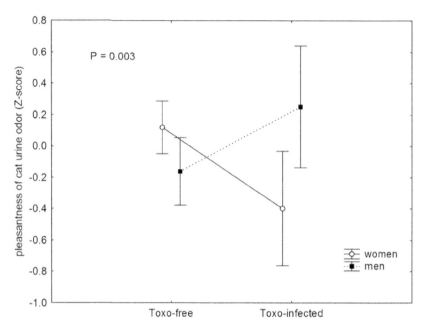

Fig. 48 The effect of Toxoplasma *infection on the perception of the odor of cat urine.* Toxoplasma-*infected and uninfected students evaluated on a 7-point scale the pleasantness or repulsiveness of the urine odor of various animals (cat, horse, dog, hyena, and tiger). Only in case of cat urine was there a substantial effect – infected men liked the smell of cat urine more than did uninfected men, whereas infected women disliked it more than uninfected women. Our results demonstrate that* Toxoplasma *significantly changes the olfactory preferences of infected people; and that the phenomenon of fatal attraction, described originally on Toxo-infected Norwegian rats and mice, is also true for humans. It is interesting that the originally described attraction occurs only in men, whereas women react in the opposite way. The Z score calculated for individual evaluators (y axis) represents unpleasant odors with negative numbers, and pleasant with positive numbers. The evaluators were exposed only to small amounts of each sample, so the intensity of the odor was very low. For this reason, very few students actually guessed the true nature of the samples. For example, they usually guessed horse urine to be mushrooms or manure, and cat urine to be from the hospital or sea.*

What currently interests me the most is the role of the Rh factor in protecting against the negative effects of latent toxoplasmosis. I'd like to know which effects are influenced by the Rh factor; how Rh positivity can be beneficial or harmful whether the protective effect of Rh positivity is due to the gene for Rh positivity or other genes closely associated with it. And above all, I'd like to know if Rh positivity protects against further negative effects, not just those of latent toxoplasmosis[102,103]. Then, of course, we're also interested in discovering the mechanism behind all this. But I'm afraid that unraveling this mystery will have to wait for a physiologist or molecular biologist. Until the function of the RhD molecule is discovered, we evolutionary biologists cannot explain how Rh positivity can protect against *Toxoplasma*. So fellow scientists, hop to it – I'm eager to see what we'll find.

As I'm nearing old age and growing forgetful, it might be in my own interest to explore the possibility that toxoplasmosis is associated with **Alzheimer's**. There is evidence to suggest that dopamine production – specifically, the death of dopamine-producing cells – plays an important role in the disease. According to our results, latent toxoplasmosis in both mice and humans is accompanied by an **increase in dopamine levels** in the brain, which may be related to the presence of two genes coding for enzymes involved in dopamine formation. It's possible that when dopamine is produced excessively in the brain, the dopamine-producing cells die off more quickly.

A similar mechanism might also cause **Parkinson's disease**, since dopamine is known to play an important role in its onset. So far results are ambiguous: in 2010 two independent articles were published by Turkish researchers, one proving and the other refuting a relationship between latent toxoplasmosis and Parkinson's disease[82,83].

Toxoplasmosis is involved in other neurological effects, too. Aside from **migraines**, *Toxoplasma* plays a role in some forms of **epilepsy**[123].

So far, this disease has but a few studies to its name. One of the more convincing articles comes from Turkish authors, and found that the frequency of toxoplasmosis was 52% among 50 patients with cryptic epilepsy, 22% among 50 patients with other forms of epilepsy, and 18% among 50 persons without epilepsy[124]. Other studies show that toxoplasmosis could trigger obsessive compulsive disorder in some people[125]; and several articles indicate a connection between *Toxoplasma* and autism[126].

Don't think that I'm blaming toxoplasmosis for all the health problems we face today. (That's why I haven't mentioned the opinions of Ukrainian doctor Vladimir Krivonos, who claims that this parasite is even responsible for balding – which could be explained by the increased synthesis of testosterone in infected men – and primarily for some kinds of cancer, including prostate cancer. Since I'm writing this in parentheses, it doesn't actually count, and I am free to distance myself at any time.) I try to be as objective as possible, and judge *Toxoplasma* fairly, so I readily confess that there exist a number of diseases for which no connection to Toxo has been proven. But even objectivity and fairness can't be overdone: one could argue that no connection has been proven simply because these diseases have never been tested for a connection to Toxo. Well, at least we have a despicable suspect, as our most famous playwright, poet, composer, teacher, traveller, philosopher, mathematician, inventor, detective, and sportsman (of course not Václav Havel, but Jára Cimrman) says in the play "Murder in a Parlor Car Compartment."

Meanwhile, *Toxoplasma* flourishes under the disinterested eye of the public. In most European countries, it's decreasing in the population, which may be due to the fact the kids who once played in the sandbox now spend their days in front of a computer screen. But whatever we may tell ourselves, the events in the western-most periphery of Asia supercontinent are not so important. Unless current trends are rudely interrupted, China and India will finally achieve a consumer society. Then their households will not only get 3D television, but also house cats. I'd be surprised if they didn't – having a cat makes life much more enjoyable than owning a 3D TV (I know from experience, because recently I had six of them in my house – six cats, that is, not TVs).

As a result, the global prevalence of toxoplasmosis certainly isn't decreasing. And be warned, today's 30% world-wide prevalence includes everybody, including infants – which means that every other individual will become infected with *Toxoplasma* sometime in his life. Latent toxoplasmosis cannot be cured. To be honest, no one (aside from the before-mentioned Vladimir Krivonos) has actually tried it – and why would they, since the latent form is officially harmless. Actually, already infected woman aren't at risk from catching *Toxoplasma* during pregnancy, so their children are safe from congenital toxoplasmosis. It would probably be worthwhile to see if latent toxoplasmosis can be effectively treated by certain antipsychotics, which have been shown to specifically and strongly inhibit the reproduction of *Toxoplasma* in tissue cultures[127]. It would also be advisable to see if the temporary health problems in a significant number of people given preventative anti-malaria drugs aren't actually the side-effect of dying *Toxoplasma* cysts. *Toxoplasma* is closely related to the *Plasmodium* which causes malaria (both of them are sort of like strange plants – their cells actually contained modified chloroplasts known as apicoplasts). Therefore, it's quite likely that the same drugs may kill both of these parasites. We certainly should look at the concentration of *Toxoplasma* specific antibodies in people using various anti-malaria drugs.

But the most important weapon against *Toxoplasma* should be prevention. Cats – and primarily today's domestic cats – are the definitive hosts of *Toxoplasma*. The spread of toxoplasmosis in the human population could probably be contained using an oral vaccination, which would immunize even feral cat populations around human settlements.

Getting rid of *Toxoplasma* isn't feasible, since it's too clever a parasite with a wide range of intermediate hosts. The only way might be too kill off the entire cat population – but I wouldn't dare to suggest this even jokingly, for fear that my family would disinherit me and perhaps even tell our tomcat Freddy (he already suspects me; whenever I'm typing this book in bed, he decides to interfere by lying on the keyboard). But it would be feasible, through a good vaccination program, to decrease the global prevalence of toxoplasmosis to under 5%, a prevalence seen in many parts of Asia. With an effective form of pharmacotherapy, it might even be possible to significantly decrease the health and subsequent economic effects of all forms of toxoplasmosis. In a world without *Toxoplasma*, women might be less social, friendly and stylish, men about three centimeters shorter and have lower levels of testosterone; but when we consider that lack of Toxo would also decrease the number of car accidents, suicides and schizophrenics, I think that it would be worth it. In a world without the lovely *Toxoplasma*, I'd have to find another controversial and exciting research topic. Attentive readers[*] of this book might think that this would be an endeavor, the difficulty of which would only be comparable to that of developing a *Toxoplasma* vaccine. But you needn't worry. The other day I was returning to Prague after giving a lecture in Brno. At home, I realized that I wasn't at all tired from the long bus ride, although I'm usually weary after traveling more comfortably in a train. I've observed a similar thing when coming home from the university. I rise from the computer at five thirty, still chipper, but after a forty-minute ride in the subway, I have to stretch out on the bed and the most difficult task I can accomplish in the next half hour is to lend my body heat to the above-mentioned Freddy, who lays on my belly while purring in sympathy.

---

[*] Mythical creatures that appear in the particularly wild dreams (of a slightly erotic character) of the authors of popular science books.

What if my two observations were related? And what if this meant that… But someone surely would have discovered already. Although… It wouldn't be too much trouble to quickly run a questionnaire… Tomorrow a hundred of my students are taking an exam, and I could give them a short questionnaire to complete afterwards to determine when they feel tired. In a couple of hours, I'd know whether there's a grain of truth in my hypothesis. And if I discovered a statistically significant effect or at least some trend, I can put a similar questionnaire on my blog and the frequently visited blogs of my friends; likewise, I can post a questionnaire on a popular web page devoted to health. Furthermore, I could organize an entertaining experiment on the Prague metro with volunteers who sign up on my Facebook page, Guinea pigs… Do you want to hear our results? I won't tell you about them just yet, but get ready – it's gonna be the bomb!

The end (for now, at least…)

Reference List

1. Lafferty KD. Can the common brain parasite, *Toxoplasma gondii*, influence human culture? Proc R Soc Biol Sci Ser B. 2006;273:2749-55.

2. Wang AL, Wang CC. A linear double stranded RNA in *Trichomonas vaginalis*. J Biol Chem. 1985;260:3697-702.

3. Flegr J. A rapid method for isolation of double stranded RNA. Prep Biochem. 1987;17:423-33.

4. Flegr J, Cerkasov J, Kulda J, Cerkasovova A, Stokrova J. Double stranded RNA in *Trichomonas vaginalis*. Acta Universitatis Carolinae - Biologica. 1986;30:281-6.

5. Flegr J, Cerkasov J, Kulda J, Tachezy J, Stokrova J. The dsRNA of *Trichomonas vaginalis* is associated with virus like particles and does not correlate with metronidazole resistance. Folia Microbiol (Praha). 1987;32:345-8.

6. Flegr J, Cerkasov J, Stokrova J. Multiple populations of double-strranded RNA in two virus-harbouring strains of *Trichomonas vaginalis*. Folia Microbiol (Praha). 1988;33:462-5.

7. Hampl V, Horner DS, Dyal P, Kulda J, Flegr J, Foster PG, et al. Inference of the phylogenetic position of oxymonads based on nine genes: Support for Metamonada and Excavata. Mol Biol Evol. 2005;22:2508-18.

8. Kolisko M, Cepicka I, Hampl V, Kulda J, Flegr J. The phylogenetic position of enteromonads: a challenge for the present models of diplomonad evolution. Int J Syst Evol Microbiol. 2005;55:1729-33.

9. Kostka M, Hampl V, Cepicka I, Flegr J. Phylogenetic position of *Protoopalina intestinalis* based on SSU rRNA gene sequence. Mol Phylogenet Evol. 2004;33:220-4.

10. Dawkins R. The selfish gene. Oxford: Oxford University Press; 1976. 224 p.

11. Flegr J. Frozen evolution or, that's not the way it is, Mr. Darwin A farewell to selfish gene. Praque: Charles University in Praque Press; 2008. 224 p.

12. Hubbard G, Bayarri MJ. Confusion over measures of evidence (p's) versus errors (α's) in classical statistical testing. The American Statistician 2003;57(3):171-8.

13. Ninio J. A ternary cellular-complex between lymphocytes-B and lymphocytes-T and antigen-presenting cells. Immunol Today. 1986;7:354-.

14. Lanzavecchia A. Antigen-specific interaction between T-cells and B-cells. Nature. 1985;314:537-9.

15. Flegr J, Zitkova S, Kodym P, Frynta D. Induction of changes in human behaviour by the parasitic protozoan *Toxoplasma gondii*. Parasitology. 1996;113:49-54.

16. Flegr J, Hrdý I. Influence of chronic toxoplasmosis on some human personality factors. Folia Parasitol. 1994;41:122-6.

17. Flegr J, Kodym P, Tolarová V. Correlation of duration of latent *Toxoplasma gondii* infection with personality changes in women. Biol Psychol. 2000;53(1):57-68.

18. Flegr J. Influence of latent toxoplasmosis on the phenotype of intermediate hosts. Folia Parasitol. 2010;57:81-7.

19. Berdoy M, Webster JP, Macdonald DW. Fatal attraction in rats infected with *Toxoplasma gondii*. Proc R Soc Biol Sci Ser B. 2000;267(1452):1591-4.

20. Vyas A, Kim SK, Giacomini N, Boothroyd JC, Sapolsky RM. Behavioral changes induced by *Toxoplasma* infection of rodents are highly specific to aversion of cat odors. Proc Natl Acad Sci USA. 2007;104:6442-7.

21. Vyas A, Kim SK, Sapolsky RM. The effects of *Toxoplasma* infection on rodent behavior are dependent on dose of the stimulus. Neuroscience. 2007;148:342-8.

22. Flegr J, Lenochová P, Hodný Z, Vondrová M. Fatal attraction phenomenon in humans: cat odour attractiveness increased for *Toxoplasma*-infected men while decreased for infected women. PLoS Neglect Trop D. 2011;5(11):e1389.

23. Havlíček J, Roberts SC, Flegr J. Women's preference for dominant male odour: effects of menstrual cycle and relationship status. Biol Lett. 2005;1:256-9.

24. Havlíček J, Roberts SC. MHC-correlated mate choice in humans: A review. Psychoneuroendocrinology. 2009;34:497-512.

25. Flegr J. On the "origin" of natural selection by means of speciation. Riv Biol/Biol Forum. 1998;91(2):291-304.

26. Flegr J. Elastic, not plastic species: frozen plasticity theory and the origin of adaptive evolution in sexually reproducing organisms. Biol Direct. 2010;5:2.

27. Flegr J. Microevolutionary, macroevolutionary, ecological and taxonomical implications of of punctuational theories of adaptive evolution. Biol Direct. 2013;8:1.

28. Flegr J. A possible role of intracellular isoelectric focusing in the evolution of eukaryotic cells and multicellular organisms. J Mol Evol. 2009;69:444-51.

29. Vorisek P, Votypka J, Zvara K, Svobodova M. Heteroxenous coccidia increase the predation risk of parasitized rodents. Parasitology. 1998;117:521-4.

30. Flegr J, Havlíček J, Kodym P, Malý M, Šmahel Z. Increased risk of traffic accidents in subjects with latent toxoplasmosis: a retrospective case-control study. BMC Infect Dis. 2002;2:art-11.

31. Yereli K, Balcioglu IC, Ozbilgin A. Is *Toxoplasma gondii* a potential risk for traffic accidents in Turkey? Forensic Sci Int. 2006;163:34-7.

32. Kocazeybek B, Oner YA, Turksoy R, Babur C, Cakan H, Sahip N, et al. Higher prevalence of toxoplasmosis in victims of traffic accidents suggest increased risk of traffic accident in *Toxoplasma*-infected inhabitants of Istanbul and its suburbs. Forensic Sci Int. 2009;187:103-8.

33. Flegr J, Klose J, Novotná M, Berenreitterová M, Havlíček J. Increased incidence of traffic accidents in *Toxoplasma*-infected military drivers and protective effect RhD molecule revealed by a large-scale prospective cohort study. BMC Infect Dis. 2009;9:art. 72.

34. Havlíček J, Gašová Z, Smith AP, Zvára K, Flegr J. Decrease of psychomotor performance in subjects with latent 'asymptomatic' toxoplasmosis. Parasitology. 2001;122:515-20.

35. Flegr J, Lindová J, Kodym P. Sex-dependent toxoplasmosis-associated differences in testosterone concentration in humans. Parasitology. 2008;135:427-31.

36. Flegr J, Novotná M, Fialová A, Kolbeková P, Gašová Z. The influence of RhD phenotype on toxoplasmosis- and age-associated changes in personality profile of blood donors. Folia Parasitol. 2010;57:143-50.

37. Flegr J, Příplatová L. Testosterone and cortisol levels in university students reflect actual rather than estimated number of wrong answers on written exam. Neuroendocrinol Lett. 2010;31:577-81.

38. Kannan G, Moldovan K, Xiao JC, Yolken RH, Jones-Brando L, Pletnikov MV. *Toxoplasma gondii* strain-dependent effects on mouse behaviour. Folia Parasitol. 2010;57:151-5.

39. Flegr J, Dama M. Does prevalence of latent toxoplasmosis correlate with nation-wide rate of traffic accidents? Folia Parasitol. 2014;6:485-94.

40. Flegr J. Two distinct types of natural selection in turbidostat-like and chemostat-like ecosystems. J Theor Biol. 1997;188:121-6.

41. Hrdá Š, Votýpka J, Kodym P, Flegr J. Transient nature of *Toxoplasma gondii*-induced behavioral changes in mice. J Parasitol. 2000;86(4):657-63.

42. Webster JP. The effect of *Toxoplasma gondii* and other parasites on activity levels in wild and hybrid *Rattus norvegicus* Parasitology. 1994;109:583-9.

43. Webster JP, Brunton CFA, Macdonald DW. Effect of *Toxoplasma gondii* upon neophobic behaviour in wild brown rats, *Rattus norvegicus* Parasitology. 1994;109:37-43.

44. Flegr J, Prandota J, Sovickova M, Israili ZH. Toxoplasmosis - A global threat. Correlation of latent toxoplasmosis with specific disease burden in a set of 88 countries. PLoS ONE. 2014;9(3).

45. Penzhorn BL, Stylianides E, van Vuuren M, Alexander K, Meltzer DGA, Mukarati N. Seroprevalence of *Toxoplasma gondii* in free-ranging lion and leopard populations in southern Africa. S Afr J Wildl Res. 2002;32:163-5.

46. Poirotte C, Kappeler PM, Ngoubangoye B, Bourgeois S, Moussodji M, Charpentier MJE. Morbid attraction to leopard urine in *Toxoplasma*-infected chimpanzees. Curr Biol. 2016;26(3):R98-R9.

47. Stibbs HH. Changes in brain concentrations of catecholamines and indoleamines in *Toxoplasma gondii* infected mice. Ann Trop Med Parasitol. 1985;79:153-7.

48. Skallová A, Novotná M, Kolbeková P, Gašová Z, Veselý V, Flegr J. Decreased level of novelty seeking in blood donors infected with *Toxoplasma*. Neuroendocrinol Lett. 2005;26(5):480-6.

49.   Novotná M, Hanušová J, Klose J, Preiss M, Havlíček J, Roubalová K, et al. Probable neuroimmunological link between *Toxoplasma* and cytomegalovirus infections and personality changes in the human host. BMC Infect Dis. 2005;5:54.

50.   Gaskell EA, Smith JE, Pinney JW, Westhead DR, McConkey GA. A unique dual activity amino acid hydroxylase in *Toxoplasma gondii* PLoS ONE. 2009;4:e4801.

51.   Prandovszky E, Gaskell E, Martin H, Dubey JP, Webster JP, McConkey GA. The neurotropic parasite *Toxoplasma gondii* increases dopamine metabolism. PLoS ONE. 2011;6(9):e23866.

52.   Skallová A, Kodym P, Frynta D, Flegr J. The role of dopamine in *Toxoplasma*-induced behavioural alterations in mice: an ethological and ethopharmacological study. Parasitology. 2006;133:525-35.

53.   Hodková H, Kodym P, Flegr J. Poorer results of mice with latent toxoplasmosis in learning tests: impaired learning processes or the novelty discrimination mechanism? Parasitology. 2007;134:1329-37.

54.   Hutchison WM, Aitken PP, Wells WP. Chronic *Toxoplasma* infections and familiarity-novelty discrimination in the mouse. Ann Trop Med Parasitol. 1980;74(2):145-50.

55.   Lindová J, Novotná M, Havlíček J, Jozífková E, Skallová A, Kolbeková P, et al. Gender differences in behavioural changes induced by latent toxoplasmosis. Int J Parasitol. 2006;36:1485-92.

56.   Lindová J, Kuběna AA, Šturcová A, Křivohlavá R, Novotná M, Rubešová A, et al. Pattern of money allocation in experimental games supports the stress hypothesis of gender differences in *Toxoplasma gondii*-induced behavioural changes. Folia Parasitol. 2010;57:136-42.

57.   Kulich T, Flegr J. Positive effects of multiple gene control on the spread of altruism by group selection. J Theor Biol. 2011;284:1-6.

58.   Kubena AA, Houdek P, Lindova J, Priplatova L, Flegr J. Justine Effect: Punishment of the unduly self-sacrificing cooperative individuals. PLoS ONE. 2014;9(3).

59.   Herrmann B, Thoni C, Gachter S. Antisocial punishment across societies. Science. 2008;319(5868):1362-7.

60.   Flegr J, Hrušková M, Hodný Z, Novotná M, Hanušová J. Body height, body mass index, waist-hip ratio, fluctuating asymmetry and

second to fourth digit ratio in subjects with latent toxoplasmosis. Parasitology. 2005;130:621-8.

61. Kratochvíl L, Flegr J. Differences in the 2nd to 4th digit length ratio in humans reflect shifts along the common allometric line. Biol Lett. 2009;5:643-6.

62. Hodkova H, Kolbekova P, Skallova A, Lindova J, Flegr J. Higher perceived dominance in *Toxoplasma* infected men--a new evidence for role of increased level of testosterone in toxoplasmosis-associated changes in human behavior. Neuro endocrinology letters. 2007;28(2):110-4.

63. Lindova J, Little AC, Havlicek J, Roberts SC, Rubesova A, Flegr J. Effect of partnership status on preferences for facial self-resemblance. Frontiers in Psychology. 2016;7.

64. Kleisner K, Kocnar T, Rubesová A, Flegr J. Eye color predicts but does not directly influence perceived dominance in men. Pers Individ Diff. 2010;49:59-64.

65. Flegr J, Lindová J, Pivoňková V, Havlíček J. Brief Communication:Latent toxoplasmosis and salivary testosterone concentration-important confounding factors in second to fourth digit ratio studies. Am J Phys Anthropol. 2008;137:479-84.

66. Flegr J, Stříž I. Potential immunomodulatory effects of latent toxoplasmosis in humans. BMC Infect Dis. 2011;11:274.

67. Kaňková Š, Kodym P, Flegr J. Direct evidence of *Toxoplasma*-induced changes in serum testosterone in mice. Exp Parasitol. 2011;128:181-3.

68. Lim A, Kumar V, Hari Dass SA, Vyas A. *Toxoplasma gondii* infection enhances testicular steroidogenesis in rats. Mol Ecol. 2013;22(1):102-10.

69. Torrey EF, Yolken RH. Could schizophrenia be a viral zoonosis transmitted from house cats. Schizophr Bull. 1995;21(2):167-71.

70. Fuller TE, Rawlings R, Yolken RH. The antecedents of psychoses: a case-control study of selected risk factors. Schizophr Res. 2000;46:17-23.

71. Saha S, Chant DC, Welham JL, McGrath JJ. A systematic review of the prevalence of schizophrenia. Schizophr Res. 2006;81:182-3.

72. Girard SL, Xiong L, Dion PA, Rouleau GA. Where are the missing pieces of the schizophrenia genetics puzzle? Curr Opin Genet Dev. 2011;21:310-6.

73.   Jones-Brando L, Torrey EF, Yolken R. Drugs used in the treatment of schizophrenia and bipolar disorder inhibit the replication of *Toxoplasma gondii*. Schizophr Res. 2003;62:237-44.

74.   Fond G, Macgregor A, Tamouza R, Hamdani N, Meary A, Leboyer M, et al. Comparative analysis of anti-toxoplasmic activity of antipsychotic drugs and valproate. Eur Arch Psychiatry Clin Neurosci. 2014;264(2):179-83.

75.   Nielbuhr DW, Millikan AM, Cowan DN, Yolken R, Li YZ, Weber NS. Selected infectious agents and risk of schizophrenia among US military personnel. Am J Psychiatry. 2008;165:99-106.

76.   Holub D, Flegr J, Dragomirecka E, Rodriguez M, Preiss M, Novak T, et al. Differences in onset of disease and severity of psychopathology between toxoplasmosis-related and toxoplasmosis-unrelated schizophrenia. Acta Psychiatr Scand. 2013;127:227-38.

77.   Flegr J, Priplatova L, Hampl R, Bicikovia M, Ripova D, Mohr P. Difference of neuro- and immunomodulatory steroids and selected hormone and lipid concentrations between *Toxoplasma*-free and *Toxoplasma*-infected but not CMV-free and CMV-infected schizophrenia patients. Neuroendocrinol Lett. 2014;35(1):20-7.

78.   Wang H, Yolken RH, Hoekstra PJ, Burger H, Klein HC. Antibodies to infectious agents and the positive symptom dimension of subclinical psychosis: The TRAILS study. Schizophr Res. 2011;129:47-51.

79.   Celik T, Kartalci S, Aytas O, Akarsu GA, Gozukara H, Unal S. Association between latent toxoplasmosis and clinical course of schizophrenia - continuous course of the disease is characteristic for *Toxoplasma gondii*-infected patients. Folia Parasitol. 2015;62.

80.   Horacek J, Flegr J, Tintera J, Verebova K, Spaniel F, Novak T, et al. Latent toxoplasmosis reduces gray matter density in schizophrenia but not in controls: Voxel-based-morphometry (VBM) study. World J Biol Psychiatry. 2012;13:501-9.

81.   Hinze-Selch D, Daubener W, Erdag S, Wilms S. The diagnosis of a personality disorder increases the likelihood for seropositivity to *Toxoplasma gondii* in psychiatric patients. Folia Parasitol (Praha). 2010;57(2):129-35.

82.   Miman O, Kusbeci OY, Aktepe OC, Cetinkaya Z. The probable relation between *Toxoplasma gondii* and Parkinson's disease. Neurosci Lett. 2010;475:129-31.

83. Celik T, Kamisli O, Babur C, Cevik MO, Oztuna D, Altinayar S. Is there a relationship between *Toxoplasma gondii* infection and idiopathic Parkinson's disease? Scand J Infect Dis. 2010;42:604-8.

84. Kusbeci OY, Miman O, Yaman M, Aktepe OC, Yazar S. Could *Toxoplasma gondii* have any role in Alzheimer disease? Alzheimer Dis Assoc Disord. 2011;25:1-3.

85. Sutterland AL, Fond G, Kuin A, Koeter MW, Lutter R, van Gool T, et al. Beyond the association. *Toxoplasma gondii* in schizophrenia, bipolar disorder, and addiction: systematic review and meta-analysis. Acta Psychiatr Scand. 2015;132(3):161-79.

86. Webster JP, Lamberton PHL, Donnelly CA, Torrey EF. Parasites as causative agents of human affective disorders? The impact of anti-psychotic, mood-stabilizer and anti-parasite medication on *Toxoplasma gondii* 's ability to alter host behaviour. Proc R Soc Biol Sci Ser B. 2006;273:1023-30.

87. Arling TA, Yolken RH, Lapidus M, Langenberg P, Dickerson FB, Zimmerman SA, et al. *Toxoplasma gondii* antibody titers and history of suicide attempts in patients with recurrent mood disorders. J Nerv Ment Dis. 2009;197:905-8.

88. Koseoglu E, Yazar S, Koc I. Is *Toxoplasma gondii* a causal agent in migraine? Am J Med Sci. 2009;338:120-2.

89. Flegr J. Neurological and neuropsychiatric consequences of chronic *Toxoplasma* infection. Parasitology. 2015;2:163-72.

90. Yuksel P, Alpay N, Babur C, Bayar R, Saribas S, Karakose AR, et al. The role of latent toxoplasmosis in the aetiopathogenesis of schizophrenia - the risk factor or an indication of a contact with cat? Folia Parasitol. 2010;57:121-8.

91. Kolbeková P, Kourbatova E, Novotná M, Kodym P, Flegr J. New and old risk-factors for *Toxoplasma gondii* infection: prospective cross-sectional study among military personnel in the Czech Republic. Clin Microbiol Infec. 2007;13:1012-7.

92. Novotná M, Havlíček J, Smith AP, Kolbeková P, Skallová A, Klose J, et al. *Toxoplasma* and reaction time: Role of toxoplasmosis in the origin, preservation and geographical distribution of Rh blood group polymorphism. Parasitology. 2008;135:1253-61.

93. Flegr J, Novotná M, Lindová J, Havlíček J. Neurophysiological effect of the Rh factor. Protective role of the RhD molecule against

Toxoplasma-induced impairment of reaction times in women. Neuroendocrinol Lett. 2008;29:475-81.

94. Haldane JBS. Mutation and the Rhesus reaction   Nature. 1944;153:106.

95. Fisher RA, Race RR, Taylor GL. Mutation and the rhesus reaction. Nature. 1944;153:106.

96. McFadden D, Loehlin JC, Breedlove SM, Lippa RA, Manning JT, Rahman Q. A reanalysis of five studies on sexual orientation and the relative length of the 2nd and 4th fingers (the 2D : 4D ratio). Arch Sex Behav. 2005;34:341-56.

97. Kraemer B, Noll T, Delsignore A, Milos G, Schnyder U, Hepp U. Finger length ratio (2D : 4D) and dimensions of sexual orientation. Neuropsychobiology. 2006;53:210-4.

98. Manning JT. Digit ratio: A pointer to fertility, behavior, and heatlh. New Jersey: Rutgers University Press; 2002. 1-173 p.

99. Flegr J, Preiss M, Klose J. Toxoplasmosis-associated difference in intelligence and personality in men depends on their Rhesus blood group but not ABO blood group. PLoS ONE. 2013;8(4).

100. Flegr J, Geryk J, Volny J, Klose J, Cernochova D. Rhesus factor modulation of effects of smoking and age on psychomotor performance, intelligence, personality profile, and health in Czech soldiers. PLoS ONE. 2012;7(11):e49478.

101. Cattell RB. Blood-groups and personality traits. Am J Hum Genet. 1972;24:485.

102. Flegr J, Hoffmann R, Dammann M. Worse health status and higher incidence of health disorders in Rhesus negative subjects. PLoS ONE. 2015;10(10). doi: 10.1371/journal.pone.0141362.

103. Flegr J. Heterozygote advantage probably maintains rhesus factor blood group polymorphism: Ecological regression study. PLoS ONE. 2016;11(1):e0147955.

104. Kaňková Š, Holáň V, Zajícová A, Kodym P, Flegr J. Modulation of immunity in mice with latent toxoplasmosis - the experimental support for the immunosupression hypothesis of *Toxoplasma*-induced changes in reproduction of mice and humans. Parasitol Res. 2010;107 1421-7.

105. Snol SE. Fiziko-khimicheskie faktory biologicheskoi evolyutsii (Physikochemical factors of biological evolution). Moscow: Nauka; 1979.

106. Flegr J. Does a cell perform isoelectric focusing? BioSystens. 1990;24:127-33.

107. Meili R. Lehrbuch der Psychologischen Diagnostik. Bern: Verlag Hans Huber; 1961.

108. Flegr J, Kuba R. The relation of *Toxoplasma* infection and sexual attraction to fear, danger, pain and submissiveness. Evolutionary Psychology. 2016:1-10.

109. Jozífková E, Flegr J. Dominance, submissivity (and homosexuality) in general population. Testing of evolutionary hypothesis of sadomasochism by internet-trap-method. Neuroendocrinol Lett. 2006;27:711-8.

110. Flegr J, Hrdá Š, Kodym P. Influence of latent 'asymptomatic' toxoplasmosis on body weight of pregnant women. Folia Parasitol. 2005;52:199-204.

111. Kaňková Š, Flegr J. Longer pregnancy and slower fetal development in women with latent "asymptomatic" toxoplasmosis BMC Infect Dis. 2007;7:art: 114.

112. Kaňková S, Šulc J, Křivohlavá R, Kuběna A, Flegr J. Slower postnatal motor development in infants of mothers with latent toxoplasmosis during the first 18 months of life. Early Hum Dev. 2012;88(11):879-84.

113. Benjamini Y, Hochberg Y. Controlling the false discovery rate: A practical and powerful approach to multiple testing. J Roy Stat Soc B Met. 1995;57(1):289-300. PubMed PMID: ISI:A1995QE45300017.

114. Kaňková Š, Šulc J, Nouzová K, Fajfrlik K, Frynta D, Flegr J. Women infected with parasite *Toxoplasma* have more sons. Naturwissenschaften. 2007;94:122-7.

115. Kaňková Š, Kodym P, Frynta D, Vavřinová R, Kuběna A, Flegr J. Influence of latent toxoplasmosis on the secondary sex ratio in mice. Parasitology. 2007;134:1709-17.

116. Hostomská L, Jírovec O, Horáčková M, Hrubcová M. The role of toxoplasmosis in the mother in the development of mongolism in the child (in Czech). Československá Pediatrie. 1957;12:713-23.

117. Kaňková Š, Šulc J, Flegr J. Increased pregnancy weight gain in women with latent toxoplasmosis and RhD-positivity protection against this effect. Parasitology. 2010;137:1773-9.

118. Flegr J, Hrdá Š, Tachezy J. The role of psychological factors in questionnaire-based studies on routes of human toxoplasmosis transmission. Cent Eur J Public Health. 1998;6:45-50.

119. Flegr J, Klapilová K, Kaňková Š. Toxoplasmosis can be a sexually transmitted infection with serious clinical consequences. Not all routes of infection are created equal. Med Hypotheses. 2014;83:286-9.

120. Flegr J, Escudero DQ. Impaired health status and increased incidence of diseases in *Toxoplasma*-seropositive subjects – An explorative cross-sectional study. Parasitology. 2016; 143:1974-1989.

121. Priplatova L, Sebankova B, Flegr J. Contrasting effect of prepulse signals on performance of *Toxoplasma*-infected and *Toxoplasma*-free subjects in an acoustic reaction times test. PLoS ONE. 2014;9(11).

122. James WH. Potential solutions to problems posed by the offspring sex ratios of people with viral and other infections. Folia Parasitol. 2010;57.2:114.

123. Ngoungou EB, Bhalla D, Nzoghe A, Darde M-L, Preux P-M. Toxoplasmosis and epilepsy - systematic review and meta analysis. PLoS Neglect Trop D. 2015;9(2).

124. Yazar S, Arman F, Yalcin S, Dimirtas F, Yaman O, Sahin I. Investigation of probable relationship between *Toxoplasma gondii* and cryptogenic epilepsy. Seiz Europ J Epil. 2003;12:107-9.

125. Flegr J, Horáček J. *Toxoplasma gondii*-infected subjects report an Obsessive-Compulsive Disorder diagnosis more often and score higher in Obsessive-Compulsive Inventory. European Psychiatry. 2016;in press.

126. Prandota J. Neuropathological changes and clinical features of autism spectrum disorder participants are similar to that reported in congenital and chronic cerebral toxoplasmosis in humans and mice. Res Autism Spectr Disorders. 2010;4:103-18.

127. Flegr J. Schizophrenia and *Toxoplasma gondii*: an undervalued association? Expert Review of Anti-Infective Therapy. 2015;13(7):817-20.

INDEX

Kulda Jaroslav, 13, 16, 35, 104, 120, 138
Kulich Tomáš, 243
kyneuric acid, 274, 276
Lanzavecchia Antonio, 62
leopards, 213
Leptospira icterohaemorrhagiae, 206
Leucochloridium macrostomum, 26
life cycle, 40
Lindová Jitka, 93, 241
linear regression, 98
linkage disequilibrium, 299
lions, 213
lipopolysaccharide, 30
literature review, 115
logistic regression, 98
log-linear analysis, 99
long-eared owl, 155
longitudinal study, 165, 276
long-term partners, 130
lymphokines, 220
Lysenko Trofim Denisovich, 27
Lysenkoism, 27
macrophages, 86
magnetic resonance imaging, 279
major urinary proteins, 375
malaria, 297
MANCOVA, 98
manipulation hypothesis, 205
manipulative parasite, 44
manipulatory activity, 221
Mann-Whitney U-test, 96, 99
MANOVA, 98
manuscript, 158
masculinity, 259
masochistic sexual preferences, 336
maturation of cysts, 367
measurement quality of science, 112

medium-term memory, 330
Meili's test of selective memory, 332
memory B cells, 87
menstrual cycle, 131, 263
meta-analysis, 310
methods established, 91
methods scientific, 91
MHC antigens, 88, 144
MHC class I proteins, 145
MHC class II proteins, 145
MHC proteins, 132, 134, 144
microchimera, 290, 292
Microtus arvalis, 152
migraines, 377
mitochondria, 17
model, 107, 202
modeling process vs. system, 109
Mokrejš Martin, 147
molecular phylogenetics, 28, 128
monkeys, 213, 231
Monte Carlo tests, 345
MRI, 279
multidimensional linear regression, 99
mutations, 228, 367
Myodes glareolus, 114
N-70 test, 63
natural selection, 139, 228
negative heritability of fitness, 134
neocortex, 280
NEO-PI-R, 63
Neubauer Zdeněk, 14
neurotransmitter, 59, 216
Ninio Jacques, 62
Nobel Prize, 63
nonparametric tests, 97
Norwegian rat, 206
Novák Vladimír Jan Amos, 27

randomization tests, 98, 343, 344

rank correlation test, 96

ratio of the 2nd and 4th fingers, 250

ratios, 253

Rattus norvegicus, 206

reaction time, 151, 160

red blood cell, 286

Red Queen Hypothesis, 134

reindeer, 119

religion, 131

repeated measures tests, 284

repetitive DNA, 19

research project, 115

resistance to fatigue, 186

respiratory chain, 19

retrovirus, 180

reverse theory of personality, 61

review, 158

reviewers, 158

Reward dependence, 217

Rh factor, 287

Rh negative women, 362

Rh negative women-pregnancy, 362

Rh polymorphism, 286, 288, 292

Rh positivity, 377

RhD molecule, 377

risk factors for toxoplasmosis, 364, 370

risk of suicide, 285

RNA viruses, 367

r-strategy, 201

Sacculina, 44

sadomasochistic sexual preference, 332

Sarcocystis dispersa, 155

scent of cat, 124

scientific ethics, 77

scientific etiquette, 62

scientific grants, 110

scientific journals, 159

scientific publications, 126

scientometrics, 114

SCL-90 test, 63

secondary immune response, 87

selection for heterozygotes, 294, 297

selfish gene theory, 227

selfish organelles, 17

selfishness, 242

self-similar faces, 263

self-similarity, 261

Self-transcendence, 217

sensitivity, 37

serotonin, 285

sex ratio, 352

sex ratio at birth, 351

sexually reproducing organisms, 140

Shakespeare William, 231

short-term memory, 186

short-term sexual partner, 130

schizophrenia, 273

sickle-cell anemia, 297

side-effect of infection, 221

sieve effect, 193

significance of luck in science, 286

size of the fetus, 84

smell, 130

Smith Andrew, 161

social feedback loop hypothesis, 265

social norms, 234

sorting on the basis of stability, 142

South America, 183

Spearman's rank correlation test, 96, 99

specificity, 37

variable binary, 95
variable categorical, 95
variable confounding, 81
variable continuous, 95
variable dependent, 80
variable discrete, 95
variable independent, 80
variable ordinal, 95
variable qualitative, 95
variable quantitative, 95
Velvet Revolution, 14
verbal questioning, 369
virions, 92
Vitáková Martina, 161
VMT questionnaire, 308

vomeronasal organ, 136
Votýpka Jan, 122, 153
Webster Joanne, 206
weight, 338
weight gain, 362
white biology, 11
Wilcoxon test, 99
within subject effect, 284
World Health Organization, 157
written exams, 176
Yolken Robert H., 273
Zajícová Alena, 358
Zemková Michaela, 147
Zitková Štěpánka, 121, 199
Zrzavý Jan, 119

Printed in Great Britain
by Amazon